Penny Brady

Dept of Mental

# PRINCIPLES
## OF
# MEDICAL
# STATISTICS

BY

## AUSTIN BRADFORD HILL
### C.B.E., D.Sc., Ph.D., F.R.S.

*Professor Emeritus of Medical Statistics in the University of London; Past Honorary Director of the Statistical Research Unit of the Medical Research Council; Past President of the Royal Statistical Society; Civil Consultant in Medical Statistics to the Royal Navy and the Royal Air Force; Member of the International Statistical Institute*

SEVENTH EDITION
REVISED AND ENLARGED

New York
## OXFORD UNIVERSITY PRESS
1961

*First Edition,* 1937
*Second Edition,* 1939
*Third Edition,* 1942
*Third Edition Reprinted,* 1945
*Third Edition Reprinted,* 1946
*Fourth Edition,* 1948
*Fourth Edition Reprinted,* 1949
*Fifth Edition,* 1950
*Fifth Edition Reprinted,* 1952
*Sixth Edition,* 1955
*Sixth Edition Reprinted,* 1959
*Seventh Edition,* 1961

Translated into
Spanish, *First Edition,* 1950
*Second Edition,* 1958
Russian, 1958
Korean, 1960
Polish, 1962

To

# F. M. H.

PRINTED IN GREAT BRITAIN
BY R. & R. CLARK, LTD., EDINBURGH

# FOREWORD TO FIRST EDITION

In clinical medicine to-day there is a growing demand for adequate proof of the efficacy of this or that form of treatment. Often proof can come only by means of a collection of records of clinical trials devised on such a scale and in such a form that statistically reliable conclusions can be drawn from them. However great may be our aversion to figures, we cannot escape the conclusion that the solution of most of the problems of clinical or preventive medicine must ultimately depend on them. Even those who pretend to despise this method of approach find that any assessment of success or failure which is based on fact rather than on opinion must nearly always be expressed in some numerical form—*e.g.* when the medical observer reports that he has treated so many cases with a favourable result in such and such a proportion, or the public health worker assesses the attack-rate on a population inoculated against some infection. But often, unfortunately, the figures used are either insufficient in number or documentation or too limited in their scope to bear the weight of the interpretation that is placed upon them. An additional difficulty is that few medical men have been trained to interpret figures or to analyse and test their meaning by even an elementary statistical technique. We have reason to believe that there is now a steadily increasing demand among both clinical and public health workers for some knowledge of that technique and a realisation that it is not much good collecting figures more or less haphazardly and then to expect a professional statistician to draw conclusions from them.

Acting upon this belief, last year we invited Dr. A. Bradford Hill to prepare for our columns a series of short simple articles on such methods as his experience of medical statistics had shown him would be most useful in that

iii

field. He has succeeded beyond our hopes in demonstrating some of the ways in which investigations can be planned and figures derived from them can be analysed in order to yield fruitful results. He has chosen examples from medical publications to illustrate both the types of problem with which the medical worker is faced and the kinds of error he is most liable to make; and wherever possible he has either avoided mathematical presentation of his material or has led up to it so skilfully as to rob equations and even square roots of their traditional horrors. This consideration for those who are not mathematically minded has resulted in an exceptionally clear exposition of a difficult subject. We are happy to accede to the many requests we have received for the reissue of these articles in book form.

EDITOR OF "THE LANCET"

*June* 1937

# PREFACE TO SEVENTH EDITION

Two long sea voyages provided me with an opportunity to give a great deal of uninterrupted reflection to this book and, as a result, to make considerable changes in it. I have added (I fear, the consequence of *too* much leisure) three new chapters, namely Chapters II and IV concerned with the elements of sampling and the carrying out of scientific investigations, and Chapter XIX dealing with the problems of defining and measuring sickness. In some compensation for this increase I have reduced the space previously given to the standardisation of death-rates and have incorporated its customary rates and indices in one chapter (XVII) instead of the previous two.

Other major revisions that I have thought it wise to make include an extension of the section on graphs and diagrams (Chapter V), the introduction of the " $t$ " test (Chapter XII) and of a $\chi^2$ test of the trend in a series of percentages (Chapter XIV), and a rather more detailed account of the construction of a life table as a means of observing and analysing the follow-up of a group (Chapter XVIII). Additions to Chapter XX on Clinical Trials comprise a discussion of trials made " within," rather than " between," patients, and an emphasis on the importance of being wary of subsequent exclusions of patients, for any reason, from originally randomly constructed groups. I have also taken pleasure in adding a few more " fallacies and difficulties " (Chapters XXI to XXIII) and in rearranging the examples in those three chapters in a more logical order.

While making revisions on this scale I have also taken the opportunity to alter the order of some of the chapters, which, with succeeding editions, had become awry ; and throughout the book I have rewritten many phrases and sentences. With the increasing use of statistics in medicine it is my hope that these many changes will not offend old friends and will enable the book to continue to aid newcomers to the field—and to continue to aid them as much towards clear ways of thinking as in the use of the simple methodology that it expounds.

I am greatly indebted to Dr. P. Armitage and Mr. I. D. Hill for reading my expanded text and for their advice and criticisms. Contrary to custom, for the faults that remain I trust sincerely that the reader may hold them largely responsible. The values in the table of " $t$ " I extracted from the Biometrika Tables for Statisticians and I am grateful to the Biometrika Trustees for permission to do so.

A. BRADFORD HILL

*January* 1961

# PREFACE TO FIRST EDITION

" Statistics are curious things. They afford one of the few examples in which the use, or abuse, of mathematical methods tends to induce a strong emotional reaction in non-mathematical minds. This is because statisticians apply, to problems in which we are interested, a technique which we do not understand. It is exasperating, when we have studied a problem by methods that we have spent laborious years in mastering, to find our conclusions questioned, and perhaps refuted, by someone who could not have made the observations himself. It requires more equanimity than most of us possess to acknowledge that the fault is in ourselves."

THESE are the opening words of a leading article which introduced the chapters of this book to the readers of *The Lancet*, where they appeared weekly during the first four months of 1937. As a statistician I may be permitted to view the problem the other way round. No statistician (in spite of views to the contrary) particularly enjoys refuting other workers' conclusions, especially when he knows that much patience and much hard work have been expended in the collection of data. He has no burning desire to be called in as an expert witness at the conclusion of the case for the plaintiff (on a subject-matter he may not fully understand) to say that this is " significant " and that is, statistically speaking, nonsense. It even requires some equanimity to be unmoved when he is transferred to the dock on a charge of being merely an armchair critic or a confirmed sceptic. In other words, neither party to the transaction is particularly happy.

There seems to me to be only one way of escape. The worker in medical problems, in the field of clinical as well as preventive medicine, must *himself* know something of statistical technique, both in experimental arrangements and in the interpretation of figures. To enable him to acquire some knowledge of this technique I have tried to set down as simply as possible the statistical methods that experience has shown me to be most helpful in the problems with which medical workers are concerned. I have used examples taken from medical inquiries

vii

in the attempt to make clear these methods of analysis, and have sought to show by illustration where and why workers make mistakes in their interpretation of figures. I know that I have been guilty of some repetition ; my excuse is the repetition in published papers of those elementary statistical errors which a very little knowledge of statistics would be sufficient to prevent.

I am much indebted to Professor Major Greenwood, F.R.S., Professor W. W. C. Topley, F.R.S., Dr. J. O. Irwin, and Mr. W. T. Russell, for reading the whole or part of the manuscript or proofs. I have gained much from their criticisms. The original articles were written for *The Lancet* at the suggestion of Dr. M. H. Kettle, and I owe a very great deal to her encouragement and interest.

The table of $\chi^2$ is reproduced by kind permission of the author and publishers from *Statistical Methods for Research Workers*, by Professor R. A. Fisher, Sc.D., F.R.S. (6th edition, 1936, Oliver & Boyd, Edinburgh and London).

A. BRADFORD HILL

*June* 1937

# CONTENTS

ix

# I

## THE AIM OF THE STATISTICAL METHOD

" Is the application of the numerical method to the subject-matter of medicine a trivial and time-wasting ingenuity as some hold, or is it an important stage in the development of our art, as others proclaim ? " Whatever may have been the reactions of medically qualified readers to that question, propounded by the writer of an article on medical statistics in 1921 (*Lancet*, 1, 985), it must be admitted that in subsequent years there has been a continual and substantial increase in the number of papers contributed to medical journals of which the essence is largely statistical. Not only has there developed an enhanced knowledge of, and respect for, the national registers of life and death which the Registrars-General of the United Kingdom (and similar authorities in other countries) annually publish and analyse, but there is an increasing number of workers who endeavour to apply numerical methods of analysis to their records obtained, by observation or experiment, in clinical and other branches of medicine. Many such workers, however, have had little or no training in statistical method, and many of them find the more mathematical methods of the professional statistician, as has been said, " obscure and even repellent." Often enough, indeed, the argument is put forward that the use of such mathematical methods is quite unjustifiable, that the accuracy of the original material is not sufficient to bear the weight of the treatment meted out to it. This assertion is not strictly logical. If a collection of figures is worth a statistical analysis at all, it is, obviously, worth the best form of statistical analysis—*i.e.* the form which allows the maximum amount of information to be derived from the data.

1

Whether mathematical statistical methods *are* the best form in particular cases, whether they are essential or may be regarded as an unnecessary elaboration must turn rather upon this question : Can we in any of the problems of medical statistics reach satisfactory results by means of relatively simple numerical methods only ?  In other words : Can we satisfactorily test hypotheses and draw deductions from data that have been analysed by means of such simple methods ? The answer is undoubtedly yes, that many of the figures included today in medical papers can by relatively simple statistical methods be made to yield information of value, that where the yield is rather less than that which might be obtained by more erudite methods which are not at the worker's command the best should not be made the enemy of the good, and that even the simplest statistical analysis carried out logically and carefully is an aid to clear thinking with regard to the meaning and limitations of the original records.  If these conclusions are accepted, the question immediately at issue becomes this : Are simple methods of the interpretation of figures only a synonym for common sense or do they involve an art or knowledge which can be imparted ?  Familiarity with medical statistics leads inevitably to the conclusion that common sense is *not* enough. Mistakes which when pointed out look extremely foolish are quite frequently made by intelligent persons, and the same mistakes, or types of mistakes, continue to crop up again and again.  There is often lacking what has been called a " statistical tact, which is rather more than simple good sense."  That tact the majority of persons must acquire (with a minority it is undoubtedly innate) by a study of the basic principles of statistical thought and method.

The object of this book is to discuss these basic principles in an elementary way and to show, by representative examples taken from medical literature, how these principles are frequently forgotten or ignored.  There is no doubt that the discussion will often appear too simple and that some of the mistakes to which space is given will be thought too futile to need attention.  That such is not the case is revealed by the recurrence of these mistakes and the neglect of these elementary principles, a feature with which every professional statistician is familiar in the papers submitted to him by their authors for " counsel's opinion."

## Definition of Statistics

Whereas the laboratory worker can frequently exclude variables in which he is not interested and confine his attention to one or more controlled factors at a time, the worker in clinical or preventive medicine is often unable to experiment and must inevitably use records which may be influenced by factors which he cannot control but have essentially to be taken into account. The essence of the statistical method lies in the elucidation of the effects of these multiple causes. By statistics, therefore, we mean " quantitative data affected to a marked extent by a multiplicity of causes," and by statistical method " methods specially adapted to the elucidation of quantitative data affected by a multiplicity of causes " (Yule and Kendall, *An Introduction to the Theory of Statistics*, Charles Griffin & Co., Ltd., London).

For example, suppose we have a number of children all of whom have been in contact with measles and to a proportion of them is given an injection of gamma globulin. We wish to know whether the treatment prevents the development of a clinical attack. It is possible that the risk of developing an attack is influenced by age, by sex, by social class and all that that denotes, by duration and intimacy of contact, by general state of health. A statistical analysis necessitates attention to *all* these possible influences. We must endeavour to equalise the groups we compare in every possibly influential respect except in the one factor at issue —namely, the treatment. If we have been unable to equalise the groups *ab initio* we must equalise them to the utmost extent by the mode of analysis. As far as possible it is clear, however, that we should endeavour to eliminate, or allow for, these extraneous or disturbing causes when the observations are planned ; with such planning maybe we can determine not only whether the treatment is of value but whether it is more efficacious at one age than another, etc. It is a serious mistake to rely upon the statistical method to eliminate disturbing factors at the completion of the work. *No* statistical method can compensate for badly planned observations or for a badly planned experiment.

## Planning and Interpretation of Experiments

It follows that the statistician may be able to advise upon the statistical lines an experiment such as that referred to above should follow. Elaborate experiments can be planned in which quite a number of factors can be taken into account statistically at the same time (see, for example, *Experimental Designs* by W. G. Cochran and G. M. Cox and *Planning of Experiments* by D. R. Cox). It is not the intention to discuss these more complex methods of planning and analysis ; attention is mainly confined to the simpler types of experimental arrangement with which medical workers are familiar. Limitation of the discussion to that type must not be taken to mean that it is the best form of experiment in a particular case.

The essence of the problem in a simple experiment is, as emphasised above, to ensure beforehand that, as far as is possible, the control and treated groups are the same in all *relevant* respects. The word " relevant " needs emphasis for two reasons. First, it is obvious that no statistician, when appealed to for help, can be aware of all the factors that are, or may be, relevant in particular medical problems. From general experience he may well be able to suggest certain broad disturbing causes which should be considered in planning the experiment (such as age and sex in the example above), but with factors which are narrowly specific to a particular problem he cannot be expected to be familiar. The onus of knowing what is likely to be relevant in a specific problem must rest upon the experimenter, who is, presumably, familiar with that narrow field. Thus, when the statistician's help is required it is his task to suggest means of allowing for the disturbing causes, either in planning the experiment or in analysing the results, and not, as a rule, to determine what *are* the relevant disturbing causes. At the same time successful collaboration demands that the statistician learn all he can of the problem at issue and the experimenter (clinician, medical officer of health, etc.) all he can of the statistical approach. Without substantial knowledge on both sides the blind may well lead the blind.

The second point that must be observed as regards the equality of groups in all relevant respects is the caution that must attend the interpretation of statistical results. If we find that Group A differs from Group B in some characteristic, say, its mortality-rate, can we be certain that that difference is due to the fact that Group A was inoculated (for example) and Group B was uninoculated ? Are we certain that Group A does not differ from Group B in some other character relevant to the issues as well as in the presence or absence of inoculation ? For instance, in a particular case, inoculated persons might, on the average, belong to a higher social class than the uninoculated and therefore live in surroundings in which the risk of infection was less. We can never be *certain* that we have not overlooked some relevant factor or that some factor is not present which could not be foreseen or identified. It is because he knows a complex chain of causation is so often involved that the statistician is, as it appears to many persons, an unduly cautious and sceptical individual.

## Statistics in Clinical Medicine

The essence of an experiment in the treatment of a disease lies in comparison. To the dictum of Helmholtz that " all science is measurement," we should add, Sir Henry Dale has pointed out, a further clause, that " all true measurement is essentially comparative." On the other hand there is a common catch-phrase that human beings are too variable to allow of the contrasts inherent in a controlled trial of a remedy. Yet if each patient is " unique " it is difficult to see how any basis for treatment can be sought in the past observations of other patients—upon which clinical medicine is founded. In fact, of course, physicians must, and do, base their " treatment of choice " upon what they have seen happen before—whether it be in only two or three cases or in a hundred.

However, though, broadly speaking, human beings are not unique in their responses to some given treatment, there is no doubt that they are likely to be variable, and sometimes extremely variable. Two or three observations may, therefore, give, merely through the customary play of chance, a favourable picture in the hands of one doctor, an unfavourable picture in the hands of another. As a result, the medical journals become an arena for conflicting claims—each in itself, maybe, perfectly true of what the doctor saw but insufficient to bear the weight of the generalisation placed upon it.

Far, therefore, from arguing that the statistical approach is impossible in the face of human variability, we must realise that it is *because* of variability that it is often essential. It does not follow, to meet another common criticism, that it invariably demands large numbers. It may do so ; it depends upon the problem. But the responses to treatment of a single patient are clearly a statement of fact—so far as the observations were truly made and accurately recorded. Indeed that single case may give, in certain circumstances, evidence of vital importance.

If, for example, we were to use a new drug in a proved case of acute leukaemia and the patient made an immediate and indisputable recovery, we should have a result of the most profound importance. The reason underlying our acceptance of merely one patient as illustrating a remarkable event—not necessarily of cause and effect—is that long and wide experience has shown that in their response to acute leukaemia human beings are *not* variable. They one and all fail to make immediate and indisputable recoveries. They one and all die. Therefore, although it would clearly be most unwise upon one case to pass from the particular to the general, it would be sheer madness not to accept the evidence presented by it.

If, on the other hand, the drug were given to a patient suffering from acute rheumatic fever and the patient made an immediate and indisputable recovery, we have little basis for remark. That recovery may clearly have followed the administration of the drug without the slightest probability of a related cause and effect. With this disease human beings *are* variable in their reactions—some may die, some may have prolonged illnesses but recover eventually with or without permanent damage, some may make immediate and indisputable recoveries—whatever treatment we give them. We must, therefore, have more cases before we can reasonably draw inferences about cause and effect. We need a statistical approach and a designed experiment (the details are discussed in Chapter XX).

While, therefore, in many instances we do need larger numbers for a sound assessment of a situation, it certainly does not follow — as is sometimes asserted — that the statistician would have rejected some of the original and fundamental observations in medicine on the grounds of their small number. To take a specific example, *fragilitas ossium* was originally described on two cases and this, a later writer said, statisticians would regard as useless evidence. But why should they ? If exact descriptions and illustrations were given of these two cases, then, of course, they form part of the body of scientific knowledge. They are undeniable evidence of an occurrence. What *can* happen, what *does* exist, quite regardless of the *frequency* of occurrence and irrespective of causation or association, may be observed, as already stated, even on a sample of one. It can only be in relation to an appeal from the particular to the general that a statistician—and, equally, any trained scientific worker—could object. If on the basis of the two cases the clinician, in practice, let us say, near the London meat market, should argue that the condition was specific to butchers, then one might suggest that the experience was too limited in size and area to justify any such generalisation.

In short, there is, and can be, no magic number for either clinician or statistician. Whether we need one, a hundred, or a thousand observations turns upon the setting of our problem and the inferences that we wish to draw.

It must be clear, too, that almost without statistics, and certainly without accurate measurement, the mental, or

B

quite rough, contrasting of one treatment (or some other
course of action) with another, will give a truthful, if not
precise, answer, *if* the treatment has a very real and considerable effect.    Without a strictly controlled trial the
merits of penicillin could not fail to come to light.    With
such " winners " it is easy for the critics of the, often
relatively slow, statistical approach to be wise after the
event, and to say that the general evidence available at the
start of a long, and perhaps tedious, trial made it unnecessary
or pedantic.    They forget the many occasions when the trial
has shown that a vaunted treatment has little, if any, value
—in spite of all the general " evidence " that was available.
Without a trial it might well have lingered on, to the detriment of patients.    Further, it is difficult to determine
through general impressions whether some drug is quite
useless or of some slight but undoubted value—and to
reduce, say, a relapse rate from 6 to 3 per cent. would not
be unimportant.    It is even more difficult to determine with
uncontrolled and unco-ordinated observations whether one
powerful drug is more valuable than another in particular
situations.    Only a carefully designed clinical trial is likely
to serve this purpose.    But that is not by any means to say
that the statistically guided experiment is the *only* profitable
means of clinical investigation or invariably the best way of
advancing knowledge.    It is merely one way.

One difficulty, in view of the variability of patients and
their illnesses, is in classifying the patients into, at least,
broad groups, so that we may be sure that like is put with
like, both before and after treatment.    But unless this
problem can be solved in specific instances, can clear-cut
answers be reached at all to the fundamental questions " is
this treatment of value, of how great a value, and with what
types of patients ? "    Even if the treatment is not of general
value but apparently of benefit in relatively isolated cases,
satisfactory evidence of that must lie in statistics—viz. that
such recoveries, however rare, do not occur with equal
frequency amongst equivalent persons not given that treatment.    Sooner or later the case is invariably based upon
that kind of evidence, but in the absence of a planned

approach it is often later rather than sooner. As Sir Robert Platt has emphasised, in a more general setting, records in clinical research are likely to be disappointing " unless they have been kept with an end in view, as part of a planned experiment. . . . Clinical experiment need not mean the subjection of patients to uncomfortable procedures of doubtful value or benefit. It means the planning of a line of action and the recording of observations designed to withstand critical analysis and give the answer to a clinical problem. It is an attitude of mind."

Returning to the problems of classification, by the statistical process of condensation of the individual items of information into a few groups, and, further, into averages and other values briefly descriptive of the data, we are clearly sacrificing some of the original detailed information. We must be particularly careful, therefore, that we sacrifice nothing relevant to the issues or more than is essential to clarity and ease in handling, interpreting and presenting the data. It is rarely feasible in practice, however, to publish the full case histories of a large number of patients specially treated and similar details of an equally large control group ; and even were it feasible, that material alone cannot supply the reader (or the writer) with the information he needs until it has been appropriately condensed. The question is, was the special treatment of value, *i.e.* the elucidation of cause and effect ? That elucidation must normally be achieved by the construction, from the original mass of recorded data, of relatively short tables, and statistical values based upon them, to show the relevant position before and after treatment of the specially treated and orthodoxly treated groups.

Other examples of the application of statistics in clinical medicine are : (*a*) observations on the natural history of a disease—what is its course, how variable is it from patient to patient, with what characteristics, *e.g.* age or sex, is it associated ? ; (*b*) the follow-up and assessment of patients treated in some particular way—particularly, perhaps, in surgery ; (*c*) the definition of " normal "—at what point does the measure of some bodily characteristic become pathological ? ; (d) the accuracy of laboratory procedures constantly used in clinical medicine, e.g. blood-counts.

## Statistics in the Field of Public Health

In public health work we may sometimes be concerned with a similar planning of experiments and the analysis of their results, e.g. in a test of the efficacy of a vaccine as a means of preventing an attack from, say, whooping-cough ; or in measuring the effects on mother and infant of supplementing the diet of pregnant women in some particular way. More often, however, we have to deal in this field with statistics that come from no deliberate experiment but that arise, and are collected, from a population living and dying in an everyday course of events.   Thus we have the general death-rate of the population in a given period of time ; its death-rates at particular ages—in infancy, in childhood, in the prime of life, and in old age ; its death-rates from particular causes—respiratory tuberculosis, cancer, violence, etc. For some diseases—the infectious notifiable diseases—we have figures relating to the number of attacks occurring from time to time.   And so on.

The object of these statistics and the statistical methods applied to them may be regarded as twofold.   On the one hand we shall use them as simple numerical assessments of the state of the public health, to show by contrasts between one place and another, or between one period of time and another, whether the death-rates of the population, for example, are relatively high or low.   It is only on the basis of such evidence that we can effectively consider the problems with which preventive medicine is faced and where and when remedial measures are most needed.   For instance, we find that the frequency of death in the first year of life, i.e. the infant mortality rate, becomes considerably greater as we pass down the social scale from the professional classes to the general labourer.   Regardless of the factors that lead to this result, we know at least that such a problem exists and needs attention.   Again, we may observe that cases of typhoid fever are more frequently notified from one type of area than from another. The cause is unknown but a problem is defined. Or, finally, the records may show that the death-rates of young children from the common infectious diseases are higher in the more crowded urban communities of a country than in the less crowded. Can we counteract that unfavourable experience of the over-crowded areas ?

The initial use of such statistics, as accurately and completely collected and compiled as is possible, is therefore to *direct attention* to the problems of health or ill-health presented by the population under study. Without such figures we can have but little knowledge of the most important fields for action, and the collection and tabulation of vital statistical data are, therefore, fundamental to public health work. In other words, the certificates of death and sickness that the doctor in his daily work is required to complete are not merely ephemeral bits of paper to satisfy legal demands. They may well make serious contributions to the problems of preventive medicine. Needless to say, there will be difficulties. Diagnosis and accurate certification are not easy tasks. The aids to them and their resulting accuracy must change from time to time and vary from place to place. Every medical statistician must be aware of that. But if we await perfection we shall wait for ever. So long as we are not ignorant of the imperfections much can be learnt from these imperfect records of mortality and sickness. For instance, in spite of some undoubtedly wrong diagnoses we are perfectly well aware of the marked seasonal distribution of poliomyelitis in Great Britain and the problem that that distribution raises in the epidemiology of this disease. In spite of the errors in determining the cause of death we are aware that more men than women die of cancer of the lung. And so on.

The second, and of course closely associated, object in the collection of such figures is the determination of the basic *reasons* for the contrasts observed. For unless we can determine those reasons, the development of effective preventive measures must obviously be hampered and may be misdirected. Why, to take the examples given above, do infants of the more impoverished classes die at a higher rate than

those of the wealthier ?   To what extent, for instance, is it
due to the malnourishment of the mother and child, to what
extent to overcrowding in the home and a more frequent
risk of specific infections, to what extent to ignorance of how
to care for the infant, or even, sometimes, to frank neglect
of it ?

Is a higher incidence, or an epidemic, of typhoid fever
in a particular area or type of area due to a defective water
supply, to milk-borne infections, or to some other form of
transmission ?   Does the pre-school child die more frequently
under conditions of overcrowding because such conditions
expose it to a greater risk of infection early in life, or does
it succumb more easily to the infection it has acquired
through factors associated with overcrowding, such as malnutrition or, possibly, lack of skilled attention in the early
stages of illness ?

Here the statistical method comes into play, endeavouring
to disentangle the chain of causation and allowing us, sometimes, to determine the most important factors in need of
correction.   Since we are dealing with uncontrolled observations, often liable to errors, the task may be very difficult ;
the effects of the " multiplicity of causes " often cannot be
completely distinguished, e.g. the effects on health of overcrowding *per se* as apart from the features of poverty which
invariably accompany it.   But the original vital statistics
having indicated the problem and their analysis having, at
least, suggested a cause and effect, we may be able to progress
further by a more deliberate collection of additional data or
sometimes by a specifically designed experiment.

However that may be, good vital statistics must be
the essential forerunner of the development of preventive
measures designed to promote the health and well-being of
any population, or of some particular fraction of it, and must
serve as one of the fundamental " yardsticks " for determining the success or failure of such measures.   They are fundamental to the study of epidemiology in the modern sense
of that word, *i.e.* the community characteristics of every
disease.

## Summary

The statistical method is required in the interpretation of figures which are at the mercy of numerous influences, and its object is to determine whether individual influences can be isolated and their effects measured.  The essence of the method lies in the determination that we are really comparing like with like, and that we have not overlooked a relevant factor which is present in Group A and absent from Group B.  The variability of human beings in their illnesses and in their reactions to them is a fundamental reason *for* the planned clinical trial and not *against* it.  Large numbers are not invariably required and it is clear that in particular circumstances even one or two cases well observed may give information of vital importance.

Vital statistics and their analysis are essential features of public health work, to define its problems, to determine, as far as possible, cause and effect, and to measure the success or failure of the steps taken to deal with such problems. They are fundamental to the study of epidemiology.

## II

## COLLECTION OF STATISTICS : SAMPLING

READERS of the early volumes of the *Journal of the Royal Statistical Society* will be struck by one marked characteristic. In their surveys of the state of the housing, education, or health of the population in the 1830's, it was the aim of the pioneers of that time to study and enumerate *every* member of the community with which they were concerned —the town in Lancashire, the borough of East London, the country village, whatever it may have been. That aim was frequently brought to nought by the very weight of the task. Sometimes the collection of the data was beyond their capacity in time, staff, and money ; sometimes, having done their best to collect them, they were weighed down by the statistical analysis that the results demanded. In contrast, the worker today would (or should) instinctively reflect on the possibility of solving such a problem by means of sampling.

By the method of sampling he may make these, and many other, tasks not only practicable but, often, more, rather than less, accurate. He will, of course, be introducing an additional error, the sampling error due to the fact that he has studied only a proportion of the total. However perfect the sample may be, that is inevitable. But owing to the fact that the work of observation and recording is made so much lighter, it may well be that it can be carried out with more precision and more uniformly by a smaller number of workers and, perhaps, by more highly skilled workers. Further, with a sample of, say, 1 in 10 it may be possible to pursue and complete the records for all, or very nearly all, the persons included. The attempt to enumerate the whole population may lead, through the practical difficulties, to a loss of an appreciable number of the observations required.

With such an incomplete " whole " population we are then, in fact, left not only with a sample but with one that raises doubts that we cannot resolve as to whether it is representative. With the completed random sample of 1 in 10 we can, on the other hand, justifiably infer the values that exist in the whole population—or, more strictly, the limits between which they are likely to lie.

It follows that in setting in train the collection of statistical data to illuminate some problem the first questions that the worker must ask himself are : Precisely what data do I need ? Can I adequately investigate the problem by means of a sample ? If so, how shall I set about obtaining a sufficiently large and representative sample ?

## Drawing a Sample

Let us suppose first of all that there is a population, or " universe," which can be readily sampled—whether, for example, it be of houses in a town, clinical records in a hospital, or medically qualified men and women on a register. Experience has shown that an apparently quite haphazard method that leaves the choice to the worker is very unlikely to be truly haphazard. He will unconsciously pick too many (or too few) houses at the corner of the street, too many (or too few) bulky clinical files, too many (or too few) surnames beginning with a particular letter. The bias may be quite unknown either in kind or degree. But it is no less likely to be there and must be avoided. It must be avoided by setting up rules of choice, to make that choice completely random and quite free of any element of personal selection.

In their simplest form the rules will give everyone in the population a precisely *equal* chance of appearing in the sample. If the individual components of the population are already numbered serially, say from 1 to 970, then the required sample can be readily drawn with the aid of tables of random sampling numbers (see pp. 344 to 359). Starting randomly at, say, Set VII (p. 350), columns 14, 15, and 16, row 12, the numbers of the " individuals " required (whether they be houses, files, or names) are 682, 708, 732, 167, 190, etc., (987 is ignored as it is outside the range. Similarly if any number appears for a second or third time it is ignored.) The process is continued until a sample of the size regarded as sufficient has been drawn, *e.g.* a total of 97 numbers, a sample of 1 in 10. Every number has had an equal chance of appearing and thus the sample is free from bias.

It does not inevitably follow that the sample is a " good " sample, in the sense that it is a true cross-section of the population. The play of chance itself must, of course, sometimes produce an unusual and, therefore, unrepresentative picture. If the sample is large (some hundreds) it is not likely to be seriously distorted ; if it is very small (20 or less) it could easily be grossly in error. The solution to that dilemma must lie principally in a larger sample, but it can also sometimes be partially found by the device of *stratification*.

### The Stratified Sample

Given sufficient knowledge of the universe to be sampled we may divide it into well-defined sub-groups or *strata* and then draw our sample of 1 in *n* from each of these strata separately. Within each stratum the choice is still entirely random, but automatically we have ensured that the final total sample includes the right proportion of each of the strata. For example, in sampling a population of children to measure their heights and weights we might first divide it into boys and girls and, within each sex, into the age groups 5–8, 9–12, and 13–15 years. Within each of these 6 groups we would then draw our sample of, say, 1 in 8 by the method given above. The total sample will clearly be 1 in 8 and at the same time it must contain the correct proportions of boys and girls of the different age groups.

Sometimes it may be better to go one stage further and to use a different sampling fraction in the different strata. Thus, suppose the population of children to be sampled was as follows :—

| Years of age | Boys | Girls |
|:---:|:---:|:---:|
| 5–8 | 156 | 148 |
| 9–12 | 624 | 635 |
| 13–15 | 49 | 52 |

If we use the same sampling fraction, 1 in 8, throughout we may have a sufficient number of the 5–8 year group, more than we need of the 9–12 year group, and too few of the 13–15 year group—particularly if we wish to examine the measurements within each group separately. We might, therefore, choose to take 1 in 5 of the 5–8 year group, 1 in 20 of the 9–12 year group, and as many as 1 in 2 of the 13–15 year group (giving 25–30 observations in each stratum). Within each stratum the choice is still random and the chance of appearing is equal. Between the strata the chance has been allowed to vary but its level is *known* for each component group and it can, therefore, be taken into account in reaching a figure for the total sample. Thus we might reach the following results :—

| Years of age | (1) Number of children in the sample | | (2) Mean height in the sample (cms.) | | (3)=(2)×(1) Sum of heights in the sample (cms.) | | (4) Sampling fraction | | (5)=(3)×(4) Estimated sum of heights in population (cms.) | |
|---|---|---|---|---|---|---|---|---|---|---|
| | Boys | Girls | Boys | Girls | Boys | Girls | Boys | Girls | Boys | Girls |
| 5–8 | 31 | 30 | 115 | 113 | 3565 | 3390 | 1 in 5 | 1 in 5 | 17,825 | 16,950 |
| 9–12 | 31 | 32 | 138 | 135 | 4278 | 4320 | 20 | 20 | 85,560 | 86,400 |
| 13–15 | 25 | 26 | 156 | 159 | 3900 | 4134 | 2 | 2 | 7,800 | 8,268 |

The estimated mean height of all the children in the population will then be the sum of the column (5) above (222,803 cms.) divided by the total population of children (1664) or 134 cms. In reaching this result we have, it will be seen, allowed for the unequal sampling fractions which were adopted. (Since the samples are not quite perfect fractions it would be slightly more accurate to " weight " the sample means directly by the total numbers of children in the population, *i.e.*

$$[(115 \times 156) + (113 \times 148) + (138 + 624) + (135 \times 635) + (156 \times 49) + (159 \times 52)] = (222,413 \div 1664) = 134 \text{ cms.})$$

If stratification is to be worth while it is clear that we must know, or have good grounds to suspect, that the strata differ appreciably from one another in the characteristic, or characteristics, in which we are interested, *e.g.* that men differ

from women, that one age group differs from another, that
doctors differ from lawyers. If the strata do not differ or, in
other words, the population as a whole is relatively uniform,
then there is no point in dividing the population into sub-
groups. Obviously there can be no gain in accuracy in such
circumstances. It is, therefore, necessary to think closely
before adopting the rather more involved technique. And
clearly it is impossible to adopt it if the universe is not
defined in the necessary detail.

## Sampling by Stages

Sometimes a strictly random sample may be very difficult
indeed to draw and it may be more practicable to take the
required sample in a series of stages. Suppose, for example,
we wished to learn the number of X-ray examinations made
of all the patients entering hospital in a given week in
England and Wales. It would be very difficult, if not impossible, to devise a scheme which would allow the universe
of patients to be directly sampled. On the other hand it
would be relatively simple to list the towns and rural districts of the whole country and randomly to draw a sample
of, say, 1 in 12. Within this sample of areas all the hospitals
could then be listed by name and a random sample of these
be drawn, say 1 in 5. Within this sample of hospitals 1 in 4
of the patients entering in the given week could be randomly
chosen for observation and recording. Thus by stages we
have reached the required sample. If appropriate, stratification could be introduced at one or more stages, e.g. the areas
could be sampled in broad regions and subdivided into
urban and rural, the hospitals could be broadly classified
and sampled according to their function, and the patients
could be subdivided by their sex and age and then randomly
selected.

## Other Methods of Sampling

It will be seen that the use of random sampling numbers
requires that the universe be already numbered—or, at least,
be numbered as the required numbers are drawn. If that is

not the case, one method of sampling a list of items that is *usually* effective is to start from a random number and then systematically take every *n*th name (or file, etc.).    In this way, suppose that from a list of 1000 clinical case records 125, or 1 in 8, are to be drawn for study.    For the starting-point a number between 1 and 8 is randomly selected, say 3. Every 8th file from that point is then drawn—3, 11, 19, 27, 35, etc.    This procedure is known as " systematic " sampling.

It should be fully realised that in certain circumstances it can give a biased result.    For example, every fiftieth house in a series of streets might conceivably produce a sample with too many corner houses and too few in the centre of the street.    More generally, the population to be sampled may have some periodicity in its characteristics.    The fixed interval method of sampling may then produce relatively too many high (or too many low) values according to where the interval happens to fall in relation to the periodicity.

Occasionally some other simple method may present itself.    For instance, every man serving in the Royal Air Force has a service number allotted to him at entry.    It would be proper to choose a 1 in 10 sample by selecting all men whose number ended in, say, an 8, or a 1 in 1000 sample by selecting all men whose number ended in, say, 345.    On the other hand, to choose all the men whose surnames began with certain letters is open to grave objection.    Suppose we take the letters M, J, W, and O.    In Great Britain the sample will certainly include unduly large numbers of the Scotch (Mackintosh, etc.), the Welsh (Jones and Williams), and the Irish (O'Brien, etc.).    Yet if we deliberately leave out the letters M, J, W, and O we shall have too few of these nationals.    The method is not a good one and should be rejected.

Another procedure that is likely to be quite satisfactory in many situations is to select persons born on specified dates in any month in any year, *e.g.* on the 9th, 16th, and 27th, giving a sample of almost 1 in 10 (36 in 365).

With such special methods we have constantly to reflect on this question : " In relation to the observations we seek to make, will this mode of choice bring one kind of person rather than another into the net ? In short, will it result in a biased picture ? " Much thought must be given to that before embarking upon a sampling scheme and particularly upon one of an unorthodox nature.

## Non-response

One of the most difficult problems that will arise in working with a random sample is that of " non-response." Some of the persons included in the sample may refuse to be interviewed ; some may be too ill ; some, perhaps, cannot be traced ; some of the children, in the example above, may be absent when we visit the school to take the measurements ; even dealing merely with a file of clinical case histories the information required may be missing from some proportion. Every missing " individual " (person or item of information) detracts from the randomness of the sample. We do not know, and usually cannot know, that the individuals that we *can* include give a true picture of the total population. The absentees, whatever the cause of their non-response, may have different characteristics from those who are present. In other words, the sample observed has thus become a biased sample and if the number of missing items is large it may be very seriously biased. It is for this reason that every possible effort must be made to gather into a drawn sample all those originally included in it. Indeed, one should remember that the best-laid sampling scheme is quite meaningless unless this effort is made. If there are missing individuals (and almost always there are some) then much thought must be given to them, as to whether their absence is likely to distort the sample in relation to the particular facts under study.

Sometimes, inevitably, the missing items may be numerous and it may be worth while drawing a random sub-sample upon which more intensive efforts can be made to draw in 100 per cent. of the required individuals. The complete, or nearly complete, sub-sample can then be compared with the less satisfactory main sample to measure the amount of bias, if any, that may exist in the latter. To give a specific example, in one inquiry into the earnings of doctors, before the advent of the National Health Service in Great Britain, nearly 6000 medically qualified men and women were approached for information. It was realised that the non-response rate would almost certainly be high—in fact it proved to be as much as 27 per cent. A small random sub-sample of 1 in 10 (or 600) was, therefore, specially drawn. This much smaller number could then be more extensively studied from available records (*e.g.* the nature of their speciality) and more assiduously pursued for a reply. Its results strongly indicated that the more extensive income figures derived from the larger but incomplete group could not be very seriously at fault.

Another procedure that may sometimes reduce the tendency of non-response lies in brevity and simplicity in one's requirements. Too many and too difficult questions do not encourage co-operation—particularly in the approach by questionnaire. There is always a desire to learn many things at the same time and by giving way to it one may end in learning nothing because of the resulting excessively high incidence of non-response. Once again a partial solution may sometimes be sought by using sub-samples for different questions. Thus in studying the services given by general practitioners to their patients over a calendar year a sample of 6000 doctors was drawn. To reduce substantially the amount of work required of each, they were allocated randomly in sub-samples of 500 to one month of the year. During that one month only they were asked to keep a complete record of the number of attendances by and visits to patients. Thus for every month a fairly large sample of the universe of practitioners was available to give a measure of the services rendered in that month and a summation of the sample values would give the figure for the year. Further, each doctor was asked to carry out a relatively small task although an appreciable proportion (one-third) of the total body was used. In addition, information was sought on five other matters by randomly dividing the sub-samples of 500 into five further sub-samples of 100 each. One such group was asked to record the number of operations performed, a second group the number of injections given, a third the number of night visits paid, and so on.

Thus the demands on any individual were carefully restricted and the non-response rate proved to be very satisfactorily small (2–3 per cent.). The original random sampling scheme was thereby maintained practically unimpaired. (For a full discussion of these sample surveys of the " doctor's day and pay " see the *Journal of the Royal Statistical Society*, 1951, Series A, **114**, 1.)

### Confidence Intervals

The methods of random sampling described above have one further advantage. When an average value or a proportion is calculated from the sample we can estimate with a given degree of probability what that value or proportion must be in the population sampled. More strictly speaking we can calculate the interval in which we can be fairly confident that the population value will lie. Thus if in a sample of 100 observations we find the proportion of persons hard of hearing to be 18 per cent., we can be fairly confident that the proportion of such persons in the universe sampled lies between 10 and 26 per cent. If that range is too wide for our purposes, then the only solution is to take a larger sample of observations. More attention will be paid to these aspects of samples in later chapters.

In conclusion, the importance of this concept of random sampling could not be more clearly emphasised than in the illuminating comment once made by a newcomer to that field :—

" The necessity of using a true random sample of the population in a survey of this nature is well known and needs no emphasis ; nevertheless, it may be added that contact with such a sample provided a new experience. The actual practice of medicine is virtually confined to those members of the population who either are ill, or think they are ill, or are thought by somebody else to be ill, and these so amply fill up the working day that in the course of time one comes unconsciously to believe that they are typical of the whole. This is not the case. The use of a random sample brings to light those individuals who are ill and know they are ill, but have no intention of doing anything about it, as well as those who never have been ill, and probably never will be till their final illness. These would have been inaccessible to any method of approach but that of the random sample. Perhaps one of the deepest impressions left in my mind after conducting the survey is the fundamental importance of the random sample—unusual as it is in most medical work. It does not make for ease of working : all sorts of inaccessible personalities may be encountered, and it is more time-consuming ; but the degree of self-selection imposed by the population on itself in regard to its approach to doctors inevitably gives anything other than a random sample a considerable bias. It has, however, one disadvantage in that the percentage of refusals may be high." ("The Social Medicine of Old Age." The Report of an inquiry in Wolverhampton made in 1948 by Dr. J. H. Sheldon, C.B.E., F.R.C.P.)

## Summary

In statistical work in the different fields of medicine we are constantly studying samples of larger populations. Sometimes we shall wish deliberately to draw such a sample from the population. Although in so doing we shall introduce a sampling error (which can be estimated), we shall nevertheless often gain in precision by the greater and more skilful attention that can be given to the collection of a smaller amount of data.

The sample should be drawn by some strictly random process that gives every individual in the parent population an equal chance (or known chance) of appearing in the sample. Random sampling numbers provide such a process. If groups within the population vary widely in their relevant characteristics, it may well be advantageous first to divide the population into those groups, or strata, and then to draw

c

a sample from each stratum appropriately. Sampling by stages may sometimes be necessary, *e.g.* by selecting towns within a region, hospitals within the selected towns, and patients within the selected hospitals. When these methods are impracticable a sample may sometimes be effectively derived by taking every $n$th name, or unit, from a list. This method, however, calls for careful thought.

Every effort must be made to keep non-response (or missing items) to a minimum. The most careful sampling scheme is of no value if a large proportion of the required data is not in the end obtained.

(*For exercise see p. 312*)

# III

## COLLECTION OF STATISTICS : SELECTION

In the previous chapter attention was devoted mainly to the situations in which a sample of observations could be deliberately drawn for study from some known universe. The basic problems are then to define the universe and to find an appropriate means of drawing a random sample from it. Often in medicine, and particularly in clinical medicine, we are not in that situation at all. We have to accept whatever sample of observations (persons, records, etc.) may present itself in the natural course of daily events. *What is the nature of the sample* then becomes the crucial question. What are its characteristics ? Are we entitled to argue from the particular to the general ? For that is what we are invariably hoping to do. In seeking to advance knowledge we are, for example, not very interested in the fact that a particular and relatively small number of patients with a specific disease rapidly recovered when treated in some defined way. We are intensely interested in knowing whether that form of treatment is the method of choice for the generality of patients with that disease. We must then consider very carefully whether the sample is representative of all such patients and not in any way biased or " selected."

It is important to be clear on the meaning the statistician attaches to the word " selected." By a selected sample he denotes a sample which is not representative of the universe of which it is a part. The selection may have been deliberate, in which case the form of selection is known and the lack of comparability between the sample and the universe is usually perfectly clear. For instance, if, in addition to the use of appropriate antibiotics, the treatment of respiratory tuberculosis by means of some form of surgery were confined in a sanatorium to patients with signs of disease in one lung only, then it is obvious that these patients are *not* a representative sample of all patients with phthisis, but are selected

25

on the criterion of only one lung affected. To compare their mortality experience with that of all patients is, therefore, a very doubtful procedure, for we are clearly not comparing like with like in all respects except with regard to surgical treatment. Even without that treatment the death-rate of patients with only one lung affected may differ materially from the death-rate of the general run of patients.

More often, however, the " selection " is not deliberate but is quite unforeseen or is unrealised. To say, therefore, that Mr. So-and-so's figures relate to a selected sample of patients is not an aspersion on Mr. So-and-so's scientific honesty ; the statement implies only that owing to the method of collection of the figures, or to the limited field in which Mr. So-and-so was able to operate, it is quite impossible for his sample to be representative. It may be that with care that selection might have been avoided ; often it is unavoidable. Its possible presence cannot be too carefully remembered or taken into account in interpreting all statistics. As, however, it is frequently overlooked by the authors of studies in medicine, this chapter is devoted to a series of examples.

### Examples of Selection

#### SEX RATIO AT BIRTH

As a simple illustration I once took from *The Times* newspaper the frequency with which male and female births were recorded in the birth column. In 1935 the number of male births was 3304 and female births 3034, so that the sex ratio was 1089 males for each 1000 females. According to the Registrar-General's figures for England and Wales, the sex ratio of births in the country as a whole rarely exceeds 1050. It is clear that from the point of view of sex ratio the births recorded in *The Times* are unlikely to be representative of the births in the country as a whole. It is possible that first births are more frequently recorded in those columns than births of a later order, and that such births have a different sex ratio ; or that proud parents are more likely to record their heirs than their daughters ; or that the sex ratio differs between social classes. Whatever the explanation, with such a sample of births, if that were all that were available, one could not generalise about the universe with any security.

## HOSPITAL STATISTICS

Turning to a more medical problem, hospital statistics can very rarely be regarded as unselected.  The patients are frequently drawn from particular areas and from particular social classes.  Still more important, in many diseases only those patients who are seriously ill are likely to be taken to hospital.  It is obvious that we cannot determine with any approach to accuracy the fatality-rate of any disease, say, measles at ages 0–5 years, if our statistics are based mainly upon the seriously ill—patients, for example, in whom a secondary pneumonia has developed—and ignore the mass of children whose symptoms are so slight that they can safely be treated in their own homes.  Of *all* children with measles those in hospital would then form only a small and stringently selected group ;  our deductions from such a group are correspondingly limited, especially with regard to such factors as the incidence of complications and the rate of fatality or recovery.  It is not too much to say that there is hardly any disease in which a hospital population must not initially be regarded with suspicion if it is desired to argue from the sample to the universe of all patients.  No such argument should be attempted without a preliminary and rigorous examination of the possible ways in which selection may have occurred.

The same difficulty arises with secular comparisons— *e.g.* when we wish to see whether the fatality from some disease has changed from one year to another.  In each year the fatality-rate is measured upon the patients admitted to hospital, and in each year those patients are a sample of all patients with the disease in question.  It must be considered whether that sample has changed in type.  In both years the sample may be a selected sample but the selection may not be identical.  The kind of patient admitted may have changed.  For example, in a group of American hospitals it was reported that the fatality-rate from appendicitis declined from 6 per cent. in 1928 to 3·5 per cent. in 1932. Is that a " real " decline, due to more efficient treatment maybe, or was there a concurrent change in the types of patients admitted ?  Examination of the basic figures shows that in these hospitals in 1928 some 2500 patients were operated upon, while in 1932 the number had risen to 3500, an increase of 40 per cent.  It is impossible to believe that an increase of 40 per cent. in five years is a real increase in the incidence of appendicitis.  It is more likely that the desire for admission to these particular hospitals or some criterion of admission had changed, that some patients who were admitted in 1932 would not have entered them in 1928.  It is possible, therefore, that the type of entry has changed as well as the volume—perhaps that milder cases were admitted and operated upon in 1932 which were not present in the 1928 series.  In the absence of positive evidence on that point the change in fatality cannot be accepted at its face value or as satisfactory evidence of the effect of a change in some other factor—*e.g.* the benefit of earlier admission to hospital in 1932 than in 1928.  The following two questions must always be considered.  Has there been a change in the population from which the samples are drawn at two dates —*i.e.* a change relevant to the question at issue ?  At each date was there an equal probability that a particular type of patient would be included in the sample ?

### DAY OF TREATMENT

In measurements of the value of some form of treatment statistics of the following type are frequently given :—

| Day of Disease upon which Treatment was first given | Fatality-rate per cent. of Treated Patients |
|:---:|:---:|
| 1 | 1·3 |
| 2 | 3·6 |
| 3 | 7·5 |
| 4 | 9·3 |
| 5 | 12·8 |
| 6 or later | 16·4 |

It is possible that the level of this fatality-rate at the different stages is seriously influenced by selection.  Let us suppose, as is often the case, that the treatment is given to patients brought to hospital and that *all* patients do not necessarily go to hospital.  Then on the first day of disease a variety of patients will be taken to hospital, in some of whom, in the absence of the special treatment, the disease is destined to run a mild course, in others a severe course.  The presence of a proportion of mild cases will ensure a relatively low fatality-rate, even if the special treatment has no specific effect.  But as time passes this proportion of mild cases in the hospital sample is likely to decline.  By the time, say, the fourth day of disease is reached, a number of patients who were not seriously ill will have recovered or be on the way to recovery.  Their removal to hospital is unnecessary. On the other hand, patients who have made a turn for the worse or whose condition has become serious are likely to be taken to hospital for immediate treatment.  Thus on the later days of disease the sample removed to hospital for treatment may well contain an increasing proportion of persons seriously ill, it obviously being unnecessary to transfer those who are making an uninterrupted recovery. In other words the patients removed to hospital on the fourth day of disease may not be a random sample of all patients who have reached that day of the disease but may consist rather, perhaps mainly, of patients still seriously ill.  Such a group will certainly have a relatively high fatality-rate.

Another example of this statistical difficulty may be taken from some fatality-rates recorded for appendicitis.  It has been reported that in a group of cases 2 per cent. died of those admitted to hospital within 24 hours of the onset of symptoms compared with 10 per cent. of those whose admission was delayed till after 72 hours.  But it is likely that the group of patients admitted early is composed of a proportion of the seriously ill and a proportion that would do well whether admitted to hospital or not.  On the other hand, those who are admitted after a delay of three days from onset are likely to be patients whose condition is serious, and clearly those whose condition has become quiescent are unlikely to be taken to hospital at that point of time.  If such a sequence of events occurs, it is clear that the group of patients admitted early is not in *pari materia* with the group of patients admitted late.  Selection may not be the whole explanation of the difference between the fatality-rates ; indeed it is not likely to be, for there are excellent reasons for the early treatment of appendicitis.  But it is a possible factor with statistics such as these, which makes it very difficult to measure accurately the *magnitude* of the advantage.

### Post-mortem Statistics

In an attempt to obtain more accurate data emphasis is sometimes placed upon post-mortem statistics.  One has, however, to remember that this increased accuracy is gained only at the risk of very selective material.  It is rare for every death to be subjected to autopsy and those that are chosen are by no means chosen randomly.  They are more likely to be chosen *because* the cause of death is obscure or because the case presents features of special interest.  No measure of these or other selective factors is likely to be easily made.

In this field of autopsy statistics it is, too, important to note that the interpretation of the observed frequency of occurrence of *two* disorders in the same person is very difficult indeed.  Thus it may appear that the number of persons found to have the two conditions is appreciably more than would be expected on a purely chance basis, *i.e.* based upon the known frequency of the occurrence of each condition separately.  But the occurrence of two disorders in the same person not only may make it more likely that he will seek hospital care, it may also make it more likely that he will die and thus come to autopsy.  Such a possible selective mechanism must always be thought upon with much care in the specific study.

### Follow-up Studies

Because of their incompleteness, follow-up studies of patients are often subject to selective influences.  In basing conclusions upon the patients who *are* successfully followed-up we are presuming that the results we record for such a group would be unchanged if we succeeded in tracing and adding in the lost-to-sight patients ; in other words, we presume that the characteristic " being followed-up " is not correlated with the characteristic that we are measuring, *e.g.* survival. Is that likely to be true ? On the one hand it might be easier to learn that a patient is dead—through the Registrar-General or other official records—than that he is alive and gone to Australia. On the other hand the living may answer inquiries more readily than the relatives of the dead. Once more all we can do is to consider the likelihood and nature of selective factors in any specific situation, or, of course, better still, avoid them by making at all costs the follow-up comprehensive.

### Infant Feeding

That on *a priori* reasoning there is a very strong case for the breast feeding of infants is obvious, but to secure a measure of the degree of its advantages is, owing to selective factors, extremely difficult.

Under actual conditions of life we cannot obtain two groups of infants, exclusively breast-fed and exclusively bottle-fed from birth, who will remain in their respective groups whether their progress is good or bad. If a baby on the breast is not thriving, its diet is likely to be changed to partial or complete artificial feeding. Thus, a purely breast-fed group would contain mainly babies who are doing well ; those who are doing badly would often be transferred at different ages to the artificially fed group to the detriment of the latter in statistical comparisons. Even if one were to preclude any such selective additions to the artificially fed group, one would still have by the withdrawals from the breast-fed group a differentially selected group of breast-fed babies—unless the babies selected for artificial feeding were deliberately retained in the breast-fed group in spite of the change of feeding ; but such a group could not truly be designated " breast-fed " and a comparison would be valueless.

Such selective factors must be closely considered in interpreting results in this field.

## Self-selection

An interesting, if old, example of what may be termed *self-selection* is worth notice.   In 1931 the Industrial Pulmonary Disease Committee of the Medical Research Council was initiating its inquiries into whether the working health and capacity of coal-miners were impaired by the inhalation of pure anthracite dust.   To begin with, a study was made of the size and age constitution of the working population at the South Wales anthracite collieries.   Underground workers had to be excluded from the investigation, since such workers, as well as being exposed to various concentrations of anthracite dust in the atmosphere, may in addition have been exposed to silica or other dust.   If the health of these workers was found to be impaired it would be impossible to implicate pure anthracite dust as the responsible agent.   The impairment might equally well be due to exposure to stone dust containing silica, which, it is well known, can produce serious damage to health.   In addition, it was considered necessary to exclude surface workers who had at any time worked underground, since the effects of exposure to silica dust will not necessarily be immediately apparent and also because impaired health may have been the reason for transference from underground to surface work.   This was, in fact, known to be the reason in numerous cases, so that such workers would be a highly select group.   Attention was therefore turned to workers who were exposed to anthracite dust on the surface and had *always* worked on the surface.   Such workers, it was found, are employed on a relatively light task.   Not only, as stated, was there a tendency to draft to it operatives who had previously worked underground and had for one reason or another become partially incapacitated, but in addition it was clear that a large number of boys were initially employed upon this work but rapidly moved away to other work.   In the main these boys were drafted underground where the physical labour was heavier but the rate of pay superior.

The inevitable inference is that the healthy and strong individuals will transfer to underground work while those who remain on the surface are likely to be of under-average physique and health. In other words, there has been a form of self-selection. If the examination of such surface workers showed that they included a high proportion with impaired health or that they suffered an unduly high rate of sickness in comparison with some standard, this result could not with security be ascribed to the effects of dust inhalation. It might be considerably influenced by the fact that these surface workers were, through the operation of selection, initially less healthy than a random sample of all surface workers. Such features of physical (and mental) selection must necessarily bear heavily upon the characteristics of persons entering, and remaining in, all specific occupations.

This investigation in South Wales also revealed an example of selection through volunteers being accepted for examination. For the reasons outlined above no inquiry was at that time made at the collieries and the field of study was transferred to dock-workers exposed to anthracite dust. Of 250 such workers it was arranged to examine, clinically and radiologically, a sample of 40 operatives—namely, 15 workers employed for only 3–4 years and 25 older workers with 15–40 years' service. These two groups were selected at random from the complete list of operatives, to ensure, as far as possible with such small numbers, a representative sample. At the examination eleven of these men were absent and to make good the deficiency in numbers volunteers were secured in place of the absentees.

The results of the examinations suggested that there was a readiness to volunteer on the part of individuals who, on account of some known or suspected disability, desired to be medically examined. Such substitutions may, therefore, result in the sample ceasing to be random and representative of the population from which it was drawn. The stipulated *quantity* had been maintained but the *quality* had been lost.

It should also be noted that if no substitutes had been accepted we still would not know that the 29 operatives who did attend were a cross-section of the originally chosen 40. Why did the 29 choose to come, why did the 11 stay away ? If it was for any reasons connected directly or indirectly with their state of health, then the sample attending *must* give a biased picture. The neurotically inclined may more readily seek medical examination, they may more readily avoid it. The physically fit man may regard it as a waste of time ; or, having nothing to fear he may be quick to submit. We do not know (or very rarely know) the motives at work and the greater, therefore, the departure from the original sample, the greater must be our doubts in interpreting the results we record.

### Volunteers for Treatment

For very similar reasons a sample which is composed of volunteers, *i.e.* self-selected individuals, is not likely to be representative of the population at large. If, for example, the prevention of the common cold by a vaccine is offered to some specified group of persons, the volunteers are likely to belong mainly to that section of the group which suffers most frequently or severely from the complaint. They hope for some advantage from the treatment. Those who have been free from colds for a long time are unlikely to come forward. Those vaccinated are, therefore, a select group, not comparable with the remainder of the population from which they were drawn (or, more strictly, drew themselves). In such a position the question must always arise : is the act of volunteering correlated with any factor which may influence the final results of the experiment ? In the present example, if the vaccinated volunteers are mainly the common cold " susceptibles " and the non-volunteers are mainly the " resistants," then clearly the contrasts between their attack rates that we might make to measure the value of the vaccine are quite meaningless.

### Questionnaires

Inquiries carried out by means of questionnaires are *par excellence* those in which selection must be suspected. In all such inquiries replies to the questions put—even to the simplest question—are received from only a proportion of the individuals to whom the form is sent.    There can never be the slightest certainty that the individuals who choose to reply are a representative sample of all the individuals approached ; indeed very often it is extremely unlikely that they are representative.    For a simple example, one may take the inquiry made by the Editor of *The Lancet* into the Present-day Openings of Medical Practice (*Lancet*, 1935, 2, 512).    To measure the success with which recent graduates had been attended in their profession a questionnaire of three relatively simple questions was addressed to the 1490 men and women who in 1930 registered their names with the General Medical Council, viz. (1) What branch of medicine have you taken up ?    (2) What led you to this choice ? and (3) What was your approximate income from professional work last year ?    To overcome objections to providing such personal information no clue to the identity of the corre- spondent was required.    Yet of the individuals approached only 44 per cent. replied.    Are these persons a representative sample of the 1490 ?    It is possible, as is clearly pointed out in the report, that there might be a tendency for those who have been successful in their profession to be more eager to register their success than for those who have failed to register their failure.    Alternatively, the latter might under the veil of secrecy be glad of the opportunity of stating frankly the drawbacks of the profession.    Those who have turned to other professions might tend not to reply, under the im- pression that the inquiry cannot concern them.    Successful and busy individuals might be unwilling to give time to the inquiry.    It is impossible to determine whether any such factors are operative in the determination to answer or not to answer.    The difficulty is inherent in all inquiries carried out by this method and must never be ignored.

It almost invariably *is* ignored by the daily press, which will report that 70 per cent. of some body, for example, think this or that about atomic warfare, the National Health Service, or the President of the United States, and overlooks the fact that the 70 per cent. is based upon the quite small proportion of the body who chose to answer.

It is possible sometimes, however, to see whether the final sample is or is not biased in certain known respects. For example, suppose the population to be approached consists of all the persons on the medical register at a given time. For each of these persons we may know such characteristics as sex, age at qualification, degrees or other qualifications obtained, type of medical work upon which the person is engaged—general practice, public health, etc. Only 50 per cent. of the total population, let us suppose, answer the questionnaire addressed to them all. In the statistical analysis of the available answers we can at least see, and it is of course essential to do so, whether the sample is representative of the universe in relation to the *known* characteristics of the latter. If 50 per cent. of the men and 50 per cent. of the women answered, then the sample obtained is not biased in its sex ratio ; but if 60 per cent. of the men and only 25 per cent. of the women answered, then a bias has been introduced, for the ratio of males to females in the sample is different from the real ratio in the universe. We must make some allowance for that fact in analysing the results and cannot merely use the sample as it stands. Similarly, we may see whether older and younger persons answered to an equal degree and whether those engaged upon different types of work were equally forthcoming. By such means we can then determine whether or no certain classes of persons have tended to answer more or less readily than others, and thus know whether or no our sample is biased in these known respects and, if necessary, make allowances for it. While such a check is highly important, indeed essential, it cannot be entirely conclusive. Even if the sample *is* representative in the known respects, we cannot be sure that those who chose to answer were in other respects representative of the total. For instance, 50 per cent. of men and 50 per cent. of women may answer, but in *each* group those who answer may mainly consist of those who feel more deeply upon the questions addressed to them, or be those, *mirabile dictu*, who like filling in forms. In other words, the sample is correct in its sex proportions, but for neither sex do we know that the sample is such that it will accurately express the views of the total men and women originally approached.

In reporting these, or similar, inquiries a statement should always be made of the number of missing questionnaires or items. Clearly if 90 per cent. of the required data were obtained, more reliance can be placed upon the results than if the proportion were only 45 per cent., and the reader should be in a position to judge.

The type of simple correction one can sometimes make for a known bias can be demonstrated arithmetically from the following hypothetical figures :—

|  | Male | Female | Total |
|---|---|---|---|
| Number of persons in the universe, all of whom were sent questionnaires    .    .    .    . | 10,000 | 2000 | 12,000 |
| Number of persons who answered . | 6,000 | 500 | 6,500 |
| Mean Income reported by those who answered    .    .    . | £1,200 | £800 | £1,169 |

Using the sample as it stands, we see that the mean income reported by the 6000 men who answered was £1200, and of the 500 women who answered was £800. The mean income of all persons in the sample is, therefore,

$$(6000 \times £1200 + 500 \times £800) \div 6500,$$

which equals £1169. But this figure is clearly too high, since men, on the average, earned more than women, and in the sample we have a ratio of 12 men to 1 woman, whereas in the universe the real ratio is only 5 men to 1 woman (due to the fact that 60 per cent. of the men answered and only 25 per cent. of the women). If we are prepared to believe that for both sexes those who answered were a representative cross-section of the total approached, then the correct estimate of the average income of a person must be obtained by " weighting " the observed mean incomes of the sexes by the correct numbers of persons of each sex. Thus we have (10000 × £1200 + 2000 × £800) ÷ 12000 = £1133. In other words, we are accepting the sample figures as giving a true picture for each sex, but must combine them by using the known true proportion of men to women in the population sampled, in place of the untrue proportion given by the sample.

## House Sampling

Finally an interesting example of selection in taking a sample of houses is suggested in the Ministry of Health's report on the influenza pandemic of 1918 (Reports on Public Health and Medical Subjects, No. 4). To obtain facts as to the incidence and fatality from influenza in 1918–19 a house-to-house inquiry was undertaken in five areas of Leicester, information being obtained *so far as possible* at every fifth house. However, houses which were found closed at the time of visit had to be ignored in this census. But houses in which there are young children are less often found closed and this would tend to affect the age-distribution of the population recorded in the sample. Compared with the population from which it was drawn the sample would be likely to contain an undue proportion of young children and a deficit in the number of adults. Any substitution of another house for the original randomly chosen one cannot correct for this bias in the sample, and such substitutions are to be avoided in sampling inquiries.

It will be noted that a selection of this type would be difficult to foresee. It is here that the statistician has some advantage, for his experience of such inquiries makes him familiar with the methods that are likely to ensure a random sample and those that are likely to lead to one that is unrepresentative of the population from which it is taken. Workers who are unfamiliar with sampling inquiries but wish to embark upon one may, therefore, find his advice of assistance.

## Summary

If we wish to generalise from some sample group of observations—which is invariably the case in practice—we must possess a sample which is representative of the population to which it belongs. In taking samples, deliberately, or in accepting samples that arise in the daily course of events, we must realise that " selection " may occur through the operation of various factors. A selected sample is one which is not representative of the universe, in which one member of the universe sampled has more chance of appearing than another, whether that bias be due to deliberate choice or unconscious selection of the members incorporated in the sample. Self-selection of the members of a group is a common form of bias, e.g. in the physical or mental status of those who follow a certain occupation. Another exceedingly common form of bias lies in the absence of some of the required records, e.g. by persons (uninterested, busy, or lazy, whatever the reason may be) who do not reply to a questionnaire. In generalising from a sample, or in making comparisons between one sample and another, the possible presence of selection must always be very closely considered.

# IV

## COLLECTION OF STATISTICS : FORMS OF
## RECORD AND INQUIRY

IN all scientific work we are involved in asking questions.
In medicine, for example, we may seek to learn the effects
of a specific treatment used upon patients with a specific
disease. But whether we require the population concerned
to make reply themselves to a questionnaire, whether we
seek the information by oral inquiry through ourselves or
trained social workers, or whether we make a clinical examination or adopt some laboratory means of procedure, we
are, in the last analysis, always asking questions. Accordingly, we need a form of record upon which to ask those
questions and to record the answers. One of the first and,
indeed, most decisive steps in any inquiry, therefore, is the
construction of that form—*what* should be included and *how*
it should be included. Each question must be given the
closest thought to see whether it is clear and definite ; what
the possible answers are ; whether the answers can be
adequately, if not wholly accurately, obtained ; how they
can be analysed and put into a statistical table at the end
of the inquiry or experiment. If the questions are incomplete, ill-conceived, or inadequately answered no statistical
analysis, however erudite, can compensate for those defects
or produce the answers that the worker had hoped to get.
The time to remember that is not at the end of an investigation but at its beginning.

We must also remember two other things—on the one
hand that the drafting of clear and unambiguous questions
is an extremely difficult task and, on the other hand, that
many persons find the completion of any form an extremely
difficult task. As the report on the Census of England and

Wales in 1891 emphasised, " those who are conversant with forms and schedules scarcely realise the difficulty which persons, not so conversant, find in filling them up correctly."

## Questions and Answers

In formulating questions, or headings, for inclusion on a form there are a number of basic principles to bear in mind.

(i) To begin with one should consider closely whether there is any *ambiguity in the question* and, consequently, in the answers received. A very simple example can be found in that innocent question which appears on so many forms— age. Age last birthday ? or age nearest birthday ? Generally, one would probably expect to be given the age last birthday. But at any moment of time, about one person in 12 is within one month of their *next* birthday and might therefore consider that the more appropriate age to give. Perhaps it does not matter. But that certainly does not mean that preliminary consideration should not be given to the question ; *a decision should be taken that it does not matter*. In certain circumstances it certainly would matter. For instance, in a group of 100 children aged 5 years *last birthday*, the average age would be $5\frac{1}{2}$ years, or close to it (the individual ages would run from 5 to less than 6). In a group of 100 children aged 5 years to the *nearest birthday* the average age would be 5 years, or close to it (the individual ages would run from $4\frac{1}{2}$ to less than $5\frac{1}{2}$). The bodily measurements of the two groups would obviously differ appreciably since the average ages differ by 6 months. With a form on which " age " is asked for we shall be unaware of what in fact is given. We should, therefore, specify " age last birthday " (or ask for " date of birth " and then make the required calculation ourselves).

Ambiguity in the question also arises if use is made of what may be called " overlapping groups." Thus, in an inquiry into prematurity, the recipient of a form was asked to state the number of babies born within three birth weight groups, (*a*) $2\frac{1}{2}$ to $3\frac{1}{2}$ lb., (*b*) $3\frac{1}{2}$ to $4\frac{1}{2}$ lb., and (*c*) $4\frac{1}{2}$ to $5\frac{1}{2}$ lb. Suppose a baby is born weighing precisely $3\frac{1}{2}$ lb. ; does it

belong to group (*a*) or to group (*b*) ?  Probably most persons
would answer (*b*).  Suppose a baby is born weighing precisely
$4\frac{1}{2}$ lb., does it belong to group (*b*) or to group (*c*) ?  Probably
most persons would answer (*c*).  But suppose a baby is born
weighing precisely $5\frac{1}{2}$ lb.  Does it belong to the table at all ?
On the previous decisions one must say no.  But since the
definition of prematurity is *$5\frac{1}{2}$ lb. or less* it certainly was
intended to belong.  The form of inquiry is therefore poor
since it is ambiguous.  It will be interpreted and answered
differently by different recipients.

(ii) As far as possible *every question should be self-
explanatory* and not require the respondent to consult a
separate sheet of instructions.  The importance of this principle will, of course, vary with the circumstances.  If a few
highly trained persons are making the observations, conducting the clinical examinations, whatever it may be, then
clearly they can be relied upon to turn to, and follow, detailed instructions.  But if the form is to be completed by
large numbers of less trained and less interested persons,
then experience shows that they cannot be relied upon to
read and remember extensive footnotes or instructions.  For
example, in a trial of a vaccine against whooping cough
details might be sought for each affected child of any known
exposure to another case.  Some definitions of the possible
varieties of exposure which are of interest must be given or
some of the answers will undoubtedly be vague and un-
certain.  If possible the definitions should be incorporated
in the question on the form itself.  Thus for each case
occurring the following alternatives of exposure might be
specified *within the question* :—

(*a*) Within the child's own home.
(*b*) At a day nursery.
(*c*) At school.
(*d*) Elsewhere : specify place.
(*e*) No known exposure.

The respondent is thus shown on the form itself the categories
of information that are sought and can answer clearly and
without undue trouble.

(iii) Almost invariably *every question should require some answer*. Without that precaution it is often impossible to know for certain whether a person did not possess some characteristic or whether no information was in fact sought or obtained. For instance, the question at issue may be " did the patient during pregnancy suffer an attack of rubella ? " An answer " yes " is a clear positive but no answer at all, or merely a dash (—), is by no means a clear negative. It *may* mean that but it may, on the other hand, mean that the question was never asked or that no certain information was forthcoming. One does not know. The question should be given in such a form as invariably to require a clear answer ; thus it might be (i) Yes ; (ii) No ; (iii) Not Known. Every question, therefore, needs some final category to make certain that some answer must be given—whether that final category be " not known," " no information," " unspecified," or " other."

(iv) *The degree of accuracy to which measurements are required* should be specified. Should, for example, blood pressures be recorded to the nearest millimetre, to the nearest 5, or to the nearest 10 ? If no specification is given the recorders will inevitably vary amongst themselves in the accuracy to which they work. It may also be necessary sometimes to specify the nature of the measurement required —whether, for instance, body temperatures are to be taken orally or per rectum.

(v) It would seem needless to say that much thought should be given as to *whether it is likely that a particular question can be answered adequately by anyone at all* ; yet much experience of forms suggests that the advice is not so needless. For example, very few persons can give the certified cause of death of their parents or, *a fortiori*, of other relations. It is very unlikely that persons can remember accurately the minor illnesses (cold in the head, etc.) they have suffered in a previous 12 months. On the other hand it certainly does not follow that questions which it is obvious cannot be answered with complete precision are thereby rendered valueless in all circumstances. The amount of inaccuracy may be unimportant to the problem at issue or it may still allow broad conclusions to be reached. Each situation must be carefully weighed on its merits. For instance, one can be sure that few persons in their 50's or 60's can give an exact statement of their past smoking habits, the habits of a lifetime. It does not follow that they cannot give an answer which is sufficiently accurate to allow them to be classified into a few broad categories—heavy, moderate, light, or non-smoker—and for the frequency of some other characteristic, e.g. cancer of the lung, to be usefully examined within those broad categories. It should be remembered, too, that if the errors are unbiased, then the degree of association found between the two characteristics is likely to be *less* than the degree that exists in reality. (If in reality the A's differ from the B's to a certain degree, that degree will be made less if through unbiased errors of memory, etc., we have included some A's with the B's and some B's with the A's. The contrast has been rendered less " pure " and clear-cut.)

Under this heading there will also be occasions on which close attention must be paid to the problem of " *observer error or variation.*" Will doctors, or other workers, surveying the same patients classify them in the same way ? For example, it is well known that experienced school medical officers will differ among themselves in the assessment of a child's nutritional condition. After a short interval of time, they will also differ from themselves. It is equally well known that experienced readers of X-ray films will differ over interpretation of, or even over the presence or absence of, lesions in the chest. According to the examiner involved, it has been shown that clinical histories will differ in the frequency with which somewhat ill-defined conditions, such as chronic bronchitis, are discovered. It is not really the observers who are at fault ; it is the method. It is not precise enough to allow uniform and clear-cut decisions. It follows that close thought should be given to the problem of observer error or variation, whether it is likely to be an important feature and, if so, whether there are any means of reducing it.

(vi) Any form of record which must be completed by

many persons should, to the utmost extent, be made *simple in wording and logical in the order of its questions*. The amount of work required of the respondent may often be reduced by putting the question in such a form that the answer demands only a cross or a tick or the ringing of one specified category (as in number (ii) above). Such answers are also very easily tabulated (and the categories on the form can be already numbered if punched cards are subsequently to be used).

(vii) Finally, much attention should be given to *the number of questions*. Obviously this must vary widely with circumstances, but at the same time there are probably no circumstances in which the constructor of a form should not ask himself of *every* question : " Is this question essential ? Can I obtain useful answers to it ? Can I analyse them usefully at the end ? " Such a self-discipline is likely to reduce the size of any form.

There are also circumstances, as described in Chapter II (see p. 21), in which it may be wise to distribute a large number of questions over different samples and thus avoid too heavy a burden being placed upon any one respondent. On the other hand there are some circumstances in which it may be profitable deliberately to include extra questions for purposes of checking the nature of the response or to encourage an unbiased response. For instance, in approaching a sample of children aged 5 years to study, say, their previous attacks of infectious diseases, it might be useful to include a question on smallpox vaccination. The frequency of vaccination is known for the universe from national statistics and so, from its frequency in the sample, one may judge whether the sample is likely to be well chosen and representative.

In certain circumstances in approaching by questionnaire a population, marked or not marked by some characteristic, it is not unlikely that the marked persons will tend to reply and the unmarked not to reply. For example, patients who have undergone a blood transfusion are followed up by post some months later and asked, with appropriate questions, whether they have had symptoms of jaundice. Those who have had symptoms, the positives, may well be inclined to reply more readily than those who have not, the negatives, so that a false measure of the incidence of serum hepatitis is reached. It may therefore be profitable to put the question in such a form as to give everyone some reason to reply, *e.g.* by listing the symptoms of various common diseases (rheumatism, etc.) and asking the respondent to put an X appropriately, or by adding some very general question applicable to everyone such as " Since leaving hospital have you been in good or poor health ? " Except to encourage an unbiased response to the real question at issue, the nature of the extra query is, of course, unimportant.

### The Pilot Inquiry

In many inquiries—and particularly very large-scale or expensive inquiries—it will be extremely profitable to conduct a small pilot investigation. A small sample of the population can be drawn and approached—and that procedure will reveal any difficulties in the sampling method itself and in reaching the respondents. The responses themselves will give a measure of the non-response rate to be expected and throw light on questions which prove to have been ill-worded or ambiguous or which cannot be answered adequately at all. Revision can then be made before the inquiry itself is set in train. Thus it has been reported that a preliminary survey in the United States showed that a proposed new income tax form was " incomprehensible to a substantial part of the public. . . . As a result of this survey a new form was devised which everyone could understand and the Treasury gained millions of dollars from the increased revenue " (P.E.P. Broadsheet on the Social Use of Sample Surveys, 1946). Apart, perhaps, from some legitimate doubts as to whether *any* income tax form could be devised which would be understood by everyone, the moral of the small pilot inquiry is clear.

The same principle may well apply in studying past records, *e.g.* clinical case notes. A small random sample will rapidly show whether the information required is available or whether there are too many gaps and omissions. It may also be made to show the scale of the proposed work in time and manpower.

## Forms of Inquiry

Leaving aside the experimental approach (the strongest weapon in the scientist's armoury) there are, of course, in detail very many ways of investigation by observation. There are, however, two broad categories of approach, each with its own merits and defects, which are worthy of con sideration—namely, the *retrospective* and the *prospective*.

In the *retrospective* inquiry the starting-point is the affected person, *e.g.* the patient with cancer of the lung, and the investigation lies in the uncovering of features in his *history* which may have led to that condition, *e.g.* cigarette smoking, industrial hazards, air pollution, etc. Does one (or more) of those features appear more frequently in the histories of affected persons than in the histories of an un-affected normal population ? This, indeed, is the classical method of epidemiology which seeks to show that of persons infected with typhoid fever, or cholera, most had consumed a particular supply of water while of those who were not attacked relatively few had done so. It is very rarely a question of all versus none since invariably some consumers are not attacked and frequently some non-consumers are attacked, *e.g.* through secondary infection. Thus, it is a comparison of *relative* frequencies and for this purpose not only the histories of the cases are required but the histories of some "controls." The choice of appropriate controls demands careful thought to ensure that the comparisons are valid. Usually the control group should be as similar as possible to the affected group except for the presence of the disease in question. Constantly it will be profitable to seek more than one control group. If a series of control groups, *e.g.* of patients with different diseases, give much the same answer and only the one affected group differs, the evidence is clearly much stronger than if the affected group differs from merely one other group.

The *prospective* method, on the other hand, starts with

an unaffected sample of the population, *e.g.* without cancer of the lung, characterises each member of the sample by one or more features, *e.g.* smoking habits, occupation, place of residence, and then records the *future* occurrence of an event (the development of cancer of the lung) in relation to those features. Does the disease appear more frequently in some groups than in others ?

### The Pros and Cons

The advantages and disadvantages of the two approaches are these. With the prospective method the sample under study can usually be clearly defined and it is easier to consider whether it is likely to be representative of some universe or is biased. It may be very difficult to identify similarly the nature of a retrospective sample or the nature of its very possible bias, *e.g.* are patients in hospital with a coronary infarct likely to be representative of all such patients in regard to some particular constitutional or environmental factor such as dietary habits ? Are the controls, selected for comparison with them, representative of the general population (or some specific population) without a coronary infarct ? What selective influences may bring the affected and the unaffected into observation ? Those are difficult questions to answer. On the other hand, following up the same example, the difficulties of interpretation are much less if we take every $n$th person in a defined normal population, determine their dietary habits, and then record subsequent events. The nature of the sample is clearer. We may, however, note that in this prospective inquiry there may be refusals to co-operate, persons lost sight of and other forms of non-response, all of which will make the sample less certain in its nature.

Neither method, of course, can provide " proof " of cause and effect. We are always seeking the *most reasonable* interpretation of an association. And usually we shall have to consider the most probable *order* of events in an association— do the dietary habits tend to lead to an infarct or does the person liable to an infarct tend to have certain dietary habits ?

One great advantage of the prospective method is that, knowing the number of persons at risk in each group, the incidence rates of the events subsequently observed can be easily calculated and compared.  Such a calculation is rarely possible with the retrospective method.  For example, we could observe pregnant women suffering an attack of rubella in the first, second, and third and later months of pregnancy and subsequently observe the incidence of congenital defects in their babies and calculate its incidence in each group. On the other hand, starting with the defective babies, we might find retrospectively that all the mothers had had rubella whereas relatively few mothers of normal control babies had been attacked.  To measure from such data the actual risks of a defective child might be impossible or, at least, very difficult.

The retrospective method, however, is likely to give an answer more speedily than the prospective with its prolonged follow-up and, in some circumstances, it is likely to be the only possible approach.  For example, with a relatively rare condition like disseminated sclerosis it might be quite impossible to categorise a sufficiently large population to give incidence rates from future occurrences within a reasonable span of time.  It would not be at all difficult to accumulate a large group of cases and retrospectively to explore their past.

The prospective method does not, however, always involve a subsequent waiting period.  It can be applied so long as a population can be defined *at any specific time* and then its subsequent events noted, *e.g.* in records already accumulated.  For instance, for the live births that took place in a given hospital over some earlier years it might be possible to determine from the available clinical records whether or not the mother had an X-ray of the abdomen. One might then determine by inquiry or other already available records, the health of the child 5 years later.  In other words, the prospective method has thus been applied to existing records.

In some circumstances one might well choose to make a pilot retrospective inquiry before embarking upon a more arduous prospective investigation.

In conclusion, though the prospective approach must usually be the " method of choice," there can certainly be no *one* right way in which to make every investigation.

## Summary

One of the most decisive and difficult tasks in any inquiry is the construction of an appropriate form of record. Care must be taken to ensure that the questions are clear and unambiguous and, as far as possible, self-explanatory. Each question should require some answer and the standard of accuracy necessary for the purpose in hand should be considered. To ensure a high rate of return a form may need to be kept short. On the other hand, to ensure an unbiased return there may be occasions when extra questions are useful. Pilot inquiries can be invaluable in revealing the difficulties and defects of a proposed large-scale investigation.

Many inquiries follow one of two forms of approach—the retrospective (looking backwards) and the prospective (looking forwards). The latter has much in its favour but with rare events may be impossible. There can be no one right or wrong way in all circumstances.

# V

## PRESENTATION OF STATISTICS

ONCE a series of observations has been made, or collected,
the first object must be to express them in some simple form
which will permit, directly or by means of further calculations, conclusions to be drawn. The publication, for instance,
of a long series of case results is not particularly helpful
(beyond providing material for interested persons to work
upon), for it is impossible to detect, from the unsorted mass
of raw material, relationships between the various factors at
issue. The worker must first consider the questions which he
believes the material is capable of answering and then determine the form of presentation which brings out the true
answers most clearly. For instance, let us suppose the
worker has amassed a series of after-histories of patients
treated for gastric ulcer and wishes to assess the value of
the treatment given, using as a measure the amount of in-
capacitating illness suffered in subsequent years. There will
be various factors, the influence of which it will be of interest
to observe. Is the age or sex of the patient material to the
upshot ? Division of the data must be made into these
categories and tables constructed to show how much subsequent illness was in fact suffered by each of these groups.
Is the after-history affected by the type of treatment ? A
further tabulation is necessary to explore this point. And
so on. The initial step must be to divide the observations
into a relatively small series of groups, those in each group
being considered alike in that characteristic for the purpose
in hand. To take another example : in Table I, showing
some past fatality-rates from scarlet fever in hospital, children within each year of age up to 10 and in each five-year
group from 10 to 20 are considered alike with respect to age.

It is, of course, possible that by this grouping we are concealing real differences. The fatality-rate at 0–6 months may differ from the fatality-rate at 6–12 months, at 12–18 months it may differ from the rate at 18–24 months. To answer that question, further sub-division—if the number of cases justifies it—would be necessary. In its present form (accepting the figures of hospital cases at their face value) the grouping states that fatality declines nearly steadily with age, a conclusion which it would be impossible to draw from

TABLE I

HOSPITAL CASES OF SCARLET FEVER, 1905–14

FATALITY-RATE AT AGES

| Age in Years | Number of Cases | Number of Deaths | Fatality-rate per cent. |
|---|---|---|---|
| (1) | (2) | (3) | (4) |
| 0– | 46 | 18 | 39·1 |
| 1– | 383 | 43 | 11·2 |
| 2– | 881 | 50 | 5·7 |
| 3– | 1169 | 60 | 5·1 |
| 4– | 1372 | 36 | 2·6 |
| 5– | 1403 | 24 | 1·7 |
| 6– | 1271 | 22 | 1·7 |
| 7– | 986 | 21 | 2·1 |
| 8– | 864 | 6 | 0·7 |
| 9– | 673 | 5 | 0·7 |
| 10– | 1965 | 14 | 0·7 |
| 15–20 | 513 | 3 | 0·6 |

The fatality or case-mortality rate is the proportion of patients with a particular disease who die.

the 11,526 original unsorted and ungrouped records. The construction of a *frequency distribution* is the first desideratum —*i.e.* a table showing the frequency with which there are present individuals with some defined characteristic or characteristics.

## The Frequency Distribution

In constructing the frequency distribution from the original unsorted records, the first point to be settled is the number of classes or groups to be used. As one of the main objects of the resulting table is to make clear to the eye the general tenor of the records, too many groups are not desirable. Otherwise, with as many as, say, 50 groups, the tabulation will itself be difficult to read and may fail to reveal the salient features of the data. On the other hand, a very small number of groups may equally fail to bring out essential points. Also, in subsequent calculations made from the frequency distribution, we shall often need to suppose that all the observations in a group can be regarded as having the value of the middle of that group, *e.g.* if in a frequency distribution of ages at death there are 75 deaths at ages 40–45 (*i.e.* 40 or over but less than 45) we shall presume that each can be taken as $42\frac{1}{2}$. In fact, of course, some will be less than $42\frac{1}{2}$, some more, but so long as the groups are not made unduly wide and the numbers of observations are not too few, no serious error is likely to arise ; $42\frac{1}{2}$ will be the mean age of the 75 deaths, or very near to it.

In general, therefore, some 10 to 20 groups is usually an appropriate number to adopt. Also it is usually best to keep the class- or group-interval a constant size. For instance, in Table I the class-interval is 1 year of age up to age 10, and it is easy to see from the figures that the absolute number of cases per year of age rises rapidly to a maximum at age 5–6 and then declines. There is, however, an abrupt and large rise in the absolute number at age 10 merely because the class-interval has been changed from 1 year to 5 years —the mean number of cases per year of age would here be only $1965 \div 5$, or 393. This change of interval makes the basic figures (not the rates) more difficult to read and sometimes makes subsequent calculations more laborious. Generally, therefore, the class-interval should be kept constant. Also, as a general rule, the distribution should initially be drawn up on a fine basis—*i.e.* with a considerable number of groups, for if this basis prove too fine owing to the numbers of observations being few, it is possible to double or treble the group-interval by combining the groups. If, on the other hand, the original grouping is made too broad, the subdivision of the groups is impossible without retabulating much of the material.

As an example of the construction of the frequency distribution we may take the following 88 death-rates taken from the Occupational Mortality Supplement (1930–32) of the Registrar-General of England and Wales. The rates, set out in four columns to save space, have been copied merely in the order of occupations as adopted in the report and it is desired to tabulate them.

THE MEAN ANNUAL DEATH-RATES PER 1000 AT AGES 20–65 IN EACH OF 88 OCCUPATIONAL GROUPS IN THE YEARS 1930–32
(Untabulated material)

| (1) | (2) | (3) | (4) |
|------|------|------|------|
| 7·5  | 10·3 | 7·7  | 6·8  |
| 8·2  | 10·1 | 12·8 | 7·1  |
| 6·2  | 10·0 | 8·7  | 6·6  |
| 8·9  | 11·1 | 5·5  | 8·8  |
| 7·8  | 6·5  | 8·6  | 8·8  |
| 5·4  | 12·5 | 9·6  | 10·7 |
| 9·4  | 7·8  | 11·9 | 10·8 |
| 9·9  | 6·5  | 10·4 | 6·0  |
| 10·9 | 8·7  | 7·8  | 7·9  |
| 10·8 | 9·3  | 7·6  | 7·3  |
| 7·4  | 12·4 | 12·1 | 19·3 |
| 9·7  | 10·6 | 4·6  | 9·3  |
| 11·6 | 9·1  | 14·0 | 8·9  |
| 12·6 | 9·7  | 8·1  | 10·1 |
| 5·0  | 9·3  | 11·4 | 3·9  |
| 10·2 | 6·2  | 10·6 | 6·0  |
| 9·2  | 10·3 | 11·6 | 6·9  |
| 12·0 | 6·6  | 10·4 | 9·0  |
| 9·9  | 7·4  | 8·1  | 9·4  |
| 7·3  | 8·6  | 4·6  | 8·8  |
| 7·3  | 7·7  | 6·6  | 11·4 |
| 8·4  | 9·4  | 12·8 | 10·9 |

The first step is to find the upper and lower limits over which the tabulation must extend. The lowest rate is 3·9 and the highest is 19·3. We have therefore a range of 15·4. A class interval of 1 will give 16 groups and clearly will be convenient to handle. On this basis we may take the groups, or classes, as 3·5 to 4·4, 4·5 to 5·4, 5·5 to 6·4, and so on. Setting out these groups, we may enter each rate by a stroke against the appropriate group. It is convenient to mark each fifth by a diagonal line as shown. Addition is then simple and errors are less likely to occur. (In making this tabulation the groups may be set out as above, 3·5–4·4, 4·5 to 5·4, etc., or as in the table, 3·5–, 4·5–, etc. It is most undesirable to have them in the form 3·5–4·5, 4·5 to 5·5, etc., since observations precisely on a dividing line, e.g. 4·5, will then sometimes be

PROCESS OF TABULATION OF 88 DEATH-RATES

*Death-rate*

| Death-rate | Tally | Count |
|---|---|---|
| 3·5– | I | 1 |
| 4·5– | IIII | 4 |
| 5·5– | IIII | 5 |
| 6·5– | IIII IIII III | 13 |
| 7·5– | IIII IIII II | 12 |
| 8·5– | IIII IIII IIII III | 18 |
| 9·5– | IIII IIII III | 13 |
| 10·5– | IIII IIII | 10 |
| 11·5– | IIII I | 6 |
| 12·5– | IIII | 4 |
| 13·5– | I | 1 |
| 14·5– | | .. |
| 15·5– | | .. |
| 16·5– | | .. |
| 17·5– | | .. |
| 18·5– | I | 1 |
| 19·5 | | |
| | | 88 |

absentmindedly put in one group and sometimes in the other.)

This method is satisfactory if the number of observations is not very large. But it always has the disadvantage that the only check of accuracy is to repeat the work, and if some differences are found it is not always easy to locate the error or errors. A better method is to enter the observations on cards, one to each card, and then to " deal " the cards into their packs. These packs can then be checked, that they contain only the correct components, and added. On a very large scale the process can be carried out by machines.

The final figures resulting from this construction of the

E

frequency distribution are given in Table II, from which it can be clearly seen that the majority of the death-rates lie between 6·5 and 11·5 per 1000 and that they are fairly symmetrically spread round the most frequent rate of 8·5–9·5. To avoid unduly lengthening the table by the inclusion of the 4 groups with no entries against them, the final group has been termed 13·5 and over.  As a rule this is an undesirable procedure unless the entries can also be precisely specified, as is done here in a footnote.  Without that specification full information on the spread of the rates has not been given to the reader and he may be hampered if he wishes to make calculations from the distribution.  A similar caution relates to the lowest group.

TABLE II

THE MEAN ANNUAL DEATH-RATE PER 1000 AT AGES 20–65 IN VARIOUS OCCUPATIONAL GROUPS IN THE YEARS 1930–32

| Death-rate per 1000 | Number of Occupational Groups with given Death-rate |
|---|---|
| 3·5– | 1 |
| 4·5– | 4 |
| 5·5– | 5 |
| 6·5– | 13 |
| 7·5– | 12 |
| 8·5– | 18 |
| 9·5– | 13 |
| 10·5– | 10 |
| 11·5– | 6 |
| 12·5– | 4 |
| 13·5 and over | 2* |
| Total | 88 |

* 1 death-rate of 14·0 and 1 death-rate of 19·3.

## Statistical Tables

Returning to Table I (p. 52), this may be used in illustration of certain basic principles in the presentation of statistical data.

(i) The contents of the table as a whole and the items in each separate column should be clearly and fully defined. For lack of sufficient headings, or even any headings at all, many published tables are quite unintelligible to the reader without a search for clues in the text (and not always then). For instance, if the heading given in column (1) were merely " age," it would not be clear whether the groups refer to years or months of life. The unit of measurement must be included.

(ii) If the table includes rates, as in column (4), the base on which they are measured must be clearly stated—*e.g.* death-rate per cent., or per thousand, or per million, as the case may be (a very common omission in published tables). To know that the fatality-rate is " 20 " is not helpful unless we know whether it is 20 in 100 patients who die (1 in 5) or 20 in 1000 (1 in 50).

(iii) Whenever possible the frequency distributions should be given in full, as in columns (2) and (3). These are the basic data from which conclusions are being drawn and their presentation allows the reader to check the validity of the author's arguments. The publication merely of certain values descriptive of the frequency distribution—*e.g.* the arithmetic mean or average — severely handicaps other workers. For instance, the information that for certain groups of patients the mean age at death from cancer of the lung was 54·8 years and from cancer of the stomach was 62·1 years is of very limited value in the absence of any knowledge of the distribution of ages at death in the two classes.

(iv) Rates or proportions should not be given alone without any information as to the numbers of observations upon which they are based. In presenting experimental data, and indeed nearly all statistical data, this is a funda-mental rule (which, however, is constantly broken). For example, the fatality-rate from smallpox in England and Wales (ratio of registered deaths to notified cases) was 42·9 per cent. in 1917 while in the following year it was only 3·2 per cent. This impressive difference becomes less convincing of a real change in virulence when we note that in 1917 there were but 7 cases notified, of whom 3 died, and in 1918 only 63 of whom 2 died. (Though the low rate of 1918 *may* mark the presence of variola minor.) " It is the essence of science to disclose both the data upon which a conclusion is based and the methods by which the conclusion is attained." By giving only rates or proportions, and by omitting the actual numbers of observations or frequency distributions, we are excluding the basic data. In their absence we can draw no valid conclusion whatever from, say, a comparison of two, or more, percentages.

It is often stated that it is wrong to calculate a percentage when the number of observations is small, *e.g.* under 50. *But so long as the basic numbers are also given* it is difficult to see where the objection lies and how such a presentation can be misleading—except to those who disregard the basic figures and who, therefore, in all probability will be misled by any presentation. If, for example, we have 9 relapses in 23 patients in one group and 4 relapses in 15 patients in another, it is difficult for the mind to grasp the difference (if any). Some common basis would seem essential, and percentages are a convenient one. In this comparison they are, in fact, 39 and 27. They will thus be seen, in view of the small numbers involved, to be not very different. The fundamental rules should be that the writer gives no percentages without adding the scale of events underlying them and the reader accepts no percentages without considering that scale. Inevitably with small numbers care will be needed in drawing conclusions ; but that is true whatever the basis from which they are viewed.

(v) On a point of detail it is sometimes helpful in publishing results to use one decimal figure in percentages to draw the reader's attention to the fact that the figure is a percentage and not an absolute number. An alternative, especially useful in tables, is to give percentages (or rates) in italics and absolute numbers in bold type. This variation in type, too, often makes a large table simpler to grasp. As a general principle two or three small tables are to be preferred to one large one. Often the latter *can* be read but its appearance may well lead to it going unread.

(vi) Full particulars of any deliberate exclusions of observations from a collected series must be given, the reasons for and the criteria of exclusion being clearly defined. For example, if it be desired to measure the success of an operation for, say, cancer of some site, it might, from one aspect, be considered advisable to take as a measure the percentage of patients surviving at the end of 5 years, *excluding those who died from the operation itself*—*i.e.* the question asked is " What is the survival-rate of patients upon whom the operation is successfully carried out ? " It is obvious that these figures are not comparable with those of observers who have included the operative mortality. If the exclusion that has been made in the first case is not clearly stated no one can necessarily deduce that there is a lack of comparability between the records of different observers, and misleading comparisons are likely to be made. Similarly one worker may include among the subsequent deaths only those due to cancer and exclude unrelated deaths—*e.g.* from accident—while another includes all deaths, irrespective of their cause. Definition of the exclusions will prevent unjust comparisons.

Sometimes exclusions are inevitable—*e.g.* if in computing a survival-rate some individuals have been lost sight of so that nothing is known of their fate. The number of such individuals must invariably be stated, and it must be considered whether the lack of knowledge extends to so many patients as to stultify conclusions (*vide* p. 235).

Beyond these few rules it is very difficult, if not impossible, to lay down rules for the construction of tables. The whole issue is the arrangement of data in a concise and easily read form. In acquiring skill in the construction of tables probably the best way is, as Pearl suggested, to consider critically published tables with such questions as these in mind : " What is the *purpose* of this table ? What is it *supposed* to accomplish in the mind of the reader ? . . . wherein does its failure of attainment fall ? " (Raymond Pearl, *Medical Biometry and Statistics.* Philadelphia and London : W. B. Saunders Co., Ltd.). Study of the tables published by the professional statistician—*e.g.* in the Registrar-General's Annual Reports—will materially assist the beginner.

## Graphs

Even with the most lucid construction of tables such a method of presentation always gives difficulties to the reader, especially to the non-statistically-minded reader. The presentation of the same material diagrammatically often proves a very considerable aid and has much to commend it if certain basic principles are not forgotten.

(i) The sole object of a diagram is to assist the intelligence to grasp the meaning of a series of numbers by means of the eye. If—as is unfortunately often the case—the eye itself is merely confused by a crisscross of half a dozen, or even a dozen, lines, the sole object is defeated. The criterion must be that the eye can with reasonable ease follow the movement of the various lines on the diagram from point to point and thus observe what is the change in the value of the ordinate (the vertical scale) for a given change in the value of the abscissa (the horizontal scale). The writer should

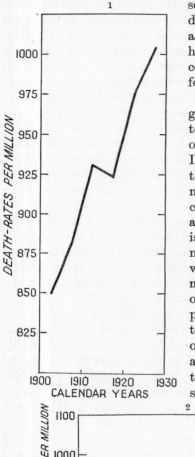

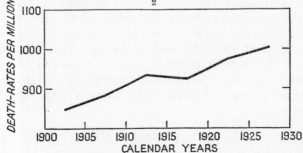

FIGS. 1 AND 2.—Standardised death-rates from cancer in England and Wales in each quinquennium from 1901–5 to 1926–30.

always remember, too, that he is familiar with the data, and what may be obvious to him is not necessarily obvious to the reader. The object of the graph is to make it obvious, or at least as clear as possible, and simplicity is invariably the keynote.

(ii) The second point to bear in mind in constructing *and in reading* graphs is that by the choice of scales the same

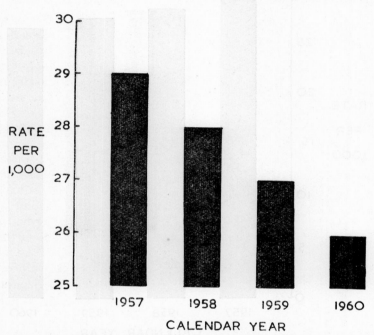

FIG. 3.—The infant mortality-rate in four consecutive years in the City of X, drawn on an exaggerated scale and omitting the zero base line.

numerical values can be made to appear very different to the eye. Figs. 1 and 2 are an example. Both show the same data —namely, the death-rates (standardised) from cancer in England and Wales in each quinquennium between 1901 and 1930. In Fig. 1 the increase in mortality that has been recorded appears at a cursory glance to be exceedingly rapid and of serious magnitude, while in Fig. 2 a slow and far less impressive rise is suggested.  The difference is, of course, due to the difference in the vertical and horizontal scales. In reading graphs, therefore, the scales must be carefully observed and the magnitude of the changes interpreted by a rough translation of the points into actual figures.  In

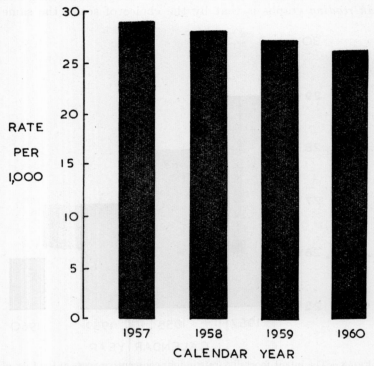

FIG. 4.—The infant mortality-rate in four consecutive years in the City of X, drawn on a reasonable scale and including the zero base line.

drawing graphs undue exaggeration or compression of the scales must be avoided.

It must be considered also whether a false impression is conveyed, as quite frequently happens, if the vertical scale does not start at zero but at some point appreciably above it. Figures 3 and 4 show what can be done in this way with infant mortality-rates of 29, 28, 27, and 26 per 1000 in four consecutive years and the aid of a little ingenuity, *i.e.* change of scale and omission of the zero base line.

(iii) Graphs should always be regarded as subsidiary aids to the intelligence and *not* as the evidence of associations or trends. That evidence must be largely drawn from the statistical tables themselves. It follows that graphs are an unsatisfactory *substitute* for statistical tables. An entirely deaf ear should be turned to such editorial pleading as this : " If we print the graphs would it not be possible to take some of the tables for granted ? Having given a sample of the process by which you arrive at the graph is it necessary in each case to reproduce the steps ? " The retort to this request is that statistical tables are *not* a step to a diagram, they are the basic data. Without these basic data the reader cannot adequately consider the validity of the author's deductions, and he cannot make any further analysis of the data, if he should wish, without laboriously and inaccurately endeavouring to translate the diagram back into the statistics from which it was originally constructed (and few tasks are more irritating). There are, of course, some occasions when the statistical data are not worth setting out in detail and a graph may be sufficient. But careful thought is advisable before that procedure is followed.

(iv) The problem of scale illustrated in Figs. 1 and 2 is also an important factor in the comparison of trend lines. Fig. 5 shows the trend of the death-rates from respiratory tuberculosis and from typhoid fever in England and Wales from 1870 to 1930. Unless the scale of the ordinate (the vertical scale) is carefully considered, the inference drawn from this graph might well be that *relatively* the mortality from respiratory tuberculosis had declined more than the mortality from typhoid fever. Actually the precise reverse is the case—relatively typhoid fever declined considerably more than respiratory tuberculosis. In 1921–30 the rate from respiratory tuberculosis was 34 per cent. of the rate recorded in 1871–80, while the rate from typhoid fever was but 3·4 per cent. of its earlier level. *Absolutely*, respiratory tuberculosis shows the greater improvement (from

2231 deaths per million in 1871–80 to 768 in 1921–30, compared with 321 and 11 for typhoid fever) ; but relatively typhoid fever shows the advantage. If it is the relative degree of improvement that is at issue Fig. 5 is insufficient. For this purpose the rates in each decade may be converted into percentages based upon the rate in the first decade, as is shown in Fig. 6, or plotted on semi-logarithmic paper which automatically shows the rate of change.

(v) It is a *sine qua non* with graphs, as with tables, that they form self-contained units, the contents of which can be grasped without reference to the text. For this purpose inclusive and clearly stated headings must be given, the meaning of the various lines indicated, and a statement made against the ordinate and abscissa of the characteristics to which these scales refer (*vide* Figs. 1 to 8).

## Frequency Diagrams

Many types of diagrams have been evolved to bring out the main features of statistical data. In representing frequency distributions diagrammatically there are two which are primarily used : (1) *the frequency polygon* and (2) the *histogram*, of which the latter is usually the better. In both these the base line is used to denote the characteristic which is being measured and the vertical scale reveals the frequency with which it occurs. In Table I it was shown that the numbers of deaths from scarlet fever were as follows :—

| Age in Years | Number of Deaths |
|:---:|:---:|
| 0– | 18 |
| 1– | 43 |
| 2– | 50 |
| 3– | 60 |
| 4– | 36 |
| 5– | 24 |
| 6– | 22 |
| 7– | 21 |
| 8– | 6 |
| 9– | 5 |
| 10– | 14 |
| 15–20 | 3 |

Here we have a frequency distribution of some deaths from scarlet fever in relation to age. To graph this distribution

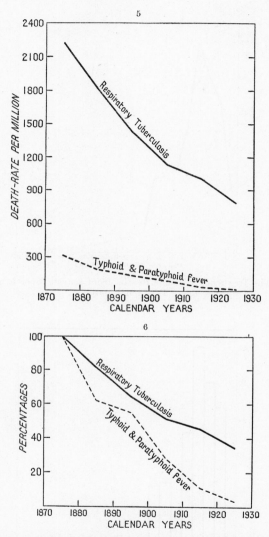

FIGS. 5 AND 6.—Standardised death-rates from (a) respiratory tuberculosis and (b) typhoid and paratyphoid fever in England and Wales. In Fig. 6 the rate from each disease in each decade is expressed as a percentage of the corresponding rate in 1871–80.

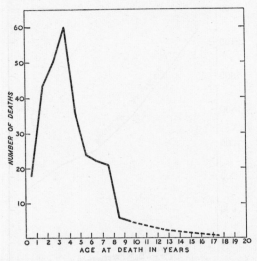

FIG. 7.—The frequency of some deaths from scarlet fever in relation to age.    Frequency polygon.

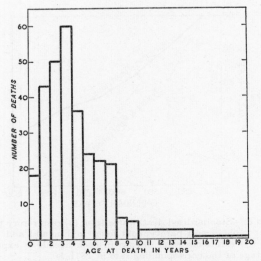

FIG. 8.—The frequency of some deaths from scarlet fever in relation to age.    Histogram.

the base line is divided into single years of age and the vertical scale is made to relate to the number of observations. To draw the frequency polygon, or line diagram, a point representing the observed frequency is made against the *middle* of the age group concerned. Thus there were 18 deaths at ages 0–1, and against the middle of the 0–1 age interval on the base-line a point is made against 18 on the vertical frequency scale. Similarly a point is made against the middle of the 1–2 age group against 43 on the vertical scale. Finally these points are joined one to another to complete the diagram (see Fig. 7).

Some difficulty, it will be noted, occurs with the final figures since the scale is here changed from one year to five years. An erroneous picture will result if the 14 deaths are plotted against the mid-point of the age group 10–15. It may then appear that the number of deaths is again rising though in terms of *per year of age* they are still declining. It will be better, therefore, to find this average number of deaths per year of age by dividing the 14 by the 5 years to which they relate, and plotting this point (2·8) against the mid-point of the age group to which it relates.

This difficulty is more clearly overcome, and the figures more clearly shown diagrammatically, by the use of the histogram, in which the frequency is represented by an area corresponding to the number of observations (or to the proportion of the total falling in each group). Thus in the present example a point is placed against 18 on the vertical scale both against age 0 and age 1 on the base line. A rectangle is then drawn to show this frequency. Similarly a point is placed against 43 both above age 1 and age 2, and this rectangle is completed. The area of each rectangle is thus proportional to the number of deaths in the year of age concerned. To maintain a correct area when the scale of age grouping changes, we must divide the recorded deaths by the new unit of grouping, *i.e.* the 14 and the 3 in the two final groups by 5, giving, on the average, 2·8 and 0·6 deaths per year of age. These figures then relate to the whole of the 5-year age group and the rectangles will extend over the ages 10–15 and 15–20. In other words, in the absence of more detailed data, we plot the figures as if there were 2·8 deaths at ages 10–11, 2·8 at ages 11–12, 2·8 at ages 12-13, and so on; 0·6 at ages 15-16, 0·6 at ages 16-17, 0·6 at ages 17–18, and so on (see Fig. 8). If thought desirable the actual number of deaths reported can be written inside, or just above, the rectangles.

Another very simple form of diagram is the *bar chart*,

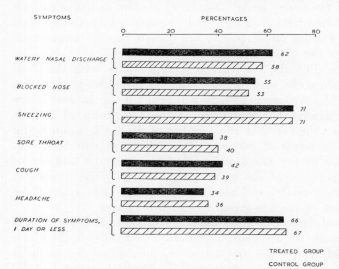

Fig. 9.—A bar chart showing the percentage of patients with defined *presenting symptoms* of the common cold in two groups, T to be treated with an anti-histamine compound and C to be treated with a placebo.

which can be used to show pictorially the absolute, or relative, frequency of events, *e.g.* the numbers of deaths due to specified causes, the percentage of patients with a particular disease showing certain symptoms, as illustrated in Fig. 9.

In a preliminary exploration of the degree of association between two characteristics, *e.g.* body temperature and the erythrocyte sedimentation rate, a *scatter diagram* is valuable (see p. 181).

## Summary

For the comprehension of a series of figures tabulation is essential ; a diagram (*in addition to tables but not in place of them*) is often of considerable aid both for publication and for a preliminary study of the features of the data. Both tables and graphs must be entirely self-explanatory without reference to the text. As far as possible the original observations should always be reproduced (in tabulated form showing the actual numbers belonging to each group) and not given only in the form of percentages—*i.e.* the percentages of the total falling in each group. The exclusion of observations from the tabulated series on any grounds whatever must be stated, the criterion upon which exclusion was determined clearly set out, and usually the number of such exclusions stated. Conclusions should be drawn from graphs only with extreme caution and only after careful consideration of the scales adopted.

(*For exercise see p.* 313)

# VI

## THE AVERAGE

WHEN a series of observations has been tabulated, *i.e.* put in the form of a frequency distribution, the next step is the calculation of certain values which may be used as descriptive of the characteristics of that distribution. These values will enable comparisons to be made between one series of observations and another. The two principal characteristics of the distribution which it is invariably necessary to place on a quantitative basis are (*a*) its average value and (*b*) the degree of scatter of the observations round that average value. The former, the average value, is a measure of the *position* of the distribution, the point around which the individual values are dispersed. For example, the average incubation period of one infectious illness may be 7 days and of another 11 days. Though individual values may overlap, the two distributions have different central positions and therefore differ in this characteristic of location. In practice it is constantly necessary to discuss and compare such measures. A simple instance would be the observation that persons following one occupation lose *on the average* 5 days a year per person from illness ; in another occupation they lose 10 days. The two distributions differ in their position and we are led to seek the reasons for such a difference and to see whether it is remediable.

In the above discussion the term " average " has been introduced according to common everyday usage, namely that the average is the mean, or, more accurately, arithmetic mean, of all the observations (the sum of all the observations divided by the number of observations). The three terms, *average, mean, arithmetic mean*, are customarily taken as interchangeable. There are, however, in common use, and sometimes of special value, two other " averages " or measures of position, namely the *median* and the *mode*, which it is necessary to study. The median of a series of observations is the value, or magnitude, of the central or middle observation when all the observations are listed in order from lowest to highest. In other words, half the observations fall below the median and half the observations lie above it, and the median therefore divides the distribution into two halves. It defines the position of the distribution in that way.

The mode, as its name indicates, is the most frequently occurring, or most fashionable, value observed in the series.

Both these measures of position have, on occasions, a special value. For instance, in discussing the length of an illness we may be interested not so much in the mean, or average, length but in the *usual* length. The average length may be high owing (in a short series of observations) to a few unduly long cases which pull up its value. We are more concerned here with the most frequent length, or the mode. If, however, we have insufficient data to determine a most frequent length, the median may give a better indication of the position than the mean. The mean may be affected by large outlying observations and the median is unaffected. For example, if most of the illnesses last between 10 and 15 days the median will not be appreciably altered by the addition of 2 patients ill for 3 and 6 months ; they merely represent two more cases lying above the middle point, and how much above is immaterial. On the other hand, the mean might be increased by their addition to 20 days and be, therefore, a poor measure of the general location of the distribution.

In general it is a sound rule in practice to calculate invariably the arithmetic mean and to use in conjunction with it, when it seems necessary, the median and the mode.

## Calculation of the Averages

With a short series of observations the calculation of the mean is quite simply made. Let us take the following

F

figures relating to the recorded age of onset of disease (age last birthday) for a group of 27 patients suffering from some specific illness.

| Age of Patient at Onset of Disease (in Years) | Age of Patient at Onset of Disease (in Years) |
|---|---|
| 39 | 36 |
| 50 | 57 |
| 26 | 41 |
| 45 | 61 |
| 47 | 47 |
| 71 | 44 |
| 51 | 48 |
| 33 | 59 |
| 40 | 42 |
| 40 | 54 |
| 51 | 47 |
| 66 | 53 |
| 63 | 54 |
| 55 | |

The arithmetic mean is the sum of all the values divided by their number. For the above example this is $39 + 50 + 26 + 45 +$ etc., giving a total of 1320. The average age of the 27 persons at onset of disease is, therefore, $1320 \div 27$, or 48·9 years (as the age taken at onset was the age of the person *last birthday*, strictly speaking this average should be increased by half a year ; for *on the average* persons aged, say, 40 last birthday will at the time of onset be $40\frac{1}{2}$—they may be anywhere between 40 and 41—and this will be the case with each person in the sample, again on the average).

Writing, now, the values in order of magnitude from lowest to highest we have the following list : 26, 33, 36, 39, 40, 40, 41, 42, 44, 45, 47, 47, 47, (48), 50, 51, 51, 53, 54, 54, 55, 57, 59, 61, 63, 66, 71. The median being the central value will be the 14th observation, there being 13 lower values than this and 13 higher values. It is, therefore, 48 years, and half the patients had lower ages of onset than this and half had higher.

The most commonly occurring observation is 47 years (three instances), but, beyond a statement of fact regarding this particular distribution of values, it is clear that with so short and widely scattered a series such a value is not likely to be a reliable estimate of the mode, or age most likely to occur in general with this disease.

A simple method of determining which value is required for the median is to divide the number of observations plus 1 by 2, or $(n+1) \div 2$; in the present instance $(27+1) \div 2 = 14$, and the 14th value is the median. If there were 171 values the median is $(171+1) \div 2 = $ the 86th value, there being then 85 lower values, the median, 85 higher values $= 171$ in all.

In these instances when the total number of observations is an odd number there is no difficulty in finding the median as defined—the central value with an equal number of observations smaller and greater than itself. Often, however, with a short series of figures the definition cannot be strictly fulfilled, namely when the total number of observations is an even number. If in the above series an additional patient had been observed with an age of onset of 73 there would have been 28 observations in all. There could be no central value. In such a situation it is usual to take the mean, or average, of the *two central values* as the median. Thus we should have : 26, 33, 36, 39, 40, 40, 41, 42, 44, 45, 47, 47, 47, (48, 50), 51, 51, 53, 54, 54, 55, 57, 59, 61, 63, 66, 71, 73. The two central values are 48 and 50, with 13 values lying on either side of them, and the median is taken as $(48+50) \div 2 = 49$ years.

The method of finding which are the required observations will, again, be to divide by 2 the number of observations plus 1 ; and the median will be the average of the values immediately above and below. Thus with 28 observations we have $(28+1) \div 2 = 14 \cdot 5$ and the 14th and 15th values are required ; with 172 observations we have $(172+1) \div 2 = 86 \cdot 5$ and the 86th and 87th values are required, there then being 85 below, 2 for the median calculation, and 85 above $= 172$.

## Difficulties with the Median

This customary extension of the definition of the median presents no difficulty and is a reasonable procedure. Often, however, in a short series of observations the definition cannot be completely fulfilled.   Thus we might have as our observations of ages of onset the following values : 26, 33, 36, 39, 40, 40, 41, 42, 44, 45, 47, 48, 48, (48), 48, 51, 51, 53, 54, 54, 55, 57, 59, 61, 63, 66, 71.   With 27 observations the middle one, the 14th, can of course be found.   But it will be seen that there are *not* 13 smaller observations than this value and *not* 13 larger, for three of them are equal to the 14th value.   In strict terms of the definition the median cannot be found in this short series.   Even with a large number of observations it may be impossible to find a median value if the characteristic under discussion changes discontinuously (Table III).   Take, for example, the following frequency distributions :—

TABLE III

TWO HYPOTHETICAL FREQUENCY DISTRIBUTIONS

| A | | B | |
|---|---|---|---|
| Height of a Group of Children, in Inches | Number of Children | Number of Children in a Family | Number of Families observed |
| 50– | 96 | 0 | 96 |
| 51– | 120 | 1 | 120 |
| 52– | 145 | 2 | 145 |
| 53– | 83 | 3 | 83 |
| 54– | 71 | 4 | 71 |
| 55– | 32 | 5 | 32 |
| 56–57 | 18 | 6 or more | 18 |
| Total | 565 | Total | 565 |

In the left-hand distribution, A, we have measurements of the heights of a group of 565 children and in the right-hand distribution, B, the number of children observed in 565 families.

The median height will be that of the 283rd child, $(565 + 1) \div 2$, when the observations are listed in order.   To a considerable extent they are already in order, in the frequency distribution.   Adding up the observations from the lower end of the distribution $96 + 120 = 216$, and we therefore need 67 more beyond this point to reach the 283rd. The median value, accordingly, lies in the group 52–53 inches, and merely putting the 145 observations in that group in exact height order the required 67th can be found.   (It can be estimated more simply but accurately by a method described later, p. 79.) Variation in stature is continuous and thus a median value can reasonably be calculated.

On the other hand, the number of children in a family cannot vary continuously but must proceed by unit steps. The 283rd family must again be the " middle " one and it must have 2 children, but there can be no central value for family size which divides the distribution into two halves, half the families having fewer children and half having more children. There is no real median value. Sometimes, however, it may be reasonable to extend the definition and to accept for the median the value which divides the distribution in such a way that half the observations are *less than or equal to* that value and half are *greater than or equal to it.*

### Calculations from Grouped Figures: the Mean

With a large number of observations it would be very laborious to calculate the mean by summing all the individual values. With no serious loss of accuracy this can be avoided by working from the grouped frequency distribution. So long as the classes into which the observations have been grouped are not too wide we can presume that the observations in that group are located at its centre. Taking the distribution A above, we presume that the 96 children whose height lies between 50 and 51 inches were all $50\frac{1}{2}$ inches, that the 120 children whose height lies between 51 and 52 inches were all $51\frac{1}{2}$ inches. With small class-intervals and a distribution that is not grossly asymmetrical that will approximate quite closely to the truth. Thus to reach the mean stature we may proceed as in Table IV.

Thus the sum of all the 565 statures is computed to be 29,743·5 inches, and the mean stature is, therefore, this sum divided by 565, or 52·64 inches.

Even this method of calculation is unduly laborious since large multiplications have to be performed. It can, fortunately, be simplified.

Suppose 7 children were measured and their statures were found to be, in inches, 45·8, 46·9, 48·8, 50·0, 52·1,

53·6, 57·0. The mean stature, summing the values, is
354·2 ÷ 7 = 50·6 inches. But instead of summing these

TABLE IV

CALCULATION OF THE MEAN, USING TRUE UNITS
OF MEASUREMENT

| Height of Children in Inches | Number of Children | Mid-point of Group | Sum of Statures of the Children measured |
|---|---|---|---|
| 50– | 96 | 50·5 | 96 × 50·5 = 4,848·0 |
| 51– | 120 | 51·5 | 120 × 51·5 = 6,180·0 |
| 52– | 145 | 52·5 | 145 × 52·5 = 7,612·5 |
| 53– | 83 | 53·5 | 83 × 53·5 = 4,440·5 |
| 54– | 71 | 54·5 | 71 × 54·5 = 3,869·5 |
| 55– | 32 | 55·5 | 32 × 55·5 = 1,776·0 |
| 56–57 | 18 | 56·5 | 18 × 56·5 = 1,017·0 |
| Total | 565 | | 29,743·5 |

values we might proceed, if it saved time, by seeing how far
each of these children differed from, say, 50 inches. Originally, indeed, we might merely have measured these differences
from a mark 50 inches high, instead of taking the statures
from ground-level, so that we would finally have the average
level of stature above or below 50 inches instead of above 0,
or ground-level. These differences from 50 inches are − 4·2,
− 3·1, − 1·2, 0·0, + 2·1, + 3·6, + 7·0, and their sum, taking
sign into account, is + 4·2 ; their mean is then 4·2 ÷ 7, or
+ 0·6. This is the mean difference of the children from
50·0, and their mean stature from ground-level will, therefore, be 50·0 + 0·6, or 50·6 inches as before.

The same process can be applied to the frequency distribution. A central group can be taken as base line and its
stature called 0 in place of its real value. The groups below
it become − 1, − 2, − 3, etc., and those above become + 1,
+ 2, + 3, etc. Using these smaller multipliers, we can more
simply find the mean stature in these units and then convert
the answer into the original real units. The figures previously used then become as set out in Table V.

The sum of the statures measured from 0 in working units
is + 393 − 312 = 81 ; their mean is 81 ÷ 565, or + 0·14. The
base line 0 was placed, it will be noted, against the group

52–53 inches, or, in other words, against the point 52·5 (the value used in Table IV working with the real values).  We

TABLE V

CALCULATION OF THE MEAN, USING ARBITRARY UNITS

| Height of Children in Inches.  Real Units | Number of Children | Height in Working Units | Sum of Statures in Working Units | |
|---|---|---|---|---|
| 50– | 96 | – 2 | 96 × – 2 = – 192 | |
| 51– | 120 | – 1 | 120 × – 1 = – 120 | |
| 52– | 145 | 0 | 145 × 0 = 0 | – 312 |
| 53– | 83 | +1 | 83 × 1 = + 83 | |
| 54– | 71 | +2 | 71 × 2 = +142 | |
| 55– | 32 | +3 | 32 × 3 = + 96 | |
| 56–57 | 18 | +4 | 18 × 4 = + 72 | |
| | | | | +393 |
| Total | 565 | | | +81 |

have found, then, that the average difference of the children's stature from this central point of 52·5 is  +0·14.   Their real mean stature from ground-level must therefore be 52·5 + 0·14 = 52·64 inches, the same value as was found previously from the more complicated sums using real values.

While the method has been demonstrated on a distribution of statures it is, of course, perfectly general.   Returning to the previous example of age of onset of a disease, the calculation of the mean from a frequency distribution will be made as in Table VI.

The mean age of the patients in working units is – 4015/7292, or  – 0·5506, and we have to translate this value into the real units.   It lies, it will be seen, 0·5506 of a working unit *below* the 0 which was placed against the group 40–45. The centre of this group is 42·5 and the real mean is, therefore,  42·5 – 5(0·5506) = 39·75 years.   The multiplier 5 is arrived at thus: the mean is found to be 0·5506 of a unit below the 0 value when the groups differ in their distances from one another's centres by unity, *e.g.* from 0 to – 1 to – 2. But in the real distribution their distance from one another's centres is 5, *e.g.* from 42·5 to 47·5.   Therefore the mean in real units must be 5 times 0·5506 below 42·5 ; if the mean in working units had been  – 1, clearly the real mean would have been 37·5, for the latter is the value for which − 1 was the substitute, *i.e.* 42·5 − 5(1).

The formula is, then—

Mean in real units = *Centre value* in real units of the group against which 0 has been placed, plus or minus

TABLE VI

CALCULATION OF THE MEAN, USING ARBITRARY UNITS

| Age of Patient at onset of Disease (in Years) | Age in Working Units | Number of Patients | Sum of Ages of Patients in Working Units | |
|---|---|---|---|---|
| 15– | − 5 | 14 | − 70 | |
| 20– | − 4 | 163 | − 652 | |
| 25– | − 3 | 861 | − 2583 | |
| 30– | − 2 | 1460 | − 2920 | |
| 35– | − 1 | 1466 | − 1466 | |
| 40– | 0 | 1269 | | − 7691 |
| 45– | 1 | 953 | + 953 | |
| 50– | 2 | 754 | +1508 | |
| 55– | 3 | 221 | + 663 | |
| 60– | 4 | 103 | + 412 | |
| 65–70 | 5 | 28 | + 140 | |
| | | .. | | +3676 |
| Total | .. | 7292 | | − 4015 |

(the mean in working units × width of class adopted in the frequency distribution in real units). The plus or minus depends, of course, upon the sign of the mean in working units.

Points especially to be remembered, on which beginners often go wrong, are these :—

(*a*) The 0 value corresponds in real units to the *centre* of the group against which it is placed and *not* to the start of that group.

(*b*) In translating the mean in working units into the real mean the multiplier, or width of the groups in real units, must be brought into play.

(*c*) The groups in real units should be, throughout, of the same width; if a group should contain no observations, nevertheless the appropriate number in the working units must be allotted to it. Otherwise the size in working units of observations farther away from the 0 is not correctly defined.

(d) Values smaller in real units than the group taken as 0 should always be taken as minus in working units and higher values always taken as plus. Otherwise confusion arises in passing finally from the working mean to the real mean.

(e) The exact value for the centre of the group against which the 0 has been placed must be carefully considered. For simplification it has been taken above as the mid-point of the apparent group, but sometimes that will not be strictly correct. For instance, in taking the age of onset of disease the age of the patient might be recorded either as age last birthday or as age to nearest birthday. With age last birthday persons placed in the group 40–45 may be any age between 40 years and 44 years + 364 days, and the centre point will be 42·5. But with age to nearest birthday a person aged $39\frac{1}{2}$ is called 40 and one aged $44\frac{1}{2}$ is called 45. The group 40–45 therefore runs from 39·5 to 44·5 and its centre point is 42 years.

Somewhat similar reasoning will apply to the stature of children, depending here upon the accuracy with which the original measurements were made, or, in other words, upon what measurements were, in fact, allocated to the group entitled, say, 50–51 inches. For instance, if the measurements were taken to the nearest 1/8th of an inch the group 50–51 inches would run from 49 15/16ths to 50 15/16ths.

The working can be checked, it may be added, by changing the position of the 0, and this is a better check than a repetition of the previous arithmetic.

### Calculation from Grouped Figures : the Median

For calculation of the median from the frequency distribution we may return to the statures of children, repeated in Table VII.

As pointed out on p. 74, the median stature will be the

height of the 283rd child when the observations are listed in
order.  In practice, however, we do not trouble to list them
in order when dealing with large numbers but make an
*estimate* of the median from the grouped values in the
frequency distribution.  The value to be found is that of
the point which divides the distribution into exactly two
halves, *i.e.* with 282·5 observations below and 282·5 above
the mid-point.  In other words, the value needed lies at
the mid-point 565/2 or 282·5.  Adding the numbers from
the start of the distribution we have $96 + 120 = 216$ and
$216 + 145 = 361$.  The mid-line at 282·5, therefore, falls in

TABLE VII

| Height of Children in Inches | Number of Children |
|---|---|
| 50– | 96 |
| 51– | 120 |
| 52– | 145 |
| 53– | 83 |
| 54– | 71 |
| 55– | 32 |
| 56–57 | 18 |
| Total | 565 |

the group with 145 children whose height lies between 52
and 53 inches.  By simple proportion it will lie at a point
66·5/145ths of one inch beyond the 52 inches at which this
group of children starts $(282·5 - 216 = 66·5)$.  The median
may, therefore, be calculated as $52 + (66·5/145)$ inches
$= 52 + 0·46 = 52·46$ inches.

Similarly with the 7292 patients with a given age at
onset (Table VI) we require the value which will divide the
distribution into its two halves or $7292/2 = 3646$ observations.
Adding again from the start we have $14 + 163 + 861 + 1460$
$= 2498$ and $2498 + 1466 = 3964$.  The mid-line falls, therefore,
in the group which starts at 35 years of age and continues up
to 40 years.  By simple proportion it will lie (1148/1466th of
5 years) beyond the age of 35 at which this group starts
(for $3646 - 2498 = 1148$).  The median is, therefore, calculated to be $35 + 1148/1466$ths of the span of 5 years which

the group covers, *i.e.* 35 (the opening point of the group) + 3·92 years (the further part of the group absorbed in reaching the required point), which equals 38·92 years.

The main point to recall in calculation is that the median lies beyond the *opening* point of the group in which it is located and *not* beyond the mid-point of that group. Again the actual starting-point of the group may have to be closely considered.

### Calculation from Grouped Figures: the Mode

The mode, as previously noted, is the observation most frequently occurring. Like the other averages, the mean and the median, it has a single value (unless the distribution is bi-modal). In other words, we may say that most children in the sample above had a height between 52 and 53 inches and most patients had an age at onset of disease of 35–40 years. But these group-intervals do not specify the mode, for where the largest number of observations will fall depends partly upon the group-intervals that we choose to adopt. For instance, the most frequent stature might lie between $52\frac{1}{2}$ and $53\frac{3}{4}$ inches and the most frequent age between 35 and 37 if we chose to put the frequencies into such groups instead of those previously adopted. What we need for the value of the mode is that value at which the curve of the distribution would, when plotted, reach its highest point if we had a vast number of observations and could make the groups in which they are placed indefinitely small. In fact, an observed curve is invariably irregular, owing to paucity of numbers. To find the highest point of it accurately it is therefore necessary to fit to the actual observations some ideal curve which well describes their trend and then calculate the highest point of this curve. This is a somewhat difficult process, but, fortunately for frequency distributions that are not very asymmetrical, we can find the mode with sufficient accuracy from the formula

$$\text{Mode} = \text{Mean} - 3(\text{Mean} - \text{Median}),$$

or the mode equals the mean less 3 times the difference between the mean and the median.

In the previous examples we found—

|  | Stature of Children | Age of Onset of Disease |
|---|---|---|
| Mean . | 52·64 | 39·75 |
| Median . | 52·46 | 38·92 |

The modes are, therefore, calculated to be

$$52·64 - 3(52·64 - 52·46) = 52·64 - 3(0·18) = 52·10 \text{ inches}$$

and

$$39·75 - 3(39·75 - 38·92) = 39·75 - 3(0·83) = 37·26 \text{ years.}$$

Certain distributions may have more than one maximum, in which case they are bi-modal or multi-modal.

### The Weighted Average

Let us suppose the following fatality-rates are observed :—

| Ages in Years | Fatality-rate per cent. | Number of Patients |
|---|---|---|
| Under 20 | 47·5 | 40 |
| 20–39 | 15·0 | 120 |
| 40–59 | 22·4 | 250 |
| 60 and over | 51·1 | 90 |

It would be wrong to compute the general fatality-rate at all ages by taking the average of these four rates, *i.e.* $(47·5 + 15·0 + 22·4 + 51·1) \div 4 = 34·0$ per cent. The rate at all ages will depend upon the number of patients who fall ill at each age, as shown in the third column. To reach the rate at all ages the separate age-rates must be " weighted " by the number of observations in each group. Thus we have $(47·5 \times 40) + (15·0 \times 120) + (22·4 \times 250) + (51·1 \times 90)$ divided by 500, the total number of patients, which equals 27·8 per cent., substantially lower than the erroneous figure. By such weighting we are in effect calculating the total number of deaths that took place in the total 500 patients. These deaths divided by the number of patients gives the required rate, and the unweighted average of the rates will not produce it unless either the number of patients at each age is the same or the fatality-rate remains the same at each age. In general it is, therefore, incorrect to take an unweighted average of rates or of a series of means.

With such a series of means it is equally simple to reach the grand mean. Thus, suppose we have the mean weight of three sets of children, namely 82 lb. for 120 children, 75 lb. for 82 children, and 91 lb. for 126 children. Remembering that the mean is the sum of the weights divided by the number of children, the total weight of the 120 children with a mean of 82 lb. must have been 9840 lb. Similarly the total weight of the other groups must have been $75 \times 82$ and $91 \times 126$, or 6150 lb. and 11,466 lb. The total weight of all 328 children was therefore 27,456 lb. and the mean of all children 83·7 lb.

### Calculation of the Mean of a Few Observations

A point to remember in taking the average of a few observations is that the whole numbers need not invariably be added. Thus we might have observations of the number of cases of an infectious disease in each week of the year in each of 3 years and require the average annual number in each week.

| Year | Week 1 | Week 2 | Week 3 | Week 4 | etc. |
|------|--------|--------|--------|--------|------|
| 1944 | 126 | 132 | 163 | 182 | |
| 1945 | 121 | 126 | 159 | 191 | |
| 1946 | 128 | 120 | 161 | 190 | |

In week 1 each total has 120 as a common feature and it is necessary to add only $6 + 1 + 8 = 15$, and dividing by 3 the mean is 125. In week 2, again using 120 as a base line, we have $12 + 6 + 0 = 18$ and the mean is 126. In week 3 we may take 160 as base line and we have $+3 - 1 + 1 = 3$ and the mean is 161. In week 4 we may take 180 as base line and have $2 + 11 + 10 = 23$ and the mean is 187·7. With experience these small differences from a base line can be accurately noted and mentally added and much labour thus saved.

### Summary

The general position of a frequency distribution is measured by an average. There are three averages in common use : (a) the arithmetic mean, (b) the median, and

(c) the mode. The arithmetic mean, usually termed the mean or average, is the sum of all the observations divided by their number. The median is the central value when all the values are listed in order from the lowest to the highest. The mode is the most frequent observation, or, strictly speaking, the value at which the ideal curve to which the observations conform reaches its highest point. It can be found approximately from the formula Mode = Mean − 3(Mean − Median) so long as the shape of the distribution is not very skew. In taking the mean of a series of sub-means the " weights " attached to the latter should be taken into account.

(*For exercises* see *p.* 314)

# VII

# THE VARIABILITY OF OBSERVATIONS

In the previous chapter we have calculated and discussed an average value for a short series of observations and for one large enough to require grouping in a frequency distribution. But the very fact that we thought it necessary to calculate an average, to define the general position of a distribution, introduces the idea of *variation* of the individual values round that average. For if there were no such variation, if, in other words, all the observations had the same value, then there would be no point in calculating an average. In introducing and using an average, usually the arithmetic mean, we therefore ignore—for the time being—that variability of the observations. It follows that, taken alone, the mean is of very limited value, for it can give no information regarding the variability with which the observations are scattered around itself, and that variability (or lack of variability) is an important characteristic of the frequency distribution. As an example Table VIII shows the frequency distributions of age at death from two causes of death amongst women. The mean, or average, age at death, does *not* differ greatly between the two, being 37·2 years for deaths registered as due to diseases of the Fallopian tube and 35·2 years for those attributed to abortion. But both the table and the diagram based upon it (Fig. 10 ; p. 87) show that the difference in the variability, or scatter, of the observations round their respective means is very considerable. With diseases of the Fallopian tube the deaths in the year's records are spread over the age-groups 0–4 to 70–74, while deaths from abortion range only between 20–24 and 45–49. As a further description of the frequency distribution, we clearly need a measure of its degree of variability round the average.

A measure commonly employed in medical (and other) papers
is the *range*, as quoted above—*i.e.* the distance between the
smallest and greatest observations.  Though this measure is
often of considerable interest, it is not very satisfactory as a
description of the general variability, since it is based upon
only the two extreme observations and ignores the distribution of all the observations within those limits—*e.g.* the

TABLE VIII

FREQUENCY DISTRIBUTION OF DEATHS OF WOMEN IN
ENGLAND AND WALES, 1934, FROM (1) DISEASES OF THE
FALLOPIAN TUBE, AND (2) ABORTION NOT RETURNED AS
SEPTIC, ACCORDING TO AGE

| Age in Years | Diseases of the Fallopian Tube | Abortion not Returned as Septic |
|---|---|---|
| 0 - | 1 | .. |
| 5- | .. | .. |
| 10- | 1 | .. |
| 15- | 7 | .. |
| 20- | 12 | 6 |
| 25- | 35 | 21 |
| 30- | 42 | 22 |
| 35- | 33 | 19 |
| 40- | 24 | 26 |
| 45- | 27 | 5 |
| 50- | 10 | .. |
| 55- | 6 | .. |
| 60- | 5 | .. |
| 65- | 1 | .. |
| 70-75 | 2 | .. |
| Total | 206 | 99 |

remainder may be more evenly spread out over the distance
between the mean and the outlying values in one distribution
than in another.  Also the occurrence of the rare outlying
values will depend upon the number of observations made.
The greater the number of observations the more likely is it
that the rare value will appear amongst them.  In publishing
observations, it is certainly insufficient to give only the mean
and the range ; as previously pointed out, the frequency
distribution itself should be given—even if no further calculations are made from it.

### THE STANDARD DEVIATION

The further calculation that the statistician invariably makes is of the Standard Deviation, which is a measure of the scatter of the observations around their mean. Put briefly, the development of this particular measure is as follows. Suppose we have, as given in Table IX, twenty observations of systolic blood pressure made on twenty different persons. The mean, or average, blood pressure is the sum of the observations divided by 20 and equals 128 mm.

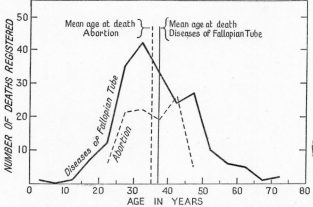

Fig. 10.—Frequency distribution of deaths of women in England and Wales, 1934, from (a) diseases of the Fallopian tube and (b) abortion not returned as septic.

It is obvious from cursory inspection that the variability of the individual values round this mean is considerable. They range from 98 to 160 ; on the other hand, a large proportion of the values lies in the narrower range 125–135 (50 per cent. of them). The mean and range are not sufficient to describe the distribution. As a further step we may calculate the amount by which each observation differs, or deviates, from the average, as is shown in column (2). If these differences are added, *taking their sign into account*, the sum must equal nought, for a characteristic of the arithmetic mean, or average, is that the sums of the positive and of the negative deviations of the observations from itself are equal. In this example the sum of the deviations above the mean

G

is $+93$ and below the mean $-93$. Two ways of avoiding this difficulty are possible : we may add all the deviations, regardless of their sign, or we may square each deviation so that each becomes positive. If the deviations be added in the example, ignoring their sign, the sum is 186 and the *mean deviation* is, therefore, 186 divided by 20 (the number of observations) or 9·3 mm. This is a valid measure of the

TABLE IX

| Twenty Observa-<br>tions of Systolic<br>Blood Pressure in mm. | Deviation of each<br>Observation from the<br>Mean (Mean = 128) | Square of each<br>Deviation from<br>the Mean |
|:---:|:---:|:---:|
| (1) | (2) | (3) |
| 98 | − 30 | 900 |
| 160 | +32 | 1024 |
| 136 | + 8 | 64 |
| 128 | 0 | 0 |
| 130 | + 2 | 4 |
| 114 | − 14 | 196 |
| 123 | − 5 | 25 |
| 134 | + 6 | 36 |
| 128 | 0 | 0 |
| 107 | − 21 | 441 |
| 123 | − 5 | 25 |
| 125 | − 3 | 9 |
| 129 | + 1 | 1 |
| 132 | + 4 | 16 |
| 154 | +26 | 676 |
| 115 | − 13 | 169 |
| 126 | − 2 | 4 |
| 132 | + 4 | 16 |
| 136 | + 8 | 64 |
| 130 | + 2 | 4 |
| Sum 2560 | 0 | 3674 |

variability of the observations around the mean, but it is one which, for reasons involved in the problems of sampling, discussed later, is of less value in general statistical work than the *standard deviation*. To reach the latter the squared deviations are used. Their sum is 3674, so that the mean squared deviation is this sum divided by 20, which equals 183·7. This value is known as the *Variance*. The standard deviation is the square root of this value (for having squared the original deviations the reverse step of taking the square root must finally be made) and in this example is, therefore, 13·55 mm.

This is, in truth, the standard deviation of *these particular 20* observations. We are, however, in practice almost invariably using such a set of observations to allow us to estimate the variability *in the population, or universe,* of which they merely form a sample. For this purpose it can be shown that on the average a slightly better estimate of the population value is reached by dividing the observed sum of the squared deviations from the mean by one less than the total number of observations, *i.e.* by $n - 1$ instead of by $n$ (see p. 105). Thus in the present instance we should calculate as the variance 3674/19, or 193·4, and the standard deviation is the square root of 193·4 or 13·91. The importance of this step is obviously greater when, as in the present instance, the number of observations is quite small.

Turning to the meaning of the result, a large standard deviation shows that the frequency distribution is widely spread out from the mean, while a small standard deviation shows that it lies closely concentrated about the mean with little variability between one observation and another. For example, the standard deviation of the widely spread age distribution of deaths attributed to diseases of the Fallopian tube (given in Table VIII) is 11·3, while of the more concentrated age distribution of deaths attributed to abortion it is only 6·8. The frequency distributions themselves clearly show this considerable difference in variability. The standard deviations have the advantage of summarising this difference by measuring the variability of each distribution in a single figure ; they also enable us to test, as will be seen subsequently, whether the observed differences between two such means and between two such degrees of variability are more than would be likely to have arisen by chance.

In making a comparison of one standard deviation with another it must, however, be remembered that this criterion of variability is measured in the same units as the original observations. The mean height of a group of school-children may be 48 inches and the standard deviation 6 inches ; if the observations were recorded in centimetres instead of in inches, then the mean would be 123 cm. and the standard deviation 15·4 cm. It follows that it is not possible by a comparison of the standard deviations to say, for instance, that weight is a more variable characteristic than height ; the two characteristics are not measured in the same units and the selection of these units—*e.g.* inches or centimetres, pounds or kilogrammes—must affect the comparison. In fact, it is no more helpful to compare these standard deviations than it is to compare the mean height with the mean weight. Further, a standard deviation of 10 round a mean of 40 must indicate a relatively greater degree of scatter than a standard deviation of 10 round a mean of 400, even though the units of measurements are the same.

### THE COEFFICIENT OF VARIATION

To overcome these difficulties of the comparison of the variabilities of frequency distributions measured in different units or with widely differing means, the Coefficient of Variation is utilised. This coefficient is the standard deviation of the distribution expressed as a percentage of the mean of the distribution—*i.e.* Coefficient of Variation = (Standard Deviation ÷ Mean) × 100. If the standard deviation is 10 round a mean of 40, then the former value is 25 per cent. of the latter ; if the standard deviation is 10 and the mean 400, the former value is 2·5 per cent. of the latter. These percentage values are the coefficients of variation. The original unit of measurement is immaterial for this coefficient, since it enters into both the numerator and the denominator of the fraction above. For instance, with a mean height of 48 inches and a standard deviation of 6 inches the coefficient of variation is $(6/48) \times 100 = 12 \cdot 5$ per cent. If the unit of measurement is a centimetre instead of an inch, the mean height becomes 123 cm., the standard deviation is 15·4 cm. and the coefficient of variation is $(15 \cdot 4/123) \times 100 = 12 \cdot 5$ per cent. again. Similarly the coefficient of variation of the blood pressures of Table IX is $(13 \cdot 55/128) \times 100 = 10 \cdot 6$ per cent.

These measures of variability are just as important characteristics of a series of observations as the measures of position—*i.e.* the average round which the series is centred.

The important step is to " get out of the habit of thinking in terms of the average, and think in terms of the frequency distribution. Unless and until he [the investigator] does this, his conclusions will always be liable to fallacy. If someone states merely that the average of something is so-and-so, it should always be the first mental question of the reader : ' This is all very well, but what is the frequency distribution likely to be ?  How much are the observations likely to be scattered round that average ?  And are they likely to be more scattered in the one direction than the other, or symmetrically round the average ? '  To raise questions of this kind is at least to enforce the limits of the reader's knowledge, and not only to render him more cautious in drawing conclusions, but possibly also to suggest the need for further work " (G. Udny Yule, Industrial Health Research Board, Report No. 28, 1924, p. 10).

### EXAMPLES OF VARIABILITY

The practical application of these measures of variability may be illustrated by the figures tabulated below, which are taken from an early statistical study of blood pressure in

THE BLOOD PRESSURE IN 566 HEALTHY ADULT MALES. MEANS, STANDARD DEVIATIONS, COEFFICIENTS OF VARIATION, AND THE RANGE OF MEASUREMENT

|  | Mean | Standard Deviation | Coefficient of Variation | Range |
|---|---|---|---|---|
| Age (years)    .    .    . | 23·2 | 4·02 | 17·31 | 18– 40 |
| Heart-rate  (beats  per minute)    .    .    . | 77·3 | 12·83 | 16·60 | 46–129 |
| Systolic B.P. (mm.) .    . | 128·8 | 13·05 | 10·13 | 97–168 |
| Diastolic B.P. (mm.) .    . | 79·7 | 9·39 | 11·78 | 46–108 |
| Pulse pressure (mm.)    . | 49·1 | 11·14 | 22·69 | 24– 82 |

healthy adult males by P. L. McKinlay and A. B. Walker (*Edinb. Med. J.*, 1935, 42, 407). In the original the full frequency distributions are also set out.

The variability of these physiological measurements, which is apparently compatible with good health at the time of measurement, is striking. It leads the authors to conclude that we must hesitate to regard as abnormal any isolated measurements in otherwise apparently fit individuals. Some of the measurements they found are definitely within the limits usually regarded as pathological, and study is necessary to determine whether such large deviations from the " normal " have any unfavourable prognostic significance. It is clear that the mean value alone is a very insecure guide to " normality."

As a further example of the importance of taking note of the variability of observations, the incubation period of a disease may be considered. If the day of exposure to infection is known for a number of persons we can construct a frequency distribution of the durations of time elapsing between exposure to infection and onset of disease as observed clinically. If these durations cover a relatively wide range, say 10–18 days with an average of 13 days, it is obvious that observation or isolation of those who have been exposed to infection for the *average* duration would give no high degree of security. For security we need to know the proportion of persons who develop the disease on the fourteenth, fifteenth, etc., day after exposure ; if these proportions are high—*i.e.* the standard deviation of the distribution is relatively large—isolation must be maintained considerably beyond the *average* incubation time. In such a case the importance of variability is indeed obvious ; but there is a tendency for workers to overlook the fact that in *any* series of observations the variability, large or small, is a highly important characteristic.

For the beginner, who at first finds the standard deviation a somewhat intangible quantity, it is useful to remember that for distributions that are not very asymmetrical six times the standard deviation includes about 99 per cent. of all the observations. Thus, in the example given above, the standard deviation of the diastolic blood pressures is 9·39, and six times this, or 56 units, should include very nearly all the observations. In fact, the observations lie within 108 – 46 = 62 units. If the distribution is symmetrical, the mean plus 3 times the standard deviation should give approximately the upper limit of the observations, and the mean minus 3 times the standard deviation should similarly give their lower limit. Thus for the diastolic blood pressure we have 79·7 + 28 and 79·7 − 28, or a range of, approximately, 52 to 108, very close to the observed range of 46 to 108.   This rule also serves, it will be seen, as a check upon the calculation of a standard deviation—not, of course, as to whether some small error has been made but as to whether there is some serious mistake which has led to a standard deviation which is quite unreasonable.   It must not, however, be expected to hold with a few dozen observations only.

In actual practice the calculation of the standard deviation is not usually carried out by the method shown above— *i.e.* by computing the deviation of each observation from the mean and squaring it.   Shorter methods are available both for ungrouped observations (like the twenty measurements of blood pressure in Table IX) and for grouped observations (like those in Table VIII).   These methods are described in the next chapter.

SYMMETRY

Another character of the frequency distribution is its symmetry or lack of symmetry.   With a completely symmetrical distribution the frequency with which observations are recorded at each point on the graph, or within certain values below the mean, is identical with the frequency of observations at the same point, or within the same values, above the mean.   With asymmetry the observations are not evenly scattered on either side of the mean but show an excess on one side or within particular values—*e.g.* with a mean of 50, observations below the mean may not fall below 20 units from that point, the lowest observation recorded being 30, while on the positive side of the mean observations 40 units above the mean may be observed, values of 90 being recorded.   The tabulated distribution and, still more, a graph of it will afford an *indication* of this characteristic.

THE " NORMAL " CURVE OR DISTRIBUTION

One particular form of a symmetrical distribution is known as the " normal " curve, or distribution, and this curve has

very great importance in statistical theory, being fundamental to the tests of significance discussed in later chapters.
It should not, however, be thought that this distribution is
the normal in the sense that all measurable characteristics
occurring in nature, *e.g.* of men, animals, or plants, should
conform to it. Many do, in fact, show this kind of distribution, but by no means all. Stature is a characteristic
in man which does, at least very closely, show such a distribution and we may examine the curve with this as an
example. (This approach, it may be noted, is adopted
merely for simplicity. The normal, or Gaussian, curve and
its characteristics can, of course, be derived mathematically.)

In Table X are given the heights of 1000 adult men
(hypothetical figures). Calculation shows that the mean
height is 68·0 inches and the standard deviation is 2·0 inches.
Examining the distribution, we can see how many men have
a height which differs from the mean of all men by not more
than 2 inches, *i.e.* whose height lies between 68 – 2 and 68 + 2
inches, or, in short, between 66 and 70 inches.   There are
152 + 193 = 345 men between 66 and 68 inches and 197 + 148
= 345 men between 68 and 70 inches.   There are, therefore,
690 men whose height is not more than 2 inches away from
the mean.   But it will be noticed that the standard deviation
of the values is 2 inches.   Instead of saying there are 690
men whose stature is within 2 inches of the mean, we may
therefore say that for 69·0 per cent. of all the men the stature
does not differ from the mean by more than one time the
standard deviation (either in the plus or minus direction).

Similarly we may see how many men have statures that
lie within 4 inches of the mean, *i.e.* between 64 and 72 inches.
Between 64 and 68 there are 43 + 86 + 152 + 193 = 474, and
between 68 and 72 there are 197 + 148 + 91 + 45 = 481 ; the
total is 955.   But 4 inches away from the mean is twice the
standard deviation and we may therefore say that for 95·5
per cent. of all the men the stature does not differ from the
mean by more than 2 times the standard deviation in either
direction.

Lastly, we may see how many men have a stature that is
not more than 6 inches distant from the mean, *i.e.* between

62 and 74 inches.   Between 62 and 68 there are $5 + 17 + 43 + 86 + 152 + 193 = 496$ and between 68 and 74 there are $197 + 148 + 91 + 45 + 16 + 4 = 501$, giving a total of 997.   But 6 inches away from the mean is three times the standard deviation, and we may therefore say that, for 99·7 per cent. of all the men the stature does not differ from the mean by more than 3 times the standard deviation in either direction.

This is a useful way of looking at a frequency distribution, namely to see how many of the observations lie within a given distance of the mean, not in terms of the actual units of measurement but in terms of multiples of the standard deviation.

Returning to the ideal normal frequency distribution as derived mathematically, its characteristics are :  (a) the mean, median, and mode all coincide ;  (b) the curve is perfectly symmetrical round the mean ;  and (c) we can calculate *theoretically* how many of the observations will lie in the interval between the mean itself and the mean plus or minus *any* multiple of the standard deviation.   This calculation gives the following results :—

Proportion of observations that lie within
   1 time the S.D. from the mean    .   68·27 per cent.
Proportion of observations that lie within
   2 times the S.D. from the mean    .   95·45 per cent.
Proportion of observations that lie within
   3 times the S.D. from the mean    .   99·73 per cent.

It will be seen that with a measurement that follows a normal distribution nearly one-third of the values observed will differ from the mean value by more than once the standard deviation, only about 5 per cent. will differ from the mean by more than twice the standard deviation, and only some 3 in 1000 will differ from the mean by more than 3 times the standard deviation.   In a normal distribution, in other words, values that differ from the mean by more than twice the standard deviation are fairly rare, for only about 1 in 20 observations will do so ; values that differ from the mean by more than 3 times the standard deviation are very rare, for only about 1 in 370 will do so.

These theoretical values, it will be seen, agree very closely with the observed values given by Table X.  In fact, it is unlikely that the stature of 1000 men would follow the normal distribution so very closely and, as already stated, the hypothetical figures of the table were selected deliberately for the present demonstration of the properties of a normal curve of distribution in place of deriving those properties mathematically.  The figures, therefore, must *not* be taken as quite true to life, though it is true that stature does follow

TABLE X

EXAMPLE OF A NORMAL DISTRIBUTION

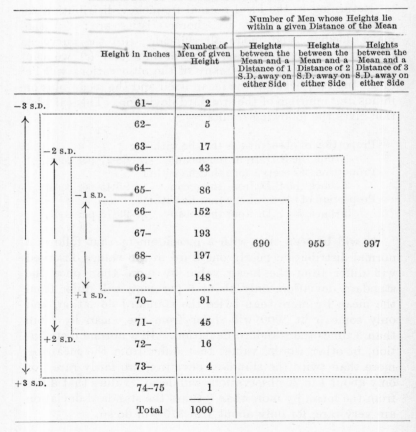

| | Height in Inches | Number of Men of given Height | Number of Men whose Heights lie within a given Distance of the Mean | | |
|---|---|---|---|---|---|
| | | | Heights between the Mean and a Distance of 1 S.D. away on either Side | Heights between the Mean and a Distance of 2 S.D. away on either Side | Heights between the Mean and a Distance of 3 S.D. away on either Side |
| −3 S.D. | 61– | 2 | | | |
| | 62– | 5 | | | |
| −2 S.D. | 63– | 17 | | | |
| | 64– | 43 | | | |
| −1 S.D. | 65– | 86 | | | |
| | 66– | 152 | | | |
| | 67– | 193 | | | |
| | 68– | 197 | 690 | 955 | 997 |
| | 69 - | 148 | | | |
| +1 S.D. | 70– | 91 | | | |
| | 71– | 45 | | | |
| +2 S.D. | 72– | 16 | | | |
| | 73– | 4 | | | |
| +3 S.D. | 74–75 | 1 | | | |
| | Total | 1000 | | | |

a fairly normal distribution. The ideal curve and the present hypothetical figures are shown diagrammatically in Fig. 11.

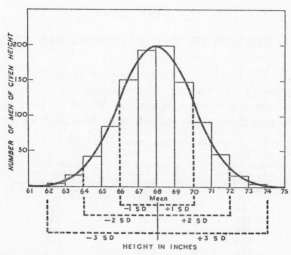

Fɪɢ. 11.—Histogram of statures of 1000 men (hypothetical figures) and normal curve superimposed.

## Summary

As descriptions of the frequency distribution of a series of observations certain values are necessary, the most important of which are, usually, the mean and standard deviation. The mean alone is rarely, if ever, sufficient. In statistical work it is necessary to think in terms of the frequency distribution as a whole, taking into account the central position round which it is spread (the mean or average), the variability it displays round that central position (the standard deviation and coefficient of variation), and the symmetry or lack of symmetry with which it is spread round the central position. With a normal distribution only 1 observation in 20 will differ from the mean by more than twice the standard deviation (plus or minus) and only some 3 in 1000 will differ from the mean by more than 3 times the standard deviation (plus or minus).

# VIII

## CALCULATION OF THE STANDARD DEVIATION

In Table IX of the previous chapter (reproduced below) there were given twenty observations of systolic blood pressure and their mean value was found to be 128. The variability of these observations was measured by means of

OBSERVATIONS FROM TABLE IX

| Twenty Observations of Systolic Blood Pressure in mm. | Deviation of each Observation from the Mean (Mean = 128) | Square of each Deviation from the Mean |
|---|---|---|
| (1) | (2) | (3) |
| 98 | − 30 | 900 |
| 160 | +32 | 1024 |
| 136 | + 8 | 64 |
| 128 | 0 | 0 |
| 130 | + 2 | 4 |
| 114 | − 14 | 196 |
| 123 | − 5 | 25 |
| 134 | + 6 | 36 |
| 128 | 0 | 0 |
| 107 | − 21 | 441 |
| 123 | − 5 | 25 |
| 125 | − 3 | 9 |
| 129 | + 1 | 1 |
| 132 | + 4 | 16 |
| 154 | +26 | 676 |
| 115 | − 13 | 169 |
| 126 | − 2 | 4 |
| 132 | + 4 | 16 |
| 136 | + 8 | 64 |
| 130 | + 2 | 4 |
| Sum 2560 | 0 | 3674 |

the standard deviation. This value, it may be noted, is sometimes referred to in short as the S.D. and sometimes designated by the Greek letter sigma ($\sigma$).* Its actual value was calculated in Chapter VII by (1) finding by how much

* In some circumstances $\sigma$ is reserved for the unknown standard deviation of the universe sampled and $s$ is used for the standard deviation estimated from the actual sample of observations under discussion.

each observation differed from the mean, (2) squaring each of these differences, (3) adding up these squares, and dividing this total by the number of observations minus one, (4) taking the square root of this number (or, taking the processes in reverse order, " the root mean square deviation," an old name for the standard deviation). This method of calculation would have been much more laborious if the mean blood pressure had not been a whole number—e.g. if it had been 128·4—and if each of the original observations had been taken to one decimal place (presuming that degree of accuracy to be possible)—e.g. the first had been 98·7. The differences between the observations and their mean, and the squares of these values, would then have been less simple to calculate. But in such cases the necessary arithmetic can still be kept simple by a slight change of method.

## The Ungrouped Series

If we call each individual observation $x$ and the mean of all 20 we call $\bar{x}$ (pronounced x-bar), then by the method of Table IX, on the opposite page, we must first find each separate deviation from the mean, $(x - \bar{x})$, as in column (2), and then we must calculate the square of each of these deviations, $(x - \bar{x})^2$, as in column (3). The required sum of all the squared deviations in column (3) can then be computed (3674) and may be described as $Sum\ (x - \bar{x})^2$. We can, however, reach this same sum *without calculating any deviations at all* by means of the following relationship :—

$$\sqrt{\frac{Sum\ (x - \bar{x})^2}{n-1}} = Sum\ x^2 - (Sum\ x)^2/n.$$

Thus in practice we square each observation, $x$, as it stands, as in column (2) of Table XI, and we find the sum of these squares ; thus $Sum\ x^2 = 331,354$. In calculating the mean we have already found the sum of the 20 observations themselves ; thus, from column (1), $Sum\ x = 2560$. Our required sum of squared deviations round the mean, $Sum\ (x - \bar{x})^2$, is therefore $331,354 - (2560)^2/20 = 3674$. The standard deviation is then, as before, $\sqrt{3674 \div 19} = 13\cdot91$ (using for the reasons given previously $n - 1$ and not $n$ as the divisor).

Thus to calculate the standard deviation in a short un-grouped series of figures we have five steps : (*a*) Square the *individual observations* themselves and find the sum of these squares. (*b*) Square the *sum* of the observations themselves and divide this by the total number of observations available. (*c*) Subtracting (*b*) from (*a*) gives the required sum of the squared deviations of the observations *around their own mean*. (*d*) Divide this value by $n-1$ to reach the variance and (*e*) take the square root of the variance to reach the standard deviation.

TABLE XI

CALCULATION OF STANDARD DEVIATION :
UNGROUPED SERIES

| Twenty Observations of Systolic Blood Pressure in mm. | Square of each Observation |
|---|---|
| (1) | (2) |
| 98 | 9,604 |
| 160 | 25,600 |
| 136 | 18,496 |
| 128 | 16,384 |
| 130 | 16,900 |
| 114 | 12,996 |
| 123 | 15,129 |
| 134 | 17,956 |
| 128 | 16,384 |
| 107 | 11,449 |
| 123 | 15,129 |
| 125 | 15,625 |
| 129 | 16,641 |
| 132 | 17,424 |
| 154 | 23,716 |
| 115 | 13,225 |
| 126 | 15,876 |
| 132 | 17,424 |
| 136 | 18,496 |
| 130 | 16,900 |
| Sum 2560 | 331,354 |

## The Grouped Series

With a large number of observations this method of squaring each observation separately would be very laborious. A shorter method which will give very nearly the same result can be adopted. The observations must first be grouped in a frequency distribution. As an example we may take the distribution given in Table VIII (p. 86) of the ages at death from diseases of the Fallopian tube. This distribution is given again in column (2) of Table XII.

To reach the mean age at death we could add up the 206 individually recorded ages and divide by 206. But at the risk of making only an immaterial error we can, as shown

TABLE XII

CALCULATION OF STANDARD DEVIATION : GROUPED SERIES

| Age in Years | Number of Deaths in each Age-group | Age in Working Units | (2)×(3) | (3)×(4) |
|---|---|---|---|---|
| (1) | (2) | (3) | (4) | (5) |
| 0– | 1 | – 6 | – 6 | 36 |
| 5– | .. | – 5 | .. | .. |
| 10– | 1 | – 4 | – 4 | 16 |
| 15– | 7 | – 3 | – 21 | 63 |
| 20– | 12 | – 2 | – 24 | 48 |
| 25– | 35 | – 1 | – 35 | 35 |
| 30– | 42 | 0 | .. | .. |
| 35– | 33 | +1 | +33 | 33 |
| 40– | 24 | +2 | +48 | 96 |
| 45– | 27 | +3 | +81 | 243 |
| 50– | 10 | +4 | +40 | 160 |
| 55– | 6 | +5 | +30 | 150 |
| 60– | 5 | +6 | +30 | 180 |
| 65– | 1 | +7 | + 7 | 49 |
| 70–75 | 2 | +8 | +16 | 128 |
| Total | 206 | .. | +195 | 1237 |

in Chapter VI, shorten this process by presuming that the individuals belonging to each 5-yearly age-group died at the centre age of that group—*e.g.* that the 42 women dying at ages between 30 and 35 all died at age 32·5. Some will have died between 30 and 32·5, some, perhaps, at exactly 32·5, some between 32·5 and 35. If the distribution is fairly symmetrical, then, as previously stated, the positive and negative errors we make by this assumption will nearly balance out. The sum of the 206 ages at death will then be $(2·5 \times 1) + (12·5 \times 1) + (17·5 \times 7) + (22·5 \times 12) + \quad . \quad . \quad . \quad +$

$(62 \cdot 5 \times 5) + (67 \cdot 5 \times 1) + (72 \cdot 5 \times 2) = 7670 \cdot 0$ and the mean age at death is $7670 \cdot 0 \div 206 = 37 \cdot 2$ years. Having found the mean in this way the standard deviation could be found by calculating how much the observations in each group deviate from it and taking the square of this value. For instance the 12 individuals in the age-group 20–25 died, on our assumption, at age $22 \cdot 5$. They differ from the mean, therefore, by $(37 \cdot 2$ minus $22 \cdot 5)$ or $14 \cdot 7$; the square of this is $216 \cdot 09$, and this value we must take 12 times as there are 12 individuals with that deviation.

Following this procedure, we should reach for the squares of the deviations of the individuals from their mean the following values :—

$$( - 34 \cdot 7)^2 \times \; 1 + ( - 24 \cdot 7)^2 \times \; 1 + ( - 19 \cdot 7)^2 \times \; 7 +$$
$$( - 14 \cdot 7)^2 \times 12 + ( - \; 9 \cdot 7)^2 \times 35 + ( - \; 4 \cdot 7)^2 \times 42 +$$
$$(0 \cdot 3)^2 \times 33 + ( \; 5 \cdot 3)^2 \times 24 + (10 \cdot 3)^2 \times 27 +$$
$$(15 \cdot 3)^2 \times 10 + (20 \cdot 3)^2 \times \; 6 + (25 \cdot 3)^2 \times \; 5 +$$
$$(30 \cdot 3)^2 \times \; 1 + (35 \cdot 3)^2 \times \; 2 = 26{,}310 \cdot 54.$$

The sum of these calculations is $26{,}310 \cdot 54$ and the standard deviation is therefore

$$\sqrt{26{,}310 \cdot 54 / 205} = \sqrt{128 \cdot 34} = 11 \cdot 33 \text{ years.}$$

### SHORT METHOD, WITH GROUPED SERIES

This is a possible method of working but, it will be observed, a laborious way. In practice a considerably shorter method is adopted. The principle of this method is merely an extension of that used in Chapter VI for finding the mean, *i.e.* instead of working in the real, and cumbersome, units of measurement we translate them arbitrarily into smaller and more convenient units, work the sums in those smaller units, and translate the results back again into the real units at the end.

Let us, for instance, in this case replace $32 \cdot 5$ by 0, $27 \cdot 5$ by $-1$, $22 \cdot 5$ by $-2$, and so on, $37 \cdot 5$ by $+1$, $42 \cdot 5$ by $+2$, and so on. (The original groups must have, it will be remembered, intervals of equal width; they were all 5-yearly in our example.) Now instead of having to multiply $-27.5$ by 35, for example, we have the simpler task of multiplying $-1$ by 35. These multiplications are made in column (4) of Table XII. Their sum, taking the sign into account (as must be done), is $+195$. The mean in these units is therefore

$$+195/206 = +0.947.$$

The standard deviation can be found in these same small units, measuring the deviations of the observations from the 0 value instead of from the mean for simplicity. The squares of the deviations in these units are merely 1, 4, 9, 16, etc., and these have to be multiplied by the number of individuals with the particular deviation—e.g. $7 \times 9$ for the $-3$ group, $24 \times 4$ for the $+2$ group, and so forth. A still simpler process of reaching the same result is to multiply column (4) by column (3), i.e. instead of multiplying 7 by 9 we multiply $(7 \times -3)$ by $-3$. This gives the figures of column (5). The sum of these squared deviations is, then, 1237.

These deviations in working units have, however, been measured round the 0 value, whereas they ought to have been measured round the mean (in working units) of $+0.947$. The correction is again made by the formula given on p. 99, namely that the required $Sum\ (x - \bar{x})^2$ equals $Sum\ x^2 - (Sum\ x)^2/n$. Therefore from the values in Table XII we can calculate $Sum\ (x - \bar{x})^2$ to be $1237 - (195)^2/206 = 1052.41$. The standard deviation in working units is, therefore, $\sqrt{1052.41/205} = 2.265$.

We have now to translate the mean, $+0.947$, and the standard deviation, $2.265$, back into the real units. This is simply done. The mean in working units is $+0.947$—i.e. 0.947 working units above our 0. In real units our 0 is equivalent to 32.5, for that is the substitution we made (note, once more, the *centre* of the group against which we placed the 0, not its beginning). The real mean must therefore be $32.5 + 5\ (0.947) = 37.2$ years, which is the same as the value we found by the long method using real units throughout. (The multiplier 5, it will be remembered, comes from the size of the interval of the original group.)

H

To reach the real standard deviation, all that has to be done is to multiply the standard deviation as found in working units by the original units of grouping—in this case by 5. For if this measure of the scatter of the observations is 2·265 when the range is only 14 units (from − 6 to + 8) it must be 5 times as much when the range is really 70 units (from 2·5 to 72·5). The real standard deviation is therefore $5 \times 2·265 = 11·33$ years. (It should be noted that if the original units are *smaller* than the working units then the standard deviation will be smaller in the real units, *e.g.* the multiplier will be 0·25 if that is the original group interval.)

### CHECKING THE ARITHMETIC

As regards the final result for the standard deviation, as well as the mean, it is immaterial where the 0 is placed ; the same answers in *real* units must be reached. From the point of view of the arithmetic it is usually best to place it centrally so that the multipliers may be kept small. For the sake of demonstration the calculations for Table XII

### TABLE XIII

CALCULATION OF STANDARD DEVIATION : GROUPED SERIES

| Age in Years | Number of Deaths in each Age-group | Age in Working Units | $(2) \times (3)$ | $(4) \times (3)$ |
|---|---|---|---|---|
| (1) | (2) | (3) | (4) | (5) |
| 0– | 1 | − 8 | − 8 | 64 |
| 5– | .. | − 7 | .. | .. |
| 10– | 1 | − 6 | − 6 | 36 |
| 15– | 7 | − 5 | − 35 | 175 |
| 20– | 12 | − 4 | − 48 | 192 |
| 25– | 35 | − 3 | − 105 | 315 |
| 30– | 42 | − 2 | − 84 | 168 |
| 35– | 33 | − 1 | − 33 | 33 |
| 40– | 24 | 0 | .. | .. |
| 45– | 27 | +1 | + 27 | 27 |
| 50– | 10 | +2 | + 20 | 40 |
| 55– | 6 | +3 | + 18 | 54 |
| 60– | 5 | +4 | + 20 | 80 |
| 65– | 1 | +5 | + 5 | 25 |
| 70–75 | 2 | +6 | + 12 | 72 |
| Total | 206 | .. | − 217 | 1281 |

are repeated in Table XIII taking another position for 0. This, in practice, is a good method of checking the arithmetic.

From the calculations in Table XIII we have :

Mean in working units $= -217/206 = -1\cdot053$,

$\therefore$ mean in real units $= 42\cdot5 - 5\ (1\cdot053) = 37\cdot2$ years

(42·5 is the centre of the group against which the 0 was placed ; note that the correction has now to be subtracted, for the sign of the mean in working units is negative).

Sum of squared deviations in working units round the mean is $1281 - (217)^2/206 = 1052\cdot41$ and, therefore, as before, the standard deviation in working units is $\sqrt{1052\cdot41/205} = 2\cdot265$ and in true units $2\cdot265 \times 5 = 11\cdot33$ years.

These values agree with those previously found.

### The Standard Deviation in Small Samples

As already pointed out, the standard deviation found for a set of observations is an estimate of the variability of the observations in the population, or universe, that has been sampled and on the average a slightly better estimate is reached by dividing the sum of the squared deviations from the mean by $n - 1$ instead of by $n$ (where $n$ is the number of observations). If the number of observations is large the difference is immaterial ; if it is small, some difference results.

An arithmetical demonstration of the advantage, on the average, of basing the calculation upon one less than the total number of observations is given in Table XIV. One hundred samples, each containing 5 individuals, or observations, were drawn from a " universe." In this " universe " the " persons " could have any value from 0 to 9. We might imagine, as in the next chapter, that the value denoted the number of colds a person had had in the previous 12 months.

The " universe " used was composed of *Random Sampling Numbers*, such as are given on pp. 344 to 359. Within such a universe the numbers 0, 1, 2, 3 up to 9 should occur with equal frequency, and it can, therefore, be calculated that its mean is 4·50 and its standard deviation 2·87. If a *large* sample be drawn from it, it will (almost certainly) be found that the mean and standard deviation of that sample do not

differ appreciably from those values.  With small samples
they may differ appreciably.  This question is discussed in
detail in the next chapter, and the present issue is merely

TABLE XIV

A COMPARISON OF THE STANDARD DEVIATIONS OCCURRING
IN 100 SAMPLES OF 5 OBSERVATIONS

WHEN BASED UPON

(a) THE NUMBER OF OBSERVATIONS IN THE SAMPLE, AND
(b) ONE LESS THAN THE NUMBER OF OBSERVATIONS

| Size of the S.D. observed in the Sample (1) | Number of Times an S.D. of the given Size occurred when the Calculation was based upon— | |
| --- | --- | --- |
| | The Number of Observations = 5 (2) | One Less than the Number of Observations = 4 (3) |
| 0·62– | 2 | 2 |
| 0·87– | 2 | .. |
| 1·12– | .. | 1 |
| 1·37– | 4 | 1 |
| 1·62– | 11 | 4 |
| 1·87– | 11 | 10 |
| 2·12– | 13 | 11 |
| 2·37– | 9 | 13 |
| 2·62– | 17    69 | 6    48 |
| 2·87– | 13 | 17 |
| 3·12– | 8 | 12 |
| 3·37– | 7 | 8 |
| 3·62– | 2 | 8 |
| 3·87– | 1 | 5 |
| 4·21–4·37 | ..    31 | 2    52 |
| Total | 100 | 100 |
| Average S.D. Value . | 2·50 | 2·81 |

whether the standard deviation of the sample is likely to be
nearer the truth when it is based upon one less than the
number of observations than when it is based upon the total
number.  Table XIV shows the number of times a standard
deviation of a given size was seen to occur in a sample of 5
" persons."  In column (2) the calculation was based upon
all 5 observations, and it will be seen that of the 100 S.D.'s
69 fell below the real value of 2·87 and only 31 were larger

than the real value (including here one which was exactly the correct value). In other words, there is a greater chance that the sample S.D. will be too low than too high when it is based upon the total number of observations. The average value for these hundred S.D.'s is 2·50, *i.e.* somewhat below the real value of 2·87.

On the other hand, when the calculation is based upon 4 observations, or one less than the total number of 5, the distribution of S.D.'s becomes much more equally spread on either side of the true value, 48 now being below and 52 above the real value. The average value for the 100 S.D.'s has become 2·81, *i.e.* very close to the real value.

Two points should, however, be noted especially.

(1) The improvement in the sample S.D. as an estimate of the universe S.D. when the former is based upon $n - 1$ is *only an average improvement*. If the S.D. of the sample is based upon *all* the observations and, already in this form, is *larger* than the real S.D. of the universe, then basing the estimate upon $n - 1$ must make it still larger and therefore still more distant from the truth. The point is that there are more values too low than too high, so that we have an average improvement by increasing all the values. Also, for the tests of significance discussed in subsequent chapters it is, on the whole, wiser to have an over-stated than an under-stated standard deviation.

(2) The second point worth noting is that, with such a very small sample, the standard deviation may, naturally, differ greatly from the real value.

(*For exercises see p.* 315)

## PROBLEMS OF SAMPLING : AVERAGES

THE observations to which the application of statistical methods is necessary are those, it has been pointed out, which are influenced by numerous causes, the object being to disentangle that multiple causation. It has also been noted that the observations utilised are nearly always only a sample of all the possible observations that might have been made. For instance, the frequency distribution of the stature of Englishmen—*i.e.* the number of Englishmen of different heights—is not based upon measurements of all Englishmen but only upon some sample of them. The question that immediately arises is how far is the sample representative of the population from which it was drawn, and, bound up with that question, to what extent may the values calculated from the sample—*e.g.* the mean and standard deviation—be regarded as true estimates of the values in the population sampled. If the mean height of 1000 men is 169 cm. with a standard deviation of 7 cm., may we assert that the values of the mean and standard deviation of all the men of whom these 1000 form a sample are not likely to differ appreciably from 169 and 7 ? This problem is fundamental to all statistical work and reasoning ; a clear conception of its importance is necessary if errors of interpretation are to be avoided, while a knowledge of the statistical technique in determining errors of sampling will allow conclusions to be drawn with a greater degree of security.

### ELIMINATION OF BIAS

Consideration must first be given, as previously noted, to the presence of selection or bias in the sample. If owing to the method of collection of the observations, those observations cannot possibly be a representative sample of the total population, then clearly the values calculated from the sample cannot be regarded as true estimates of the population values, and no statistical technique can allow for that kind of error.   If the average daily consumption of calories per adult male is found to be 3000 in a group of 200 families from whom particulars are collected of their week's consumption of food, it cannot be deduced that that value is likely to be the true average of all families.   Housewives who are willing to undertake the task of giving such particulars may be above the average level of intelligence or be the more careful and thrifty of the population.   The sample is, then, not a representative but a somewhat selected sample and there is no evidence as to the degree to which this selection affects the results.   That difficulty of interpretation was discussed in Chapter III.   In the present discussion we will presume that the sample is " unselected " and devote attention entirely to the problem of the variability which will be found to occur from one sample to another in such values as means, standard deviations, and proportions, due entirely, to what are known as the " errors of sampling." Attention may first be given to the mean.

### THE MEAN

Let us suppose that we are taking samples from a very large population, or universe, and that we know that an individual in that universe may measure any value from 0 to 9—*e.g.* we may be recording the number of attacks of the common cold suffered by each person during a specified period, presuming 9 attacks to be the maximum number possible.   The mean number of attacks per person and the standard deviation in the whole population we will presume to be known ; let the average number of attacks per person be 4·50 (*i.e.* the total attacks during the specified period divided by the number of persons in the universe) and let the standard deviation be 2·87 (as found, in the previous two chapters, by calculating how much the experience of

## TABLE XV

### NUMBER OF COLDS SUFFERED BY INDIVIDUALS, VALUES RECORDED IN SAMPLES OF 5 PERSONS (HYPOTHETICAL FIGURES)

| Sample No. | 1 | 2 | 3 | 4 | 5 | 6 | 7 | 8 | 9 | 10 | 11 | 12 | 13 | 14 | 15 | 16 | 17 | 18 | 19 | 20 | 21 | 22 | 23 | 24 | 25 |
|---|---|---|---|---|---|---|---|---|---|---|---|---|---|---|---|---|---|---|---|---|---|---|---|---|---|
| | 2 | 6 | 3 | 9 | 7 | 5 | 3 | 0 | 5 | 4 | 5 | 2 | 4 | 1 | 2 | 6 | 6 | 9 | 2 | 3 | 5 | 3 | 9 | 6 | 6 |
| | 4 | 9 | 1 | 1 | 7 | 5 | 1 | 0 | 2 | 3 | 9 | 2 | 3 | 5 | 8 | 6 | 5 | 8 | 2 | 3 | 1 | 6 | 1 | 6 | 2 |
| | 2 | 7 | 3 | 2 | 3 | 1 | 6 | 3 | 7 | 1 | 2 | 7 | 1 | 7 | 0 | 8 | 8 | 9 | 7 | 8 | 6 | 5 | 5 | 3 | 7 |
| | 0 | 5 | 1 | 6 | 6 | 8 | 4 | 3 | 8 | 6 | 9 | 2 | 9 | 3 | 2 | 8 | 1 | 5 | 6 | 5 | 2 | 2 | 4 | 7 | 2 |
| | 2 | 9 | 1 | 9 | 7 | 6 | 8 | 6 | 6 | 6 | 8 | 1 | 1 | 5 | 3 | 7 | 3 | 1 | 7 | 1 | 5 | 4 | 2 | 5 | 1 |
| Mean of each sample | 2·0 | 7·2 | 1·8 | 5·4 | 6·0 | 5·0 | 4·4 | 2·4 | 5·6 | 4·0 | 6·6 | 2·8 | 3·6 | 4·2 | 3·0 | 7·0 | 4·6 | 6·4 | 4·8 | 4·0 | 3·8 | 4·0 | 4·2 | 5·4 | 3·6 |

| Sample No. | 26 | 27 | 28 | 29 | 30 | 31 | 32 | 33 | 34 | 35 | 36 | 37 | 38 | 39 | 40 | 41 | 42 | 43 | 44 | 45 | 46 | 47 | 48 | 49 | 50 |
|---|---|---|---|---|---|---|---|---|---|---|---|---|---|---|---|---|---|---|---|---|---|---|---|---|---|
| | 7 | 7 | 8 | 7 | 9 | 4 | 1 | 3 | 3 | 9 | 4 | 2 | 5 | 9 | 5 | 9 | 7 | 3 | 0 | 2 | 1 | 6 | 9 | 4 | 4 |
| | 5 | 0 | 0 | 2 | 4 | 2 | 6 | 5 | 9 | 7 | 1 | 5 | 1 | 7 | 8 | 3 | 6 | 6 | 9 | 3 | 1 | 1 | 8 | 4 | 1 |
| | 3 | 8 | 6 | 6 | 9 | 6 | 4 | 7 | 6 | 1 | 7 | 1 | 9 | 5 | 5 | 9 | 1 | 5 | 0 | 6 | 0 | 4 | 1 | 4 | 4 |
| | 1 | 5 | 0 | 5 | 0 | 8 | 4 | 4 | 9 | 5 | 3 | 5 | 2 | 3 | 7 | 9 | 9 | 2 | 7 | 4 | 2 | 6 | 7 | 2 | 7 |
| | 6 | 5 | 4 | 9 | 4 | 7 | 3 | 5 | 9 | 2 | 4 | 4 | 5 | 8 | 7 | 7 | 3 | 2 | 7 | 0 | 7 | 1 | 8 | 1 | 6 |
| Mean of each sample | 4·4 | 5·0 | 3·6 | 5·8 | 5·2 | 5·4 | 3·6 | 4·8 | 7·2 | 4·8 | 3·8 | 3·4 | 4·4 | 6·4 | 6·4 | 7·4 | 5·2 | 3·6 | 4·6 | 3·0 | 2·2 | 3·6 | 6·6 | 3·0 | 4·4 |

| Sample No. | 51 | 52 | 53 | 54 | 55 | 56 | 57 | 58 | 59 | 60 | 61 | 62 | 63 | 64 | 65 | 66 | 67 | 68 | 69 | 70 | 71 | 72 | 73 | 74 | 75 |
|---|---|---|---|---|---|---|---|---|---|---|---|---|---|---|---|---|---|---|---|---|---|---|---|---|---|
| | 9 | 9 | 7 | 0 | 9 | 1 | 0 | 6 | 1 | 9 | 1 | 7 | 3 | 1 | 0 | 3 | 4 | 0 | 3 | 6 | 2 | 7 | 8 | 0 | 1 |
| | 9 | 9 | 8 | 9 | 4 | 0 | 6 | 7 | 5 | 2 | 7 | 8 | 7 | 5 | 7 | 6 | 1 | 6 | 3 | 4 | 0 | 2 | 9 | 6 | 9 |
| | 1 | 3 | 5 | 3 | 9 | 5 | 2 | 8 | 8 | 4 | 3 | 2 | 0 | 9 | 8 | 5 | 8 | 3 | 9 | 7 | 3 | 8 | 7 | 9 | 2 |
| | 0 | 4 | 4 | 1 | 1 | 1 | 5 | 3 | 4 | 7 | 7 | 4 | 5 | 6 | 6 | 8 | 3 | 3 | 9 | 4 | 7 | 0 | 7 | 2 | 2 |
| | 6 | 3 | 3 | 2 | 8 | 4 | 6 | 9 | 3 | 3 | 8 | 3 | 8 | 0 | 6 | 0 | 2 | 9 | 5 | 2 | 5 | 1 | 2 | 9 | 0 |
| Mean of each sample | 5·0 | 5·6 | 5·4 | 3·0 | 6·2 | 2·2 | 3·8 | 6·6 | 4·2 | 5·0 | 5·2 | 4·8 | 4·6 | 4·2 | 5·4 | 4·4 | 3·6 | 4·2 | 5·8 | 4·6 | 3·4 | 3·6 | 6·6 | 5·2 | 2·8 |

| Sample No. | 76 | 77 | 78 | 79 | 80 | 81 | 82 | 83 | 84 | 85 | 86 | 87 | 88 | 89 | 90 | 91 | 92 | 93 | 94 | 95 | 96 | 97 | 98 | 99 | 100 |
|---|---|---|---|---|---|---|---|---|---|---|---|---|---|---|---|---|---|---|---|---|---|---|---|---|---|
| | 2 | 3 | 2 | 5 | 9 | 1 | 2 | 2 | 9 | 0 | 3 | 9 | 6 | 5 | 6 | 4 | 4 | 2 | 8 | 4 | 1 | 7 | 2 | 8 | 0 |
| | 1 | 9 | 8 | 1 | 4 | 3 | 4 | 7 | 6 | 9 | 3 | 4 | 9 | 3 | 5 | 0 | 6 | 3 | 5 | 4 | 1 | 9 | 9 | 6 | 4 |
| | 0 | 1 | 2 | 3 | 7 | 1 | 2 | 1 | 2 | 3 | 8 | 1 | 0 | 1 | 4 | 4 | 3 | 1 | 2 | 1 | 0 | 7 | 2 | 3 | 5 |
| | 4 | 2 | 4 | 3 | 8 | 1 | 7 | 5 | 7 | 9 | 0 | 7 | 2 | 5 | 2 | 4 | 9 | 7 | 3 | 2 | 0 | 3 | 5 | 8 | 2 |
| | 1 | 1 | 0 | 2 | 1 | 6 | 9 | 9 | 2 | 7 | 2 | 5 | 7 | 0 | 1 | 2 | 1 | 7 | 0 | 4 | 4 | 3 | 0 | 9 | 6 |
| Mean of each sample | 1·6 | 3·2 | 3·2 | 2·8 | 5·8 | 2·4 | 4·8 | 4·8 | 5·2 | 5·6 | 3·2 | 5·2 | 4·8 | 2·8 | 3·6 | 2·8 | 4·6 | 4·0 | 3·6 | 3·0 | 1·2 | 5·8 | 3·6 | 6·8 | 3·4 |

each person deviates from the average, finding the average of the squares of these deviations, and the square root of this value).   From that universe we will draw, at random, samples of 5 individuals.   For each sample we can calculate the mean number of attacks suffered by the 5 individuals composing it.   To what extent will these means in the small samples diverge from the real mean—*i.e.* the mean of the universe, 4·50 ?

In Table XV are set out a hundred such samples of 5 individuals drawn at random from the universe.   The " universe " actually used for this and later demonstrations was composed of the *Random Sampling Numbers* arranged

TABLE XVI

MEAN NUMBER OF COLDS PER PERSON IN SAMPLES
OF DIFFERENT SIZE

| Value of Mean in Sample | Frequency with which Mean Values, as shown in Column (1), occurred | | | |
|---|---|---|---|---|
| | Samples of 5 | Samples of 10 | Samples of 20 | Samples of 50 |
| (1) | (2) | (3) | (4) | (5) |
| 0·75– | 1 | .. | .. | .. |
| 1·25– | 1 | .. | .. | .. |
| 1·75– | 4 | 1 | .. | .. |
| 2·25– | 2 | 2 | .. | .. |
| 2·75– | 12 | 5 | 2 | 1 |
| 3·25– | 15 | 8 | 9 | 5 |
| 3·75– | 12 ⎫ | 16 ⎫ | 24 ⎫ | 22 ⎫ |
| 4·25– | 10 ⎬ 39 | 26 ⎬ 58 | 31 ⎬ 77 | 45 ⎬ 91 |
| 4·75– | 17 ⎭ | 16 ⎭ | 22 ⎭ | 24 ⎭ |
| 5·25– | 8 | 15 | 10 | 3 |
| 5·75– | 6 | 8 | 2 | .. |
| 6·25– | 7 | 3 | .. | .. |
| 6·75– | 4 | .. | .. | .. |
| 7·25–7·75 | 1 | .. | .. | .. |
| Total number of means  .   . | 100 | 100 | 100 | 100 |
| Total observa-tions  .   . | 500 | 1000 | 2000 | 5000 |
| Grand means  . | 4·43 | 4·61 | 4·50 | 4·48 |

and published by L. H. C. Tippett (Tracts for Computers, No. XV, Camb. Univ. Press, 1927).   Sets of unit random numbers were taken from its columns in fives, tens, twenties, and fifties as required. For instance, in the first sample of Table XV there were 3 individuals who had 2 colds each, one fortunate person who had none, and one unfortunate who had 4. From each of these samples a mean can be calculated which, in all, gives one hundred mean values ; and of these means we can make a frequency distribution. In the first sample the mean is $2 + 2 + 2 + 0 + 4 \div 5 = 2 \cdot 0$, in the second it is $6 + 9 + 7 + 5 + 9 \div 5 = 7 \cdot 2$, and so on. The grouped distribution of these means is given in Table XVI, column (2). There was one sample in which the mean was only $1 \cdot 2$ and one in which it was as high as $7 \cdot 4$ (the possible minimum and maximum values are, of course, 0 and 9). A study of this distribution shows :—

(a) That with samples of only 5 individuals there will be, as might be expected, a very wide range in the values of the mean ; the mean number of attacks of the whole 500 individuals is $4 \cdot 43$, which is very close to the mean of the universe sampled—namely, $4 \cdot 50$ (as given above)—but in the individual samples of 5 persons the values range from between $0 \cdot 75$ and $1 \cdot 25$ (the one at $1 \cdot 2$) to between $7 \cdot 25$ and $7 \cdot 75$ (the one at $7 \cdot 4$). In samples of 5, therefore, there will be instances, due to the play of chance, in which the observed mean is very far removed from the real mean.

(b) On the other hand, these extreme values of the observed mean are relatively rare, and a large number of the means in the samples lie fairly close to the mean of the universe ($4 \cdot 50$) ; 39 per cent. of them lie within three-quarters of a unit of it (i.e. between $3 \cdot 75$ and $5 \cdot 25$).*

When in place of samples of 5 individuals a hundred samples of 10 individuals were taken at random from this universe, the distribution of the means in these samples

* The noticeable unevenness of the distribution with samples of 5 is artificial, being due merely to the group intervals used. With only whole numbers in the universe the mean of 5 observations *must* end in an even number (see Table XV). The groups $0 \cdot 75$ to $1 \cdot 25$, $1 \cdot 75$ to $2 \cdot 25$, etc., however, contain 3 possible values ($0 \cdot 80$, $1 \cdot 00$, and $1 \cdot 20$, $1 \cdot 80$, $2 \cdot 00$, etc.) while the groups $1 \cdot 25$ to $1 \cdot 75$, $2 \cdot 25$ to $2 \cdot 75$ contain only 2 possible values ($1 \cdot 40$ and $1 \cdot 60$, $2 \cdot 40$ and $2 \cdot 60$, etc.). This defect does not apply to the samples of 10, 20, and 50 and has no material effect upon the general arguments and demonstrations based upon the distribution for samples of 5.

showed a somewhat smaller scatter—as is shown in column (3) of Table XVI. The extreme values obtained now lie in the groups 1·75–2·25 and 6·25–6·75, and 58 per cent. of the values are within three-quarters of a unit of the real mean—*i.e.* the mean of the universe.

When 100 samples of 20 were taken (column 4) the scatter was still further reduced ; the extreme values obtained lay in the groups 2·75–3·25 and 5·75–6·25, and 77 per cent. of the values lay within three-quarters of a unit of the real mean. Finally, with samples of 50 (column 5) there were 91 per cent. of the means within this distance of the true mean, and 45 per cent. lay in the group 4·25–4·75—*i.e.* did not differ appreciably from the real mean. Outlying values still appeared, but appeared only infrequently.

TWO FACTORS IN PRECISION

These results show, what is indeed intuitively obvious, that the precision of an average depends, at least in part, upon *the size of the sample.* The larger the random sample we take the more accurately are we likely to reproduce the characteristics of the universe from which it is drawn. The size of the sample, however, is not the only factor which influences the accuracy of the values calculated from it. A little thought will show that it must also depend upon the *variability of the observations in the universe*. If every individual in the universe could only have one value—*e.g.* in the example above every individual in the universe had exactly 3 colds—then clearly, whatever the size of the sample, the mean value reached would be the same as the true value. If on the other hand the individuals could have values ranging from 0 to 900 instead of from 0 to 9, the means of samples could, and would, have considerably more variability in the former case than in the latter. The accuracy of a value calculated from a sample depends, therefore, upon two considerations :—

(*a*) The size of the sample.

(*b*) The variability of the characteristic within the universe from which the sample is taken.

The statistician's aim is to pass from these simple rules to more precise formulae, which will enable him to estimate, with a certain degree of confidence, the value of the mean, etc., in the universe and also to avoid drawing conclusions from differences between means or between proportions when, in fact, these differences might easily have arisen by chance.

### MEASURING THE VARIABILITY OF MEANS

As a first step we may return to Table XVI and measure the variability shown by the means in the samples of different sizes. So far we have illustrated that variability by drawing attention to the range of the means, and, roughly, the extent to which they are concentrated round the centre point ; a better measure will be the standard deviations of the frequency distributions. The results of these calculations are shown in Table XVII.

### TABLE XVII

#### VALUES COMPUTED FROM THE FREQUENCY DISTRIBUTIONS OF MEANS GIVEN IN TABLE XVI

| Number of Individuals in each Sample | The Mean, or Average, of the 100 Means * | The Variability or Standard Deviation of each 100 Means | The Standard Deviation of the Observations in the Population Sampled ÷ Square Root of Size of Sample |
|---|---|---|---|
| 5 | 4·43 | 1·36 | 1·28 |
| 10 | 4·61 | 0·91 | 0·91 |
| 20 | 4·50 | 0·61 | 0·64 |
| 50 | 4·48 | 0·44 | 0·41 |

* It happens by chance that the grand mean of the 500 observations is in fact closer to the true mean than that given by the 1000 observations, while that based on 2000 is exact and that based on 5000 differs slightly. The observed standard deviations correspond to those given by the original ungrouped data.

The standard deviation, or scatter, of the means round the grand mean of each of the total 100 samples becomes, as is obvious from the frequency distributions, progressively smaller as the size of the sample increases. It is clear, however, that the standard deviation does not vary *directly* with the size of the sample ; for instance, increasing the sample from 5 to 50—*i.e.* by ten times—does not reduce the scatter of the means by ten times. The scatter is, in fact, reduced not in the ratio of 5 to 50 but of $\sqrt{5}$ to $\sqrt{50}$—*i.e.*

not ten times but 3·16 times (for $\sqrt{5} = 2\cdot24$ and $\sqrt{50} = 7\cdot07$ and $7\cdot07/2\cdot24 = 3\cdot16$). This rule is very closely fulfilled by the values of Table XVII ; the standard deviation for samples of 5 is 1·36, and this value is 3·09 times the standard deviation, 0·44, with samples of 50. The first more precise rule, therefore, is that _the accuracy of the mean computed from a sample does not vary directly with the size of the sample but with the square root of the size of the sample._ In other words, if the sample is increased a hundredfold the precision of the mean is increased not a hundredfold but tenfold.

As the next step we may observe how frequently in samples of different sizes means will occur at different distances from the true mean. For instance it was pointed out above that with samples of 5 individuals 39 per cent. of the means lay within three-quarters of a unit of the true mean of the universe. The grand mean of these 100 samples, 4·43, is not quite identical with the true mean of the universe, 4·50, as, of course, the total 500 observations are themselves only a sample ; it comes very close to it as the total observations are increased—it is 4·48 with 100 samples of 50. Instead, therefore, of measuring the number lying within three-quarters of a unit, or one unit, of the grand mean (or true mean, taking them to be, to all intents and purposes, identical), we may see how many lie within the boundary lines " grand mean plus the value of the standard deviation " and "grand mean minus the value of the standard deviation " —i.e. $4\cdot43 + 1\cdot36 = 5\cdot79$ and $4\cdot43 - 1\cdot36 = 3\cdot07$. The calculation can be made only approximately from Table XVI, but it shows that some two-thirds of the means will lie between these limits. If we extend our limits to " grand mean plus _twice_ the standard deviation " and " grand mean minus _twice_ the standard deviation "—i.e. $4\cdot43 + 2\ (1\cdot36) = 7\cdot15$ and $4\cdot43 - 2\ (1\cdot36) = 1\cdot71$—it will be seen that these include nearly all the means of the samples, only about 3 per cent. lying beyond these values (according to theory we expect 5 per cent. beyond ± twice the standard deviation). Roughly the same results will be reached if these methods are applied to the larger samples. Our conclusions are therefore :—

(_a_) If we take a series of samples from a universe, then

the means of those samples will not all be equal to the true mean of the universe but will be scattered around it.

(b) We can measure that scatter by the standard deviation shown by the means of the samples ; means differing from the true mean by more than twice this standard deviation, above or below the true mean, will be only infrequently observed.

### THE MEANS SHOW A "NORMAL" DISTRIBUTION

To be rather more precise, it can be proved that the means of the samples will be distributed round the mean of the universe in the shape of the normal curve discussed on pp. 93–97. In other words, as shown there, it can be calculated how many of them will in the long run, if we take enough samples, lie within certain distances of the real mean, those distances being measured as multiples of the standard deviation. To illustrate this more exactly than can be done with the figures of Table XVI, a further 100 samples of 10 observations were taken from random sampling numbers. The distribution shown by these 100 means is set out in Table XVIII. The true mean of the universe is 4·50 and the means of the samples will be distributed round that value with a standard deviation of 0·91 (see Table XVII). If they are following a normal curve we can theoretically calculate how many of them should lie in such intervals as (a) (real mean) to (real mean $\pm 1$ time the S.D.), (b) (real mean) to (real mean $\pm 2$ times the S.D.), etc. From Table XVIII we can similarly calculate the actual number that did " turn up " in these intervals, since the observations have been placed in groups with a class-interval of $\frac{1}{2}(0·91) = 0·455 = \frac{1}{2}$ the standard deviation.

Observation and theoretical calculation gave results shown on the next page.

The values given by the experiment are extremely close to the theoretical values expected. Some very extreme values —more than $2\frac{1}{2}$ times the standard deviation away from the real mean—would in time turn up, but as there should be only 1·24 such values in 100 it is obviously not surprising that no such observation was noted in these 100 samples.

| Number of sample means that lie between— | Observed No. | Expected No. |
|---|---|---|
| Real Mean of 4·50 and Real Mean ± 1 S.D., *i.e.* between 3·590 and 5·409 . . . . | 70 | 68·27 |
| Real Mean of 4·50 and Real Mean ± 1½ S.D., *i.e.* between 3·135 and 5·864 . . . . | 86 | 86·64 |
| Real Mean of 4·50 and Real Mean ± 2 S.D., *i.e.* between 2·685 and 6·319 . . . . | 96 | 95·45 |
| Real Mean of 4·50 and Real Mean ± 2½ S.D., *i.e.* between 2·225 and 6·774 . . . . | 100 | 98·76 |
| Real Mean of 4·50 and Real Mean ± 3 S.D., *i.e.* between 1·770 and 7·229 . . . . | 100 | 99·73 |

The numbers of means occurring within different distances from the real mean are shown in Fig. 12, together with the

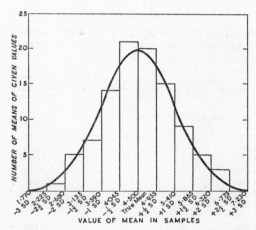

FIG. 12.—Histogram of 100 means observed in samples of 10 observations and normal curve superimposed.

superimposed normal curve. It is clear that the means occurring in the experiment do follow that curve and that we should, therefore, from our knowledge of this curve, expect only about 1 in 22 to differ from the true mean by more than twice the standard deviation (for 95·45 per cent. lie within that distance, and the 4·55 per cent. outside these limits is 1 in 22) ; and we should expect only 1 in 370 to differ from the true mean by more than 3 times the standard deviation (for

99·73 per cent. lie within that distance and the 0·27 per cent. outside these limits is 1 in 370). *In other words, we have found once more that a mean in a sample that differs from the real mean of the universe by more than twice the standard deviation shown by the sample means is a fairly rare event, and one that differs from the real mean by more than 3 times that standard deviation is a very rare event.*

In comparison with Table XVII it may be noted that this second series of samples of 10 has a grand mean of 4·57 and a standard deviation round that mean of 0·97. Within the limits of only 100 samples, open to the play of chance, we have again reached approximately the real mean and a corresponding degree of scatter round it, as measured by the standard deviation of the sample means.

TABLE XVIII

THE DISTRIBUTION OF MEANS IN 100 SAMPLES OF 10 OBSERVATIONS, THE TRUE MEAN OF THE UNIVERSE BEING 4·50

| Value of the Mean in Terms of the Actual Units of Measurement | Number of Means observed with given Value | Number of Means theoretically expected |
|---|---|---|
| Less than 1·770 | 0 | 0·135 |
| 1·770– | 0 | 0·486 |
| 2·225– | 1 | 1·654 |
| 2·685– | 5 | 4·406 |
| 3·135– | 7 | 9·185 |
| 3·590– | 14 | 14·988 |
| 4·045– | 21 | 19·146 |
| 4·500– | 20 | 19·146 |
| 4·955– | 15 | 14·988 |
| 5·410– | 9 | 9·185 |
| 5·865– | 5 | 4·406 |
| 6·320– | 3 | 1·654 |
| 6·775– | 0 | 0·486 |
| 7·230 or more | 0 | 0·135 |
| Total | 100 | 100 |

DEDUCING THE STANDARD DEVIATION

In practice, however, we do not know this standard deviation of the means, for we do not usually take repeated samples. We take a single sample, say of patients with diabetes, and we calculate a single mean, say of their body-

weight. Our problem is this : how precise is that mean—
*i.e.* how much would it be likely to vary if we did take another,
equally random, sample of patients ? What *would* be the
standard deviation of the means if we took repeated samples ?
It can be shown mathematically that the standard deviation
of means of samples is equal to *the standard deviation of the
individuals in the population sampled* divided by the square
root of the number of individuals included in the sample
(usually written as $\sigma/\sqrt{n}$). These values have been added to
Table XVII (right-hand column) and it will be seen that they
agree very closely with the standard deviations calculated
from the 100 means themselves (they do not agree exactly
because 100 samples are insufficient in number to give complete accuracy). With this knowledge we can conclude as
follows : the mean of the universe is 4·50 and the standard
deviation of the individuals within it is 2·87 (see p. 109) ; if
we take a large number of random samples composed of 5
persons from that universe, the means we shall observe will be
grouped round 4·50 with a standard deviation of $2\cdot87/\sqrt{5}$ ;
means that differ from the true mean, 4·50, by more than
plus or minus twice $2\cdot87/\sqrt{5}$ will be rare. If we take a large
number of samples of 50, then the means we shall observe
will be grouped around 4·50 with a standard deviation of
$2\cdot87/\sqrt{50}$, and means that differ from 4·50 by more than
plus or minus twice $2\cdot87/\sqrt{50}$ will be rare.

The final step is the application of this knowledge to
the single mean we observe in practice. In Chapter VII the
mean systolic blood pressure of 566 males (drawn from the
area in and around Glasgow) was given as 128·8 mm. We
want to determine the precision of this mean—*i.e.* how closely
it gives the true mean blood pressure of males in this district.

Suppose that the true mean is $M$. Then from the reasoning
developed above we know that the mean of a sample may well
differ from that true mean by as much as twice $\sigma/\sqrt{n}$, where
$\sigma$ is the standard deviation of the blood pressures of individuals *in the universe* from which the sample was taken
and $n$ is the number of individuals in the sample ; it is not
likely to differ by more than that amount—*i.e.* our observed

I

mean is likely to lie within the range $M \pm 2\,(\sigma/\sqrt{n})$. Clearly, however, we do not know the value of $\sigma$ and as an estimate of it we must use the standard deviation of the values in our sample. It must be observed that this *is* only an estimate, for just as the mean varies from sample to sample so also will the standard deviation. But the latter varies to a slighter extent and so long as the sample is fairly large the estimate is a reasonable one, and unlikely to lead to any serious error. In the example cited the standard deviation of the 566 measures of systolic blood pressure was 13·05. We therefore estimate that the standard deviation of *means* in samples of 566 would be $13 \cdot 05/\sqrt{566} = 0 \cdot 55$.

We may conclude (presuming that the sample is a random one) that our observed mean may differ from the true mean by as much as $\pm 2$ (0·55) but is unlikely to differ from it by more than that amount. In other words, if the true mean were 127·7 we might in the sample easily get a value that differed from it to any extent *up* to $127 \cdot 7 + 2(0 \cdot 55) = 128 \cdot 8$. But we should be unlikely to get a value as high as 128·8 if the true mean were lower than 127·7. Similarly if the true mean were 129·9 we might in the sample easily get a value that differed from it to any extent *down* to $129 \cdot 9 - 2(0 \cdot 55) = 128 \cdot 8$. But we should be unlikely to get a value as low as 128·8 if the true mean were higher than 129·9. In short, the true mean is likely to lie within the limits of $128 \cdot 8 \pm 2$ (0·55) or between 127·7 and 129·9, for if it lay beyond these points we should be unlikely to reach a value of 128·8 in the sample.

The value $\sigma/\sqrt{n}$ is known as the *standard error* of the mean and is used as a measure of its precision. (In publication it should be given as Standard Error or S.E. and *not* merely by the sign $\pm$ which can be misleading.)

Having calculated its value we can, as illustrated above, fix " confidence limits " to the true mean. If the mean of the sample is $\bar{x}$, then we can estimate that the true mean of the universe, $M$, is not more than twice the S.E. away (plus or minus) and we can expect to be wrong in that conclusion only once in approximately 20 times. If we wish to be more " confident," we can estimate that the true mean of the universe is not more than two and a half times the S.E.

away (*i.e.* wider limits) and we can then expect to be wrong in our conclusion only once in 80 times.

This estimation is clearly inapplicable if the sample is very small (say, less than 20 observations), for the substitution of the standard deviation of the few observations in the sample in place of the standard deviation of the whole universe, from which the few observations were taken, may be a serious error (see p. 106, where it is shown that the standard deviations shown by samples of 5 observations often differ widely from the real standard deviation of the universe).

## Summary

In medical statistical work we are, nearly always, using samples of observations taken from large populations. The values calculated from these samples will be subject to the laws of chance—*e.g.* the means, standard deviations, and proportions will vary from sample to sample. It follows that arguments based upon the values of a single sample must take into account the inherent variability of these values. It is idle to generalise from a sample value if this value is likely to differ materially from the true value in the population sampled. To determine how far a sample value is likely to differ from the true value a standard error of the sample value is calculated. The standard error of a mean is dependent upon two factors—viz. the size of the sample, or number of individuals included in it, and the variability of the measurements in the individuals in the universe from which the sample is taken. This standard error is estimated by dividing the standard deviation of the individuals in the sample by the square root of the number of individuals in the sample. The mean of the population from which the sample is taken is unlikely to differ from the value found in the sample by more than plus or minus twice this standard error. This estimation is, however, not applicable to very small samples, of, say, less than 20 individuals, and must be interpreted with reasonable caution in samples of less than 100 individuals.

(*For exercises see p.* 315)

# X

## PROBLEMS OF SAMPLING : PROPORTIONS

In the previous chapter the concept of the standard error was developed, and was illustrated by the calculation of the standard error of the mean. In addition it was pointed out that every statistical value calculated from a sample must have its standard error—*i.e.* may differ more or less from the real value in the universe that is being sampled. For example, the standard deviation, or measure of the scatter, of the observations will vary from sample to sample, and its standard error will show how much variability this value is, in fact, likely to exhibit from one sample to another taken from the same universe (see, for example, Table XIV, p. 106). In practical statistical work a value which is of particular importance, owing to the frequency with which it has to be used, is the *proportion*. For example, from a sample of patients with some specific disease we calculate the proportion who die. Let us suppose that from past experience, *covering a very large body of material*, we know that the fatality-rate of such patients is 20 per cent. (the actual figure, from the point of view of the development of the argument, is immaterial). We take, over a chosen period of time, a randomly selected group of a hundred patients and treat them with some drug. Then, presuming that our sample is a truly representative sample of all such patients —*e.g.* in age and in severity—we should observe, if the treatment is valueless, about 20 deaths (it may be noted that we are also presuming that there has been no secular change in the fatality-rate from the disease). We may observe precisely 20 deaths or owing to the play of chance

122

we may observe more or less than that number. Suppose
we observe only 10 deaths ; is that an event that is likely or
unlikely to occur by chance with a sample of 100 patients ?
If such an event is quite likely to occur by chance, then
we must conclude that the drug *may* be of value, but, so
far as we have gone, we must regard the evidence as insufficient and the case unproven. Before we can draw conclusions
safely we must increase the size of our sample. If, on the
other hand, such an event is very unlikely to occur by chance,
we may reasonably conclude that the drug is of value (that
is, of course, having satisfied ourselves that our sample of
patients is comparable with those observed in the past in
all respects except that of the treatment). Before we can
answer the problem as to what is a likely or an unlikely
event we must determine the standard error of a proportion
—*i.e.* the variability of a proportion in samples of a given
size taken from the same universe. Presuming the treatment is of no help, then the fatality-rate we should observe
on a very large sample is 20 per cent. (or nearly that). How
far is the rate likely to differ from that figure in samples of
different size ?

### SAMPLE OF ONE

If our sample comprises only one patient the fatality-rate
may be either 0 or 100 per cent. ; if the patient dies, the
fatality-rate is greater than that of past experience ; if the
patient recovers, this is obviously not very convincing evidence in favour of our treatment, for, according to past
experience, 4 out of 5 patients are likely to recover without
our treatment (20 per cent., or only 1 in 5, die).

### SAMPLE OF TWO

If the sample is increased to two patients, three events
become possible : (i) both may recover, (ii) 1 may recover
and 1 may die, (iii) both may die.

On the basis of past experience we can calculate the
probability of each of these events occurring. (i) The chance
that one may recover is 4/5 ; the chance that the other may
recover is also 4/5 ; the chance that *both* will recover is the

product of these two independent probabilities—*i.e.* 4/5 × 4/5 = 16/25.   (ii) The chance that one patient will recover is again 4/5 ;  the chance that the other will die is 1/5 ;  the chance that *both* these events will occur is, therefore, 4/5 × 1/5 ; but this value must be multiplied by 2, for the event can happen in two different ways—viz. patient A may live and patient B die, or patient A may die and patient B live.    The probability, therefore, of observing one recovery and one death is 2(4/5 × 1/5) = 8/25.    (iii) Finally the probability of each patient dying is 1/5 and of both patients dying is 1/5 × 1/5 = 1/25.    We can tabulate these values as follows :—

| Event | Probability of Event | Fatality-rate per cent. |
|-------|----------------------|-------------------------|
| Both patients recover  .    . | 16/25 = 0·64 | 0 |
| One patient recovers, one dies | 8/25 = 0·32 | 50 |
| Both patients die      .    . | 1/25 = 0·04 | 100 |
|       | 25/25 = 1·00 | .. |

The total probability is 1, for there is no alternative to these three events.    Clearly the only event that suggests that our treatment is of value is the recovery of both patients, when the fatality-rate is 0 compared with the 20 per cent. of past experience.    The death of one patient in a sample of two gives a fatality-rate of 50 per cent., and of both patients one of 100 per cent., both rates being worse than past experience. But the more favourable event, the recovery of both patients, is obviously an event which is more likely than not to occur by chance ;  it may be expected to occur 64 times in 100 trials with 2 patients even if the treatment is in-effective.    Therefore with a single sample of 2 patients and a normal fatality-rate of 20 per cent. the chance that both will recover is large, and if such a result is observed we cannot deduce from it that our special treatment is of value.

## SAMPLE OF THREE

If we increase the sample to three patients, four events become possible : (i) all 3 may recover, (ii) 2 may recover and 1 die, (iii) 1 may recover and 2 die, (iv) all 3 may die.

The probability of each event can be calculated as before. (i) The chance of the recovery of all three patients is $4/5 \times 4/5 \times 4/5 = 64/125$. (ii) The chance that two may recover and one die is $4/5 \times 4/5 \times 1/5$ ; this must be multiplied by 3, for this event can happen in three different ways since any one of the three patients may be the one to die ; this equals $48/125$. (iii) The chance that one may recover and two may die is $4/5 \times 1/5 \times 1/5$, also multiplied by 3 for this event can also happen in three ways ; this equals $12/125$. (iv) Finally, the chance that all three may die is $1/5 \times 1/5 \times 1/5$, an event which can happen only in one way, and equals $1/125$. Tabulating we have :—

| Event | Probability of Event | Fatality-rate per cent. |
|---|---|---|
| Three recover . . . | $64/125 = 0.512$ | 0 |
| Two recover, one dies . . | $48/125 = 0.384$ | 33.3 |
| One recovers, two die . . | $12/125 = 0.096$ | 66.7 |
| Three die . . . . | $1/125 = 0.008$ | 100.0 |
| | $125/125 = 100.0$ | .. |

The only event that favours our treatment is, again, the recovery of all the patients. Any other event gives a higher fatality-rate than that of past experience—viz. 20 per cent. But the recovery of all three patients is an event which is quite likely to occur by chance ; it may be expected to occur 51 times in 100 trials with three patients even if the treatment is ineffective. With a single sample of three patients, therefore, the chance that they will all recover is large, and again we cannot deduce that our special treatment is of value.

SAMPLE OF FOUR

If we increase the sample to four patients five events become possible : (i) all four may recover, (ii) three may recover and one die, (iii) two may recover and two die, (iv) one may recover and three die, (v) all four may die.

What is the probability of each of these events on the basis of past experience ? (i) The chance that all four recover is $4/5 \times 4/5 \times 4/5 \times 4/5$ ; this event can happen in only one way, and the probability equals 256/625. (ii) The chance that three recover and one dies is $4/5 \times 4/5 \times 4/5 \times 1/5$, multiplied in this case by 4, for there are four different ways in which this event can happen ; any one of the four patients can be the one to die. The probability of this event is also, therefore, 256/625. (iii) The chance that two recover and two die is $4/5 \times 4/5 \times 1/5 \times 1/5$, multiplied in this case by 6, for there are six ways in which the event can happen. For if the patients are named A, B, C, and D, the following events are possible :—

| Recover | Die |
|---------|-----|
| AB | CD |
| AC | BD |
| AD | BC |
| BC | AD |
| BD | AC |
| CD | AB |

The probability of this event is therefore 96/625. (iv) The chance that only one recovers and three die is $4/5 \times 1/5 \times 1/5 \times 1/5$, multiplied, as before, by 4 (for any one of the four may be the fortunate one to recover) ; this equals 16/625. (v) Finally, the chance that all 4 will die is $1/5 \times 1/5 \times 1/5 \times 1/5$ = 1/625. Tabulating :—

| Event | Probability of Event | Fatality-rate per cent. |
|-------|----------------------|-------------------------|
| All four recover   .    .    . | $256/625 = 0\cdot4096$ | 0 |
| Three recover, one dies    . | $256/625 = 0\cdot4096$ | 25 |
| Two recover, two die   .    . | $96/625 = 0\cdot1536$ | 50 |
| One recovers, three die .    . | $16/625 = 0\cdot0256$ | 75 |
| All four die .    .    .    . | $1/625 = 0\cdot0016$ | 100 |
| | $625/625 = 1\cdot0000$ | .. |

Once more the recovery of all the patients is the only result which gives a fatality-rate lower than that of past experience, but this, again, is an event quite likely to occur by chance ; it may be expected to occur nearly 41 times in 100 trials with 4 patients even if the treatment is ineffective.

### SAMPLE OF TEN

We can with samples of any size calculate by these methods the probability of favourable results occurring merely by chance ; as the sample increases in size, however, the calculations become progressively more laborious. But clearly we need not calculate *all* the probabilities. If, for example, we treat ten patients, then the only results which are better than that of past experience are those which give no patients at all dying or only 1 patient dying—*i.e.* fatality-rates of 0 or 10 per cent. If two of the ten patients die the fatality-rate is normal according to past experience, 20 per cent., and if three or more die then it is higher than that of past experience. The probability of all 10 patients recovering equals $(4/5 \times 4/5 \times 4/5 \times 4/5 \times 4/5 \times 4/5 \times 4/5 \times 4/5 \times 4/5 \times 4/5) = (4/5)^{10} = 0.1074$. In other words, all 10 patients would recover, according to past experience, nearly 11 times in 100 trials, or 1 in 9 times. These odds are hardly sufficient to convince us that the special treatment is of value even if all 10 patients should recover in our test of it. The probability of 9 patients recovering and 1 dying $= \{(4/5)^9 \times (1/5)\} \times 10$—since any one of the 10 may be the one to die. This equals $0.2684$. If we should observe such an event in our test it is not sufficient, however, to calculate merely its probability. What we need is the probability that we might *by chance have got just as good a result as this, or even one that is better.* In other words, how often would we be likely to see 9 *or* 10 recovering without our special treatment ? The probability of seeing all 10 recover is $0.1074$ and the probability of seeing 9 recover is $0.2684$. The probability of observing by chance one *or* the other result is the *sum* of the two probabilities, or $0.1074 + 0.2684 = 0.3758$. If, therefore, in our test 9 patients were to recover we should have to note that just as good a result as this, or even a better one, would occur nearly 38 times in 100 trials with 10 patients even if the treatment were quite ineffective. Obviously in a single sample of 10 patients a result better than that of past experience is still not an unlikely event to occur by chance, and from such an observation we cannot deduce that the drug has reduced our fatality-rate.

### SAMPLE OF A HUNDRED

If now we return to our original problem—namely, a sample of 100 patients of whom only 10 die—the probability we need is that with which this result *or a better one* might be expected to occur even if our treatment were quite ineffective—so that we ought to have observed 20 deaths on the basis of past experience. It is *possible* to calculate this by just the same means as were applied to smaller numbers. Tabulating, we have the results shown in the following table.

| Event | Probability of Event | Fatality-rate per cent. |
|-------|----------------------|-------------------------|
| All 100 recover | $(4/5)^{100}$ $= 0 \cdot 00000000020$ | 0 |
| 99 recover, 1 dies | $(4/5)^{99} \times (1/5) \times$ 100* $= 0 \cdot 00000000509$ | 1 |
| 98 recover, 2 die | $(4/5)^{98} \times (1/5)^2 \times$ 4,950 $= 0 \cdot 000000063$ | 2 |
| 97 recover, 3 die | $(4/5)^{97} \times (1/5)^3 \times$ 161,700 $= 0 \cdot 000000515$ | 3 |
| 96 recover, 4 die | $(4/5)^{96} \times (1/5)^4 \times$ 3,921,225 $= 0 \cdot 00000312$ | 4 |
| 95 recover, 5 die | $(4/5)^{95} \times (1/5)^5 \times$ 75,287,520 $= 0 \cdot 00001498$ | 5 |
| 94 recover, 6 die | $(4/5)^{94} \times (1/5)^6 \times$ 1,192,052,400 $= 0 \cdot 00005928$ | 6 |
| 93 recover, 7 die | $(4/5)^{93} \times (1/5)^7 \times$ 16,007,560,800 $= 0 \cdot 0001990$ | 7 |
| 92 recover, 8 die | $(4/5)^{92} \times (1/5)^8 \times$ 186,087,894,300 $= 0 \cdot 0005784$ | 8 |
| 91 recover, 9 die | $(4/5)^{91} \times (1/5)^9 \times$ 1,902,231,808,400 $= 0 \cdot 001478$ | 9 |
| 90 recover, 10 die | $(4/5)^{90} \times (1/5)^{10} \times$ 17,310,309,456,440 $= 0 \cdot 003363$ | 10 |

* These multipliers are the number of different ways in which the event could happen. Clearly there are 100 ways in which 1 could die and 99 survive ; there are 4950 ways in which 2 could die and 98 survive, and so on.

The sum of the probabilities will give the number of times we might expect to reach a result as favourable as the one we have observed, or one even more favourable, merely as a result of chance. This sum is $0 \cdot 0057$, and we may therefore conclude that only 57 times in 10,000 trials with a hundred patients would such a result turn up merely by chance. Such a result suggests that our treatment favourably influenced the survival-rate. But this calculation is extremely heavy and some shorter method is in practice essential.

### THE GENERAL CASE

Let us return to the tabulation regarding two patients. This shows, if we write it in percentage form, that if we had

2 patients in each of 100 hospitals the fatality-rate would (on the average) be 0 in 64 of these hospitals, 50 per cent. in 32 of them, and 100 per cent. in four of them. From these figures we can calculate the *mean* fatality-rate in the 100 hospitals and the *standard deviation* of the frequency distribution round that mean. The mean fatality-rate is $(64 \times 0) + (32 \times 50) + (4 \times 100) \div 100 = 20$ per cent.; the standard deviation is $\sqrt{[64 \times (20-0)^2 + 32 \times (20-50)^2 + 4 \times (20-100)^2]} \div 100$ which equals 28·3. A similar calculation for three patients gives a mean fatality-rate in the 100 hospitals of 20 per cent. and a standard deviation round it of 23·1 ; for four patients the mean is 20 per cent. and the standard deviation is also 20·0. The *mean* fatality-rate in samples of each size—viz. 20 per cent.—is the value, it will be noted, that we expect to reach according to past experience ; but in the individual sample we shall not necessarily observe this mean value, for round it there will be a variability in the fatality-rate from sample to sample, due to the play of chance, measured by the standard deviation and decreasing as the size of the sample increases. If we could calculate this standard deviation *without* having to find the different probabilities for each event we should have a measure of the variability that will occur by chance in the fatality-rate in samples of different sizes. This calculation is, in fact, very simply made. If on the basis of past experience we expect 20 per cent. of patients to die and 80 per cent. to recover, then the standard deviation round that expected 20 per cent. will be in samples of 2 equal to the square root of $\dfrac{20 \times 80}{2} = 28\cdot3$, in samples of 3 equal to the square root of $\dfrac{20 \times 80}{3} = 23\cdot1$, and in samples of 4 equal to the square root of $\dfrac{20 \times 80}{4} = 20\cdot0$. These values are the same as those found above by the longer calculation. In more general terms the standard deviation or, as it is usually termed, the standard error of a percentage is $\sqrt{\dfrac{p \times q}{n}}$ where $p$ is the percentage of individuals belonging to one

category (*e.g.* alive), *q* is the percentage in the other category (*e.g.* dead), and *n* is the number of individuals in the sample. We can, therefore, readily find the standard error of the percentage—*i.e.* the variability it would show from sample to sample—in samples of 100, or more, patients. With 100 patients the standard error is $\sqrt{\dfrac{20 \times 80}{100}} = 4 \cdot 0$. In other words, on the basis of past experience we should expect 20 of the 100 patients to die, but in different samples of that size we should not always observe that proportion dying ; the proportions observed in samples of one hundred will be scattered round 20 with a standard deviation of 4. We know (as was shown with the standard error of the mean in the previous section) that there will be relatively very few samples in which the proportion actually observed will differ by more than twice the standard error from the mean expected value. For instance, with 100 patients we expected 20 per cent. to die, but as this percentage has, in samples of this size, a standard error of 4, we might by chance observe a value in a single sample as high as $20 + 2(4) = 28$ or as low as $20 - 2(4) = 12$. Actually we observed a value of 10 per cent. This is beyond the value that might, *according to our criterion*, be likely to arise by chance and, *other things being equal*, we may deduce that it *appears likely* that our treatment lowered the fatality-rate. The italicised words must be emphasised. It must be recognised that we are weighing probabilities, never, as is sometimes suggested by non-statistical authors of medico-statistical papers, reaching " mathematical proof." A difference between the observed and expected values *may* be a " real " difference (in the sense that the treatment was effective) even though it is not twice the standard error ; but the calculation shows that the hypothesis that the difference has occurred by chance is equally valid. If, on the other hand, the difference between the observed and expected values is, say, four times the standard error, this does not " prove " that it is a " real " difference ; it may still be the result of chance. But the calculation shows that the hypothesis that it is due to chance is unlikely to be true, for such a chance difference is a rare event. The advantage of the calculation is that the investigator is thus enabled " critically to estimate the value of his own results ; he may be prevented from wasting his time by erecting some elaborate superstructure of argument on a difference between two averages (or proportions) which is no greater than a difference that might well be obtained on drawing two random samples from one and the same record " (G. Udny Yule, Industrial Health Research Board, Report No. 28, 1924).

Finally, presuming that the difference recorded between the observed and expected values is more than would be expected from the play of chance, then we must consider carefully whether it is due to the factor we have in mind— *e.g.* the special treatment—or to some other factor which differentiated our sample—*e.g.* age or severity of disease— from the general population of patients. Where, as Yule expresses it, " some particular interpretation is rather attractive," the investigator must be the more on his guard.

For the sake of clarity the standard error of the proportion has been deduced on the basis of a figure known from past experience. In actual practice such a figure is not often available or may be an unsatisfactory criterion of the expected level in the observed sample, owing to some secular change. The more usual procedure is the comparison of two percentages recorded over the same period of time in an experimental and a control group. The development of this test is discussed in the next chapter.

If we are interested merely in a *single* observed proportion, *e.g.* what percentage of adult persons in a given population have symptoms of rheumatoid arthritis, we can, as was shown with the mean value, estimate the true frequency in that population within given " confidence limits." If the percentage revealed by our sample is $p$ we can calculate its standard error as $\sqrt{(p \times q)/n}$. We would then expect the true frequency of the characteristic in the universe to lie within $p + 2$ S.E. and $p - 2$ S.E. and to be wrong in that conclusion only once in 20 times. To be more " confident " we would expect the true frequency to lie within $p + 2\frac{1}{2}$ S.E. and $p - 2\frac{1}{2}$ S.E. and to be wrong in that conclusion only once in 80 times. Again, we must be cautious with a small number of observations, say under 50, and also if the observed frequency is more than 95 or less than 5 per cent.

## Summary

A statistical value which is of particular importance, from the frequency of its use, is the proportion, or percentage. By simple means the standard error of this value can be calculated, that is the amount of variability it will show from sample to sample for samples of different sizes. The relation of the difference between an expected percentage and an observed percentage to this standard error shows whether that difference is likely or unlikely to have arisen merely by chance. As a convention we take twice the standard error as a criterion. If the difference is more than twice the standard error it is said to be " significant "—*i.e.* unlikely to have arisen by chance ; if it is less than twice the standard error the difference is said to be " not significant "—*i.e.*, it may easily have arisen by chance. This rule applies to samples of reasonable size and caution should be observed with numbers less than 50. With very small numbers the exact probability can be calculated. In either case the test always involves weighing probabilities, and can never amount to proof in the logical sense. The test can give no information as to the *origin* of the difference beyond saying that chance is an unlikely explanation.

(*For exercises see p.* 316)

# PROBLEMS OF SAMPLING : DIFFERENCES
# BETWEEN PROPORTIONS

In the previous chapter the calculation of the standard error of a proportion was based upon a knowledge of the proportion to be expected from some past experience—*e.g.* if past experience shows that on the average 20 per cent. of patients die, how great a discrepancy from that 20 per cent. may be expected to occur by chance in samples of a given size? In practical statistical work the occasions upon which such past experience is available as a safe and sufficient guide are relatively rare. As a substitute for past experience the experimenter takes a control group and uses it as the standard of comparison against the experimental group. For instance, as the result of the collection of data in this way, we may have :—

50 patients with a specific disease treated by the ordinary orthodox methods had a fatality-rate of 20 per cent. ;
50 patients with that disease treated by the ordinary orthodox methods *plus* special method X had a fatality-rate of 10 per cent.

Is this difference more than is likely to arise merely by chance ? It is clear that *both* these percentages will, by the play of chance, vary from sample to sample ; if method X were quite useless we should, if the results of a large number of trials were available, sometimes observe lower fatality-rates in groups of patients given that treatment, sometimes lower fatality-rates in the control groups, and sometimes no differences at all. In the long run—*i.e.* with very large samples—we should observe no material difference between the fatality-rates of the two sets of patients ; if method X is useless (but innocuous) the difference we expect to observe is, clearly, 0. Our problem is to determine how much variability will occur round that value of 0 in samples of given sizes, how large a difference between the two groups is likely to occur by chance. In other words we need *the standard error of a difference between proportions*.

### DIFFERENCES BETWEEN PROPORTIONS

To return to the example previously adopted, let us suppose we take samples from a universe in which is recorded the number of colds suffered by each individual, and for each sample we calculate the proportion of persons who have no colds at all. In the universe itself the proportion of persons having no colds is, we will suppose, 10 per cent. If we take two random samples from the universe, each containing 5 persons, we shall not necessarily observe a proportion of 10 per cent. with no colds in each of these samples;* in one sample we may obtain a percentage of, say, 20, and in the other a value of, say, 60, giving a difference of 40 per cent. Is that a difference that is likely to occur by chance in taking two samples of 5 individuals from the same universe ? As a test 100 *pairs* of samples of this size were taken from this universe. After each pair had been taken the proportion of the 5 persons in each who had had no colds was calculated, and the difference between these two proportions noted— *e.g.* in the first sample 1 of the 5 individuals had no colds, in the second sample 2 of the 5 individuals had no colds ; the percentages were, therefore, 20 and 40 and the difference between the percentages was 20. This procedure gave a distribution of *differences between the pairs* as shown below.

In nearly half the pairs of samples (45 instances) there was no difference between the percentages having no colds ; but there was a considerable scatter round that difference of 0 that we expected to see. For instance in 6 instances the percentage difference was 40 and in 1 it was as much as 60. The mean of the 100 percentage differences is very nearly 0, being −0·6, but very frequently a difference of 20 per cent. was observed between one pair of samples. The scatter of

* We certainly could not in practice, for that would imply half a person without a cold ; but that need not hinder the development of the argument.

the differences round that mean may be measured, as usual, by the standard deviation ; it is 18·0.  The distribution of

DIFFERENCES BETWEEN PERCENTAGES IN TWO SAMPLES OF
5 OBSERVATIONS

|  | Proportion of Persons having no Colds in Two Samples of 5 Persons | |
|  | Differences between Percentages in the Two Samples | No. of Pairs of Samples with Given Difference |
| --- | --- | --- |
| Smaller % in sample A than in sample B. | − 60 | 1 |
|  | − 40 | 2 |
|  | − 20 | 26 |
|  | 0 | 45 |
| Larger % in sample A than in sample B. | +20 | 22 |
|  | +40 | 4 |
|  | +60 | .. |
|  | .. | 100 |

the differences round the mean is, it will be observed, fairly symmetrical.  It is, in fact, tending to a " normal " curve (see p. 93) and for a distribution of that shape we know

DIFFERENCES BETWEEN PERCENTAGES IN TWO SAMPLES OF
20 OBSERVATIONS

|  | Proportion of Persons having no Colds in Two Samples of 20 Persons | |
|  | Differences between Percentages in the Two Samples | No. of Pairs of Samples with Given Difference |
| --- | --- | --- |
| Smaller % in sample A than in sample B. | − 25 | .. |
|  | − 20 | 6 |
|  | − 15 | 6 |
|  | − 10 | 15 |
|  | − 5 | 14 |
|  | 0 | 27 |
| Larger % in sample A than in sample B. | + 5 | 14 |
|  | +10 | 12 |
|  | +15 | 3 |
|  | +20 | 2 |
|  | +25 | 1 |
|  | .. | 100 |

that values that differ from the mean by less than plus or minus twice the standard deviation are of frequent occurrence.  We may therefore say that in samples of this size,

K

in which a percentage of 10 is expected in each, and therefore a difference of 0 between two samples, we may, in fact, easily observe by chance not that difference of 0 but one as large as $\pm 2(18) = 36$ per cent. between the proportions in two samples ; differences larger than that will be relatively rare.

Increasing the size of each sample to 20 showed a different distribution of differences between the pairs. The largest difference between 2 samples is now only 25 per cent. (larger differences would be observed if the numbers of samples taken were increased, but these large differences are so infrequent that they are unlikely to occur with only 100 pairs).

The mean of the difference between the 100 pairs is again nearly 0—namely $-1\cdot3$ per cent.—but the scatter round that mean as measured by the standard deviation now becomes $9\cdot5$ ; multiplying the size of the sample by 4 has reduced the variability of the differences by half. In samples of size 20, in which a percentage of 10 is expected in each, and therefore a difference of 0 between two samples, we conclude that differences of $\pm 2(9\cdot5) = 19$ per cent. between two samples may, in fact, easily occur by chance, while greater differences will be relatively rare.

Finally, taking pairs of samples of size 50 gave the following distribution of differences in percentages having no colds. In the 100 pairs no difference between the proportions now exceeds 14 per cent. The mean of the 100 differences is $-0\cdot5$ and the scatter round that mean as measured by the standard deviation is $5\cdot5$. In samples of size 50, in which a percentage of 10 is expected in each, and therefore a difference of 0 between two samples, differences of $\pm 2(5\cdot5) = 11\cdot0$ per cent. will, in fact, be relatively frequent and greater differences relatively rare. The standard deviation, or standard error, of the differences decreases, it will be seen, with increasing size of sample.

### STANDARD ERROR OF THE DIFFERENCE

The standard error of each proportion is, as shown in the previous chapter, $\sqrt{\dfrac{p \times q}{n}}$, where $p$ is the percentage in the universe in one category—*e.g.* having no colds—and $q$ is the percentage in the other category—*e.g.* having one or more colds—and $n$ is the number of individuals in the sample. *The standard error of difference between the two proportions* is, it may be shown, $\sqrt{\dfrac{p \times q}{n_1} + \dfrac{p \times q}{n_2}}$, where $n_1$ and $n_2$ are the numbers in the two samples. For instance in samples containing 5 individuals drawn from a universe in which $p = 10$

### DIFFERENCES BETWEEN PERCENTAGES IN TWO SAMPLES OF 50 OBSERVATIONS

| | Proportion of Persons having no Colds in Two Samples of 50 Persons | |
| --- | --- | --- |
| | Differences between Percentages in the Two Samples | No. of Pairs of Samples with Given Difference |
| Smaller % in sample A than in sample B. | − 14 | 1 |
| | − 12 | 1 |
| | − 10 | 3 |
| | − 8 | 8 |
| | − 6 | 9 |
| | − 4 | 12 |
| | − 2 | 16 |
| | 0 | 8 |
| Larger % in sample A than in sample B. | + 2 | 18 |
| | + 4 | 6 |
| | + 6 | 8 |
| | + 8 | 6 |
| | +10 | 3 |
| | +12 | .. |
| | +14 | 1 |
| | .. | 100 |

per cent. and $q$ therefore $= 90$ per cent., the standard error of the difference between the proportion in sample A and the proportion in sample B is $\sqrt{\dfrac{10 \times 90}{5} + \dfrac{10 \times 90}{5}} = 19 \cdot 0$ per cent. In other words, in a single pair of samples each containing 5 persons, drawn from the same universe, we may, instead of obtaining the expected percentage difference of 0, quite easily get a difference of $\pm 2(19) = 38$ per cent. This theoretical value, it will be observed, agrees closely with the value that was obtained practically from the test; the differences found with the 100 pairs of samples of size 5 had a standard deviation of 18. Similarly, the standard deviation of the differences between samples of size 20 was found in the test to be 9·5. The theoretical value is $\sqrt{\dfrac{10 \times 90}{20} + \dfrac{10 \times 90}{20}} = 9\cdot5$. Finally, the standard deviation of the differences between samples of size 50 was 5·5 and the theoretical value is $\sqrt{\dfrac{10 \times 90}{50} + \dfrac{10 \times 90}{50}} = 6\cdot0$.

Clearly, if we knew the proportion of individuals having no colds in the universe that we were sampling, we could calculate the size of differences between two samples that might reasonably be expected to occur merely by chance in taking samples of a given size. If, for example, from the universe used above, we took two samples of 50 persons and we treated one sample with, say, vitamin A, and found in that sample the proportion of persons having no colds over a specified period of time was 4 per cent., while in the sample not so treated it was, over the same period of time, 14 per cent., the standard error tells us that that difference is one which might easily arise by chance. The percentage difference between the two samples is $14 - 4 = 10$, and this difference, we have seen, has a standard error of 6 per cent. In other words, in taking two samples of 50 individuals from the *same* universe we might easily obtain proportions in the two samples that differed from one another by as much as twice 6 per cent. ; a difference of 10 per cent. is not, therefore, a very unlikely event to occur merely by chance with samples of this size. The lower percentage cannot safely be ascribed to the effect of vitamin A, for the same difference might quite often occur even if vitamin A were ineffective. In the example above a difference of 10 or more occurred 9 times in the 100 trials.

### THE STANDARD ERROR IN PRACTICE

In actual practice we do not, of course, know the value of $p$ in the universe ; in calculating the standard error we have to substitute for it a value calculated from the samples.  In making this substitution we act on the basis of the following reasoning.

We have observed two samples of 50 persons each and the proportion of persons with no colds is 4 per cent. in one sample and 14 per cent. in the other.  Is it reasonable to suppose that these two samples have been drawn from one and the same universe in which the percentage of persons with no colds is " $x$," and that the differences of 4 and 14 from " $x$ " are merely due to chance ?  Let us adopt the hypothesis that they *are* both samples of this one universe. Then the best estimate that we can make of " $x$ " is given by the *whole* of the observations we have—*i.e.* the percentage of persons having no colds in our total 100 observations—which is 9.  Our question now becomes this :  " If we take two samples each of 50 individuals from a universe in which the proportion of persons having no colds is 9 per cent., are we likely to reach a difference of 10 per cent. in the proportions observed in the two samples instead of a difference of 0 ? " If the answer to this question is *yes*, then we must recognise that though the difference observed *may* be a real one it is quite likely that it is only a chance difference which would disappear if we repeated, or enlarged, the experiment.  On the other hand, if the answer is *no* we can conclude that our hypothesis that these two samples are likely to be drawn from the same universe is probably not true—*i.e.* these samples differ from one another by more than is likely to be due to chance and we are entitled to look for some other explanation of the difference between them.

In the example above the difference observed is $14 - 4 = 10$ per cent.  On the hypothesis outlined above the standard error of this difference is $\sqrt{\dfrac{9 \times 91}{50} + \dfrac{9 \times 91}{50}} = 5 \cdot 7$.  The observed difference between the samples is less than twice its standard error, and we conclude that its occurrence merely by chance is not a very unlikely event—that relatively often we might observe a difference of this magnitude.  If the difference had been 15 per cent. we should have concluded that one of this magnitude was unlikely to have occurred by chance, since this difference is more than twice its standard error, and that therefore some cause (perhaps treatment with vitamin A if we are satisfied that the samples were equal in all other relevant respects) had led to the samples differing.

An alternative approach that is often used is difficult to defend logically but arithmetically may be convenient. It takes the standard error of each of the proportions separately and then, as the standard error of the difference between the proportions, the square root of the sum of the squares of these two standard errors. Thus the first value, 4 per cent., has a standard error of $\sqrt{\dfrac{4 \times 96}{50}}$; the second value, 14 per cent., has a standard error of $\sqrt{\dfrac{14 \times 86}{50}}$. The standard error of the difference between these two proportions is then taken as $\sqrt{\dfrac{4 \times 96}{50} + \dfrac{14 \times 86}{50}} = 5\cdot6$. As the observed difference of 10 per cent. is not twice this standard error, the two values might well have been derived from the same universe. In other words, there is again not sufficient evidence to lead to the conclusion that the two observed percentages differ by more than might easily be due to chance.

It will be noted that the two methods give very nearly the same results, and in practice this is usually the case. The second method is particularly convenient if the two separate standard errors have already been computed.

### LEVELS OF SIGNIFICANCE

A moment's consideration ought to be paid to the level of significance here adopted. It has been shown that values, whether of an average or a proportion, that differ from their mean by more than twice the standard deviation are relatively rare. As a conventional level, twice the standard error is therefore adopted, and differences between values in two samples which are greater than twice the standard error of the difference are said to be " significant." In fact, differences of this size would occur by chance nearly 5 times in 100 tests. If a worker regards this test as too lenient, he can raise his level of significance to $2\frac{1}{2}$ or 3 times the standard error ; with these levels, differences would occur by chance, roughly, only once in 80 tests and once in 370 tests. The problem is always one of probability and the worker is at liberty to adopt any level he wishes—so long as he makes his test clear. For this reason it is better to say in reporting results that the observed difference is, say, 2·5 times its standard error, rather than that it is " significant." The latter term will be read as implying that the difference exceeded the conventional level of twice the standard error. The worker who wishes to make the test more stringent may be reminded that he may thereby be classing as chance effects differences that are real ; he who tends to be too lenient may class as real, differences that are due to chance. With borderline cases there is only one satisfactory solution —the accumulation of more data.

### CONFIDENCE LIMITS

Having observed in two samples a difference between their values (in this case, proportions), we can go a step further. We can estimate the limits within which the true difference is likely to lie.

Thus in the hypothetical experiment of p. 138 the incidence of colds was 10 per cent. less in the group treated with vitamin A than in the group not so treated. This difference had a standard error of 5·7 and thus was not significant. Nevertheless we can still calculate " confidence limits " for the true difference. At the 1 in 20 level the difference could be as much as $10 + 2(5\cdot7)$ or 21·4 per cent. or as little as $10 - 2(5\cdot7)$ or $-1\cdot4$ per cent. In other words, it is *possible* that persons treated with vitamin A will have, roughly, one-fifth less colds than persons not so treated. On the other hand, it is also possible that they may reap no benefit whatever (even if we exclude the possibility of their being worse off). The case is non-proven as was shown by the test of significance.

It is well to remember too (and the confidence limits often reveal this fact) that a difference can be very highly significant and yet of no real importance whatever.  Given a large enough number of observations, an incidence of 60 per cent. must differ " significantly " from an incidence of 59 per cent., but that difference of 1 per cent. may be of no practical importance in the affairs of life.  " Significant " and " important " are not synonymous.

## Summary

In practical statistical work the problem that frequently arises is the " significance " of a difference between two proportions.  The difference between two such values in a pair of samples will fluctuate from one pair of samples to another, and though the samples may be drawn from one and the same universe we shall not necessarily observe a difference of 0 between them.  The object of the statistical test is to determine the size of the difference that is likely to occur by chance in samples of given magnitudes, how far it may deviate by chance from 0.  This involves the calculation of the standard error of the difference.  In reasonably large samples this standard error of a difference may be taken to be the square root of the sum of the squares of the two individual standard errors of the values in the two samples.

(*For exercises see p.* 316)

## PROBLEMS OF SAMPLING : DIFFERENCES
## BETWEEN AVERAGES

THE same type of test of significance as was applied in the last chapter to proportions is applicable to the difference between two averages, or mean values. This we may experimentally demonstrate as follows.

We may, as before, observe what, in fact, happens in practice by taking pairs of samples from the same universe, calculating the means in each pair and then the difference between them. Thus using Table XV on p. 110, we may regard samples Nos. 1 and 2 as the first pair. They have means of 2·0 and 7·2, and a difference between means of + 5·2. Samples Nos. 3 and 4 form the second pair ; they have means of 1·8 and 5·4, a difference between means of + 3·6. Samples Nos. 5 and 6 form the third pair ; they have means of 6·0 and 5·0, a difference between means of − 1·0. Proceeding in this way and adding a further 50 pairs of samples drawn in the same way gave the distribution of 100 differences between means shown on p. 144. In the long run we should expect to reach no difference between the means —since they come from the same universe. The average difference given by the 100 pairs is, in fact, + 0·08, or very little removed from the expected difference of 0. But there is as usual a wide scatter round this average which we can measure by the standard deviation. The standard deviation revealed by the 100 observations of differences is 1·99 (according to theory it should have been 1·82). The observations are, it will be seen, distributed fairly symmetrically round the average, and it can be calculated, from the original ungrouped figures, that only 5 of them are more than twice this standard deviation distant from the observed mean of $+0.08$ (*i.e.* outside the limits $-3.90$ to $+4.06$).

We note with means, therefore, that (a) in the long run the difference between samples from the same universe will be 0, (b) in individual tests the differences observed will be scattered symmetrically round 0, and (c) only about 5 differences in 100 will differ from the real value of 0 by more than twice the standard deviation. In " real life " we proceed

DIFFERENCES BETWEEN MEANS IN TWO SAMPLES OF
5 OBSERVATIONS

| Difference between Mean Number of Colds observed in 2 Samples each composed of 5 Persons | |
| --- | --- |
| Size of Difference | Number of Occasions upon which such a Difference occurred |
| $-5.49$ to $-4.50$ | 1 |
| $-4.49$ to $-3.50$ | 4 |
| $-3.49$ to $-2.50$ | 2 |
| $-2.49$ to $-1.50$ | 13 |
| $-1.49$ to $-0.50$ | 20 |
| $-0.49$ to $+0.50$ | 22 |
| $+0.51$ to $+1.50$ | 14 |
| $+1.51$ to $+2.50$ | 11 |
| $+2.51$ to $+3.50$ | 8 |
| $+3.51$ to $+4.50$ | 4 |
| $+4.51$ to $+5.50$ | 1 |
| Total | 100 |

then as follows. The mean height of a group of 6194 Englishmen is $67.38$ inches and the mean height of a group of 1304 Scotchmen is $68.61$ inches. Are Scotchmen on the average taller than Englishmen or is the difference merely due to chance, inherent in sampling ? The standard error of the mean is, it has been shown, $\sigma/\sqrt{n}$, where $\sigma$ is the standard deviation of the universe sampled and $n$ is the number of individuals in the sample. For this standard deviation of the universe we have to substitute the standard deviation of the sample. The standard deviation of the 6194 Englishmen measured was $2.564$ inches, and the standard error of their mean is therefore $2.564/\sqrt{6194} = 0.033$. The standard deviation of the 1304 Scotchmen measured was 2·497 inches, and the standard error of their mean is therefore 0·069. The standard error of the *difference* between the two means—*i.e.* the amount of variability the differences might show if we took repeated samples of this size—is $\sqrt{\dfrac{\sigma^2}{n_E} + \dfrac{\sigma^2}{n_S}}$, where $n_E$ is number of Englishmen and $n_S$ is number of Scotchmen measured. Unless the observed difference is at least twice this value it might easily have arisen by chance—*i.e.* the difference between the means ought to be 0 and differs from 0 only by chance. Methodologically we have a number of alternatives.

(i) We may substitute for the standard deviation of the universe a single estimate obtained from the whole data. Thus we may use the standard deviation of *all* our observations, Englishmen and Scotchmen, put together. The value of this standard deviation is 2·595. By its use we are asking ourselves the question : " Is it reasonable to suppose that we could draw two samples from one and the same universe, in which the standard deviation of the individuals is 2·595, and obtain two means differing from one another by as much as the difference between 68·61 and 67·38 ? " Inserting this value of the standard deviation we have as standard error $\sqrt{\dfrac{(2·595)^2}{6194} + \dfrac{(2·595)^2}{1304}} = 0·079$. The difference between the two means is 1·23 inches, and this is 15·6 times the standard error ; it is, therefore, very unlikely that we are drawing samples from the same universe. In other words, Scotchmen are on the average taller than Englishmen—presuming the samples to be representative of the nationalities.

(ii) Alternatively we may use the formula $\sqrt{\dfrac{\sigma_E^2}{n_E} + \dfrac{\sigma_S^2}{n_S}}$, $\sqrt{\dfrac{(2·564)^2}{6194} + \dfrac{(2·497)^2}{1304}} = 0·076$. In this case the difference between the averages is 16·2 times its standard error. In this test we are presuming that we have drawn the two samples from universes which differ in the variability of their individuals and we want to know whether they differ in

their means. In this example the two methods give closely
the same results and this is likely to be the case except when
the variability in the two samples is very different.

THE " t " TEST FOR SMALL NUMBERS

In both these tests of significance of the difference between the two means two points of importance will be noted :
(1) we are using the standard deviation, or standard deviations, observed in the samples as a sufficiently reliable
measure of the real, but unknown, standard deviation that
exists in the universe ; (2) we are satisfied that the differences between means of samples are distributed in the shape
of the normal curve and that therefore only 1 in 20 will
differ from zero by as much as $\pm$ twice the standard error,
if in fact no difference exists in the universe.

If, however, we have only a small number of observations
at our disposal, then we may well doubt our assumption that
their observed standard deviation will be a good measure of
the standard deviation in the universe. Obviously it may
not be (see, for instance, p. 106). Secondly, it can be shown
mathematically that with small numbers of observations the
ratio of the differences between the means of samples to their
standard error will not be distributed precisely in the shape
of the normal curve but in a rather differently shaped curve
known as the " $t$ " distribution (introduced by W. S. Gosset
under the pseudonym of Student). For these two reasons it
is necessary to use a slightly different test of significance if
the samples together contain less than about 30 observations.
The general procedure is, nevertheless, exactly the same and
calls for the same three steps, viz. (1) the calculation of the
standard deviation of the observations available (from the
two samples combined in a rather special way), (2) the use
of this standard deviation to calculate the standard error
of the observed difference between the means, and (3) the
calculation of the ratio of the actually observed difference
to this standard error. The interpretation of this ratio is,
however, determined from a special table of " $t$ " values
(given at the end of the book, p. 362) in place of the normal

distribution which was regarded as sufficiently accurate with larger numbers. In fact, it will be seen that for the probability of 1 in 20, $t$ itself approximates to the normal value of about 2 when there are some 25 observations.

EXAMPLE OF THE " $t$ " TEST

An inquiry has been made, let us suppose, into the systolic blood pressure of patients with some specified illness. The disease is a rare one and only 9 cases are available. For comparison, measurements have been taken of 11 normal persons of the same age and sex but not suffering from the disease. The resulting observations are set out in Table XIX. They give a mean figure for the 9 affected persons of 140·6 and for the 11 unaffected persons of 119·6, a difference of 21 mm. This is obviously a large difference and it is also noticeable that no affected person has a pressure under 130 and no normal person has one over 130. Nevertheless, the numbers of observations are small and there is an appreciable variation between the persons within each group. We may therefore legitimately ask whether the difference between the means might have arisen merely by chance (and of course in many such comparisons in practice the two groups would be much less clearly distinguished than imagined here).

The $t$ value we have to calculate is, as already stated, the ratio of the observed difference between the two means to the calculated standard error of that difference. In other words, as before, the ratio we require is :—

$$\frac{140\cdot6 - 119\cdot6}{\sqrt{\dfrac{s^2}{n_1} + \dfrac{s^2}{n_2}}},$$

where $s^2$ is our estimate of the standard deviation in the universe and $n_1$ and $n_2$ are the numbers of observations that we have made. To calculate $s^2$ we first proceed, as with large samples, to find for each separate group the sum of the squared deviations of the observations from their mean, i.e. $Sum\ (x_1 - \bar{x}_1)^2$ and $Sum\ (x_2 - \bar{x}_2)^2$. To calculate the two standard deviations separately we then use $n_1 - 1$ and $n_2 - 1$ as the numbers involved (as already shown in Chapters VII and VIII). Thus in making a *combined* estimate of the standard deviation we similarly have

$$s^2 = \frac{Sum\ (x_1 - \bar{x}_1)^2 + Sum\ (x_2 - \bar{x}_2)^2}{n_1 + n_2 - 2}.$$

The simplest way of calculating $Sum\ (x_1 - \bar{x}_1)^2$ is by means of the formula given previously for finding the standard deviation (Chapters VII and VIII), namely that $Sum\ (x_1 - \bar{x}_1)^2 = Sum\ (x_1{}^2) - (Sum\ x_1)^2/n_1$. Thus, taking the observations of Table XIX, we have :—

$$Sum\ (x_1 - \bar{x}_1)^2 = 178{,}665 - (1265)^2/9 = 862 \cdot 2$$
and   $$Sum\ (x_2 - \bar{x}_2)^2 = 158{,}442 - (1316)^2/11 = 1000 \cdot 5.$$

Putting these values into our formula for $s^2$ we then have

$$s^2 = (862 \cdot 2 + 1000 \cdot 5)/(9 + 11 - 2) = 1862 \cdot 7/18 = 103 \cdot 48.$$

Thus, finally, $t = 21 \cdot 0 \Big/ \sqrt{\dfrac{103 \cdot 48}{9} + \dfrac{103 \cdot 48}{11}}$

$$= 21 \cdot 0/\sqrt{11 \cdot 50 + 9 \cdot 41}$$
$$= 21 \cdot 0/4 \cdot 57$$
$$= 4 \cdot 60.$$

Turning to the table on p. 362, we have (*a*) 4·60 as our observed *t* value and (*b*) $n_1 + n_2 - 2$, or 18, as the number of values (or *degrees of freedom*) independently contributing to it. In the centre of the table are set out the values of *t*. At the top is the probability of an observed value for a given size of *n*. Thus, looking along the line against $n = 18$ we see that with this number of observations a *t* value as large as 2·878 would appear by chance only once in 100 trials, since the value of P, the probability of getting that value by chance (or a more extreme one) with 18 observations, is 0·01, as shown at the top of the column. It follows that our observed *t* of 4·60 would appear by chance even less often than this. In other words, the difference between our two means is highly significant. If, on the other hand, we had found *t* to be 1·734 then with an *n* of 18 we might have expected a value of that size to occur as often as once in

10 times (P = 0·1).  This is not so unlikely an occurrence
and we should therefore regard the difference between the
means as " not significant."

### THE " $t$ " TEST APPLIED TO A PAIRED COMPARISON

Let us suppose that the 9 patients of Table XIX are
now given a particular drug in the hope of reducing their
blood pressures.  The results of this treatment are set out
in Table XX and show that the systolic blood pressure fell

TABLE XIX

THE SYSTOLIC BLOOD PRESSURE (IN MM.) OF 9 PATIENTS
WITH A SPECIFIED ILLNESS COMPARED WITH THE
VALUES OBSERVED IN 11 COMPARABLE NORMAL PERSONS

| 9 Patients | | 11 Normals | |
|---|---|---|---|
| Observed B.P. (1) | Square of Observed Value (2) | Observed B.P. (3) | Square of Observed Value (4) |
| 132 | 17,424 | 107 | 11,449 |
| 160 | 25,600 | 98 | 9,604 |
| 145 | 21,025 | 125 | 15,625 |
| 132 | 17,424 | 129 | 16,641 |
| 140 | 19,600 | 128 | 16,384 |
| 154 | 23,716 | 114 | 12,996 |
| 136 | 18,496 | 115 | 13,225 |
| 134 | 17,956 | 126 | 15,876 |
| 132 | 17,424 | 123 | 15,129 |
| | | 123 | 15,129 |
| | | 128 | 16,384 |
| Total 1265 | 178,665 | 1316 | 158,442 |

in 6 cases, rose slightly in 2 cases, and was unchanged in 1.
The total change was a fall of 103 mm. in the 9 cases or a
mean fall of 11·4 mm. per person.  Is this reduction likely
to have arisen by chance ?  In other words, if, in the long
run, no change at all is to be expected, how likely are we in
this instance to get as large a difference from zero as 11·4
with 9 persons who have the considerable individual variability of response here revealed ?  Since we are now concerned not with two quite separate groups of persons but
with *one and the same group on two occasions*, we can obviously

and legitimately calculate the differences shown in column 3 and already referred to above. We have, in other words, a " paired comparison." It will then be more sensible to continue to work with these pairs (column 3) (and thus with a more sensitive test of significance) rather than to compare the observed values before treatment and after treatment (columns (1) and (2)) by the method demonstrated in the previous section. The question we ask of these pairs is does their mean change of $-11 \cdot 4$ mm. differ significantly from 0 ? The answer lies in calculating the ratio of this observed

TABLE XX

THE SYSTOLIC BLOOD PRESSURE (IN MM.) OF 9 PATIENTS
BEFORE AND AFTER TREATMENT WITH A SPECIFIC DRUG

| Before Treatment (1) | After Treatment (2) | Observed Difference (3) | Square of Difference (4) |
|---|---|---|---|
| 132 | 136 | + 4 | 16 |
| 160 | 130 | − 30 | 900 |
| 145 | 128 | − 17 | 289 |
| 132 | 132 | 0 | 0 |
| 140 | 130 | − 10 | 100 |
| 154 | 125 | − 29 | 841 |
| 136 | 125 | − 11 | 121 |
| 134 | 136 | + 2 | 4 |
| 132 | 120 | − 12 | 144 |
| Total 1265 | 1162 | − 103 | 2415 |

mean change to its own standard error, $s/\sqrt{n}$ (precisely as in Chapter IX), where $n$ is the number of pairs and $s$ is their standard deviation. Taking the customary formula for calculating the standard deviation, $Sum\ (x - \bar{x})^2 = Sum\ (x^2) - (Sum\ \bar{x})^2/n$, we have, in the present instance, from Table XX as follows :—

$$Sum\ (x - \bar{x})^2 = 2415 - (103)^2/9 = 2415 - 1178 \cdot 8 = 1236 \cdot 2$$
$$\text{and } s = \sqrt{1236 \cdot 2/8} = 12 \cdot 43.$$
$$\text{Then } s/\sqrt{n} = 12 \cdot 43/3 = 4 \cdot 14$$
$$\text{and, finally, } t = 11 \cdot 4/4 \cdot 14 = 2 \cdot 75.$$

Consulting the table on p. 362, we see that with $n = 8$ and $t = 2 \cdot 75$ P lies between $0 \cdot 05$ and $0 \cdot 02$. In short, a difference from zero as large as this would be expected to turn up by chance less than once in 20 times. This is a rather unlikely event and we therefore accept the difference following treatment as significant.

## Summary

With a reasonably large number of observations (which may be placed at some 25–30) the standard error of the difference between two means may be taken to be the square root of the sum of the squares of the two individual standard errors of the separate means in the two samples. A difference of twice or more this standard error may be accepted as significant, a figure of twice indicating a probability of 1 in 20. With smaller numbers this test will tend to exaggerate significance and the " $t$ " test is the more appropriate measure. With observations that are naturally paired in some way the " $t$ " test should be applied to the mean of the differences between those pairs, to see whether such a mean is significantly greater, or less, than zero.

*(For exercise see p. 316)*

L

# XIII

# PROBLEMS OF SAMPLING : $\chi^2$

IN a previous chapter (XI) attention was devoted to the appropriate test of the " significance " between two proportions. Occasions frequently arise, however, when we need to compare the characteristics of more than two groups. For instance, instead of comparing the proportion of vaccinated persons who are attacked with smallpox with the proportion of unvaccinated persons who are attacked, we wish to see whether the proportions attacked vary with the duration of time that has elapsed since vaccination. We shall then have a series of differences between groups to interpret. For the comparison of such distributions, the $\chi^2$ test has been developed (originally by Karl Pearson).

## Interpretation of a Series of Proportions

The statistical procedure may best be discussed by means of a concrete example. Table XXI shows the distribution of intelligence quotients in a group of nearly a thousand children and the number in each intelligence group that were clinically assessed as having normal or subnormal nutrition.

The percentages in the last line of the table show that amongst the more intelligent children there were proportionately fewer instances of subnormal nutrition, and the regular progression of the percentages, from 11·2 to 4·4 as the intelligence quotient rises, suggests that this relationship is unlikely to have arisen merely by chance. It is clear, however, that if another sample of 950 children were taken at random from the same universe of children we should not necessarily find in the different intelligence groups exactly 11·2, 10·6,

6·8, and 4·4 per cent. with unsatisfactory nutrition.  Each
of these percentages is certain to vary from one sample to
another, and the smaller the sample the more, as has been
previously shown, they are likely to vary.  The question at
issue then becomes this : is it likely that the magnitude of
the differences between these percentages, and also their
orderly progression, could arise merely by chance in taking
samples of the size given in line three ?  Is it likely, in other

### TABLE XXI
### INTELLIGENCE AND NUTRITIONAL STATE *

| | Intelligence Quotients | | | | |
| --- | --- | --- | --- | --- | --- |
| | Under 80% | 80–89% | 90–99% | 100% and over | Total |
| (i) Number of children with satisfactory nutrition . . . | 245 | 228 | 177 | 219 | 869 |
| (ii) Number of children with unsatisfactory nutrition . . | 31 | 27 | 13 | 10 | 81 |
| (iii) Total number of children observed . . . . . | 276 | 255 | 190 | 229 | 950 |
| (iv) Percentage in each intelligence group that had unsatisfactory nutrition . . . . | 11·2 | 10·6 | 6·8 | 4·4 | 8·5 |

* From "The Relation between Health and Intelligence in School Children," by N. J.
England (1936), *J. Hyg., Camb.*, 36, 74.

words, that, if we had observed the whole universe of children
from which the sample was taken, the percentage with
unsatisfactory nutrition would be just the same in each
intelligence group ?  To answer that question the assumption is made that the percentage with unsatisfactory nutrition ought to be identical in each of these groups—*i.e.* that
intelligence and nutrition are unrelated.  We then seek to
determine whether that assumption (often called the null
hypothesis) is a reasonable one by measuring whether the
differences actually observed from the uniform figure might
frequently or only infrequently arise by chance in taking
samples of the recorded size.  If we find that the departure
from uniformity is of the order that might frequently arise by
chance, then we must conclude that the varying percentage

of children with unsatisfactory nutrition in the different intelligence groups *suggests* that intelligence and nutrition are associated, but that these differences are not more than might have arisen by chance and might vanish if we took another sample of children. We must, therefore, be cautious in drawing deductions from them. If, on the other hand, we find that the differences from our assumed uniformity are such as would only arise by chance very infrequently, then we may reject our original hypothesis that each of the groups ought to show the same percentage. For if that hypothesis were true an unlikely event has occurred, and it is reasonable to reject the unlikely event and say that we think the differences observed are real, in the sense that they would not be likely to disappear (though they might be modified or increased) if we took another sample of children of equal size.

### THE TECHNIQUE INVOLVED

The statistical technique, therefore, involves—

(1) Calculating how many children in each intelligence group would fall in the satisfactory nutrition category, and how many in the unsatisfactory nutrition category, on the assumption that intelligence and nutrition are unrelated, so that the proportions in the nutrition categories ought to be the same in each group.

(2) Calculating the differences between these numbers expected on the hypothesis of no relationship and the numbers actually observed.

(3) Calculating whether these differences are of a magnitude likely or unlikely to be due to chance.

The first step is to determine what is the uniform percentage with unsatisfactory nutrition that we should expect to observe in each intelligence group if intelligence and nutrition are unassociated. Clearly that figure must be the percentage of malnourished children in the universe from which our sample was taken ; that is the figure we should, apart from sampling errors, expect to obtain in each intelligence group, if this characteristic is not associated with nutrition. We do not know that figure, but as an estimate of it we may take the proportion of malnourished children in our sample as a whole—namely, 8·5 per cent. Our assumption then is that the proportion of malnourished children ought to be 8·5 per cent. in each intelligence group. If that assumption is true, should we be likely to observe, in a sample of the size given, percentages of 11·2, 10·6, 6·8, and 4·4 merely by chance ? We must first calculate the number of children expected in each intelligence group on this hypothesis that 8·5 per cent. of them ought to have belonged to the malnourished category and 91·5 per cent. to the satisfactorily nourished category. These figures are given in italics in Table XXII, being calculated by simple proportion—e.g.

TABLE XXII

CALCULATION OF $\chi^2$

|  | Intelligence Quotients | | | | |
|---|---|---|---|---|---|
|  | Under 80% | 80– 89% | 90– 99% | 100% and over | Total |
| (i) Observed number with satisfactory nutrition . . | 245 | 228 | 177 | 219 | 869 |
| (ii) Expected number on hypothesis that nutrition and intelligence are unrelated . | *253* | *233* | *174* | *209* | *869* |
| (iii) Difference, observed minus expected . . . . | − 8 | − 5 | +3 | +10 | .. |
| (iv) (Difference)² . . . | 64 | 25 | 9 | 100 | .. |
| (v) (Difference)² ÷ Expected number . . . . . | 0·25 | 0·11 | 0·05 | 0·48 | .. |
| (i) Observed number with unsatisfactory nutrition . | 31 | 27 | 13 | 10 | 81 |
| (ii) Expected number on hypothesis that nutrition and intelligence are unrelated . | *23* | *22* | *16* | *20* | *81* |
| (iii) Difference, observed minus expected . . . . | +8 | +5 | − 3 | − 10 | .. |
| (iv) (Difference)² . . . | 64 | 25 | 9 | 100 | .. |
| (v) (Difference)² ÷ Expected number . . . . . | 2·78 | 1·14 | 0·56 | 5·00 | .. |
| *Total—* | | | | | |
| Observed . . . . | 276 | 255 | 190 | 229 | 950 |
| Expected . . . . | *276* | *255* | *190* | *229* | *950* |

there were 276 children whose intelligence quotient was below 80 per cent.; we expect 8·5 per cent. of these 276, or 23, to be malnourished and 91·5 per cent., or the remaining 253, to be satisfactorily nourished.

The next step is to calculate the differences between the observed and expected entries. These, given in the third line of each half of Table XXII, show that there are, in fact, more children of low intelligence with subnormal nutrition than would be expected on our hypothesis of equality and fewer with subnormal nutrition in the higher intelligence groups than would be expected on that hypothesis—*e.g.* of children in the under 80 per cent. intelligence group 31 had unsatisfactory nutrition whereas we expected only 23 ; of children in the over 100 per cent. intelligence group there were only 10 with unsatisfactory nutrition whereas we expected 20. These differences if added together according to their sign must come to zero. To get rid of this difficulty of sign, and for mathematical reasons underlying the test, each difference is squared, as shown in line (iv). Finally, the following point must be observed. If the number expected in a group is, say, 75, and the number actually observed is 100, the difference of 25 is clearly a relatively large and important one, since it amounts to one-third of the expected number. On the other hand, if the number expected in the group is 750 and the number actually observed is 775, the difference of 25 is a relatively small and unimportant one, since it amounts to only 3·3 per cent. of the expected number. To assess the importance of the difference, its square is therefore divided by the number expected in that category (in the first case above this gives a value of $(25)^2/75$ or 8·3, in the second case $(25)^2/750$ or only 0·83). The sum of these values is known as $\chi^2$ (*i.e.* chi-square). In this table it equals $0·25 + 0·11 + 0·05 + 0·48 + 2·78 + 1·14 + 0·56 + 5·00 = 10·37$.

In other words, $\chi^2$ is equal to the sum of all the values of

$$\frac{(\text{Observed number minus Expected number})^2}{\text{Expected number}}.$$

### THE INTERPRETATION OF THE $\chi^2$ VALUE

$\chi^2$, it will be observed, will be zero if the observations and expectations are identical ; in all other cases it must be a positive value, and the larger the relative differences between the observed and expected values the larger must be the value of $\chi^2$. Also the more sub-groups there are in the table the larger $\chi^2$ may become, since each sub-group contributes a quota to the sum. Therefore in interpreting the value of $\chi^2$ account must be taken both of the value itself and of the number of sub-groups contributing to it. In fact, although its mathematical foundation is complex, the interpretation of $\chi^2$ is simple by means of published tables—*e.g.* in Fisher's *Statistical Methods for Research Workers* (Edinburgh and London : Oliver & Boyd), of which an illustrative extract is given at the end of this chapter, and the complete table at the end of the book. These tables show whether the various differences found between the observed and expected values, as summed up in $\chi^2$, are sufficiently large to be opposed to our hypothesis that there ought to be a uniform proportion of malnourished children in each intelligence group. For instance in the present example $\chi^2 = 10\cdot37$ and the number of independent sub-groups is 3 (this number will be referred to in a moment) ; for these values Fisher's table gives a probability of somewhat less than 0·02. (The exact probability can be obtained from larger tables but is not always important, the main question being whether this value of $\chi^2$ is one which is likely or unlikely to have arisen by chance.) The meaning of this probability is as follows. If our hypothesis that we ought to have observed the *same* percentage of malnourished children in each of the intelligence groups is true—*i.e.* we are sampling a universe in which malnutrition and intelligence are not associated—then in the different intelligence groups of the size shown we might have reached merely by chance the differing malnourished proportions actually observed (or even larger differences from the uniformity expected) about once in fifty times (0·02 equals 2 in 100). In other words, if we had 50 separate samples of 950 children with this distribution of intelligence and ought to observe within each the same percentage of malnourished children in the intelligence groups, then in approximately only one of these 50 samples should we expect the actual proportions of malnourished children in the intelligence groups to differ between one another, by chance, by as much as (or more than) the proportions we have observed here. Once in fifty we may take to be an unlikely event and we may therefore conclude that our original null hypothesis of equality is wrong, and that it is more likely that the intelligence groups really differ in the incidence of malnourishment. If on the other hand our $\chi^2$ value had turned out to be 4·64, then the probability figure would have been 0·2. In other words, once in five trials we might reach differences of the observed magnitude between observation and expectation merely by chance. Once in five trials is a relatively frequent event, and we should have to conclude that the differences between the proportions of malnourished children in the intelligence groups might easily have arisen by chance, and we can draw from them no more than very tentative conclusions.

As with all tests of " significance," it must be observed that the final conclusion turns upon probabilities. There is no point at which we can say the differences could not have arisen by chance or that they must have arisen by chance. In the former case we say chance is an unlikely cause, in the latter that it could easily be the cause. It may not have been the cause in the latter—real differences may exist—but our data are insufficient for us to rule out chance as a valid hypothesis.

### HOW TO USE FISHER'S $\chi^2$ TABLE

Finally, we must consider the number of sub-groups, or " cells," in the table contributing to $\chi^2$.

In Table XXI (or XXII which shows the calculations on the data of Table XXI) there are 8 such values contributing to the sum. In finding $P$, the probability, from Fisher's table we took the number, $n$, to be only 3. The rule to be followed in tables of the type taken above as an example is that $n$ is the number of cells which can be filled up independently of the totals in the margins at the side and bottom of the table. In Table XXI the expected numbers of malnourished children in three of the intelligence groups must be found, by simple proportion, by applying 8·5 per cent. to the total number of children in each of those three groups. Having found those three values, all the other expected values can, however, be found by simple subtraction, since the total expected values vertically and horizontally must be the same as the observed values—e.g. having found the expected values of 23, 22, and 16 = 61 in three intelligence groups, the expected number in the fourth group must be 20, since the total must be 81 (8·5 per cent. of 229 is nearly 20). Similarly if 23 malnourished children are expected in the intelligence group of " under 80 per cent." then the well-nourished in that intelligence group must be 253, for the total children of that type is 276. Hence only 3 values in this table need to be found independently by applying proportions, and the remainder can be found by subtraction. To use the customary statistical term, the table has 3 *degrees of freedom*.

In any practical problem these degrees of freedom, or the number of expected values which need to be found independently by simple proportion, can easily be ascertained on inspection of the table ; alternatively they can be found by means of the rule $n = (c - 1)(r - 1)$, where $c$ is the number of columns, excluding the " total " column, and $r$ the number of rows in the table, excluding the " total " row—e.g. in Table XXI, $n = (4 - 1)(2 - 1) = 3$. It is with this $n$ that Fisher's table must be consulted.

It may be pointed out that in the above example the expected numbers were taken to the nearest whole number for the sake of simplification, but it would have been more accurate to retain one decimal and in practice this should be done. A warning may be added that if the *expected* number in any cell is less than 5 the $\chi^2$ value is liable to be exaggerated and the probability derived from it may be inaccurate. In a large table, however, it seems that if not more than 1 cell in 5 has an expectation of less than 5, then a minimum expectation of 1 is allowable in each such cell. In other cases adjacent columns may have to be amalgamated to give larger expected numbers.

The following table is a short extract from Fisher's table.

In the latter the $\chi^2$ values are tabulated for each value of $n$ from 1 to 30 and for 13 probability values (see pp. 360-361).

$n$ is the number of cells that needed to be filled independently (the degrees of freedom as defined above) in the table

AN EXTRACT FROM THE TABLE OF $\chi^2$

| $n$ | $P=0.90$ | 0·70 | 0·50 | 0·20 | 0·05 | 0·02 | 0·01 |
|---|---|---|---|---|---|---|---|
| 1 | 0·0158 | 0·148 | 0·455 | 1·642 | 3·841 | 5·412 | 6·635 |
| 3 | 0·584 | 1·424 | 2·366 | 4·642 | 7·815 | 9·837 | 11·341 |
| 10 | 4·865 | 7·267 | 9·342 | 13·442 | 18·307 | 21·161 | 23·209 |
| 15 | 8·547 | 11·721 | 14·339 | 19·311 | 24·996 | 28·259 | 30·578 |

of observations under study. In the centre of Fisher's table are set out the values of $\chi^2$. At the top is the probability arising from the observed value of $\chi^2$ for a given value of $n$. For instance, in the example taken above $n$ was 3 and $\chi^2$ was 10·37. Glancing along the $\chi^2$ values against $n=3$, we see that a $\chi^2$ of 9·837 gives a $P$, or probability, of 0·02 and one of 11·341 gives a $P$ of 0·01. Our value of 10·37 must therefore give a $P$ of somewhat less than 0·02. If, on the other hand, $\chi^2$ had been 4·642, we see that the $P$ against that value is only 0·2. If $n$ had been 10 and the value of $\chi^2$ found were 18·307, then $P$ would be 0·05. As a conventional level a $P$ of 0·05 is usually taken as " significant "—i.e. the proportions observed in the different groups under examination would show by chance a departure from the assumed uniformity as great as (or greater than) that actually observed only once in twenty times. But, as pointed out in the last chapter, the worker is entitled to take any level of " significance " he wishes, so long as he makes his standard clear.

## Summary

In practical statistics occasions constantly arise on which we wish to test whether persons who are characterised in some particular way are also differentiated in some second way—e.g. whether persons of different hair colour have also a different incidence of, say, tuberculosis. Suppose we take a random sample of the population, divide it into groups according to their hair colour, and then compute for each of these groups the percentage of persons with active tuberculosis. These percentages will probably not be identical even if hair colour and incidence of tuberculosis are *not* associated. Owing to chance they will vary between themselves. We need a measure to show whether such observed differences in incidence are, in fact, likely or unlikely to be the result of chance. To this type of problem the $\chi^2$ test is applicable.

# XIV

## FURTHER EXAMPLES AND DISCUSSION OF $\chi^2$

THE $\chi^2$ test has a wide applicability and forms a useful test of " significance " in many medical statistical problems, especially those in which the observations must be grouped in descriptive categories (as in the state of nutrition) and are not capable of being expressed quantitatively ; some further examples of its use may, therefore, be supplied. First it may be noted that $\chi^2$ must always be calculated from the *absolute* observed and expected numbers and never from percentages or other proportions.

### A Test of Differences between Sera

Let us suppose that batches of serum from different groups of donors are used for the prevention of measles and give the results shown in Table XXIII. (The actual figures are imaginary, though the example is drawn from the London County Council report on the measles epidemic of 1931–32, at a time when serum was being used in this way and the relative values of different sources of sera, *e.g.* from any adult or from a convalescent patient, were at issue.) The proportion of the total 700 children who after exposure to infection and the administration of serum escaped attack was 73 per cent., but between the different serum groups the proportion varies between 53·8 and 90·0 per cent. Taking into account the numbers of children upon whom each serum was tested, are the different degrees of success in the prevention of measles more than would be likely to occur by chance ? Or is it likely that the sera were all equally valuable and the departure from uniformity in the results

162

would be quite likely to occur by chance in groups of the size used ?

As a first step we presume that an equal degree of success should have been observed in each of the groups ; we then measure the observed departure from this uniformity and see whether such departure is compatible with our hypothesis of all the tested sera being equally valuable. As the expected degree of success with each serum, on this hypothesis, we use the proportion of successes observed in the

TABLE XXIII

MEASLES INCIDENCE AND SERUM TREATMENT

| Serum No. | Number of Children in Group | Number of Children in whom Measles was "Prevented" | | Number of Children in whom Measles was Not "Prevented" | | Percentage of Children in whom Measles was "Prevented" |
|---|---|---|---|---|---|---|
| | | Observed Number | Expected Number | Observed Number | Expected Number | |
| 1 | 120 | 80 | *(87·6)* | 40 | *(32·4)* | 66·7 |
| 2 | 150 | 135 | *(109·5)* | 15 | *(40·5)* | 90·0 |
| 3 | 90 | 56 | *(65·7)* | 34 | *(24·3)* | 62·2 |
| 4 | 90 | 68 | *(65·7)* | 22 | *(24·3)* | 75·6 |
| 5 | 110 | 87 | *(80·3)* | 23 | *(29·7)* | 79·1 |
| 6 | 60 | 42 | *(43·8)* | 18 | *(16·2)* | 70·0 |
| 7 | 80 | 43 | *(58·4)* | 37 | *(21·6)* | 53·8 |
| Total | 700 | 511 | *(511)* | 189 | *(189)* | 73·0 |

total—*i.e.* 73·0 per cent. Applying this proportion to each of the groups, we find the number of children in whom we expect measles to have been "prevented" or "not prevented" (the italicised figures in parentheses, *e.g.* 73 per cent. of 120 is 87·6). We observe, for example, that with serum No. 2 considerably more children escaped attack (135) than we expect on our hypothesis of uniformity (109·5). On the other hand, with serum No. 7 fewer children escaped attack (43) than we expect on our hypothesis (58·4). Are these differences more than would be likely to arise by chance ?

$\chi^2$ is the sum of the fourteen values of (observed number minus expected number)$^2$ ÷ expected number, *e.g.* $(80 - 87·6)^2$ ÷ 87·6 = 0·66 ; this sum equals 47·42. Only six expected

values have to be calculated independently, by simple proportion, from the 73 per cent. value in the total that we took
as the degree of success anticipated with each serum ; the
remaining values can be calculated by subtraction from the
totals at the side and bottom (*e.g.* if 87·6 of 120 children are
expected to escape attack, 32·4 must be expected not to
escape attack). Or by the formula $n = (c - 1)(r - 1)$, $n =
(2 - 1)(7 - 1) = 6$. The published tables of $\chi^2$ must therefore
be consulted with $\chi^2 = 47·42$ and $n = 6$.

From Fisher's table (pp. 360-361) it will be found for
these values that $P$ must be considerably less than 0·01,
since the table shows that when $n = 6$, $P$ is 0·01 when $\chi^2$
is only 16·81. Here we have a $\chi^2$ nearly three times as large
(outside the range of this table). More extensive tables
show that $P$ is less than 0·000001. In other words, if our
hypothesis that the sera were all equally valuable in prevention of measles is true, then less than once in a million
times in groups of children of the size here tested should we
reach merely by chance results which departed from that
uniformity of success to the extent that we have observed
with these children. We may therefore reject our hypothesis
and conclude that these results differ by more than is likely
to be due to chance, that, *all other relevant factors being equal,*
some sera were more efficient than others.

Whether we need the more exact probability taken from
the larger tables is rather a matter for the individual to determine. If $P$ is less than 0·01—*i.e.* one in a hundred—then
we may perhaps be content to say, without finding any more
accurate probability, that the departure from uniformity
is an unlikely event to occur by chance. Many statisticians,
as pointed out in the last chapter, take $P = 0·05$ as a conventional level of " significance "—*i.e.* if $P$ is greater than
0·05 then the observed values do not differ from the expected
values by more than might reasonably be ascribed to chance,
while if $P$ is less than 0·05, then it is likely that they do
differ by more than might be ascribed to chance. The
smaller the value of $P$ the smaller, clearly, is the probability
that the differences noted are due to chance.

## The Hourly Distribution of Births

In Table XXIV distributions are given of a series of live and still births according to the time of day at which they took place.  With live births the figures suggest that a high proportion of the total takes place during the night and a smaller proportion during the early afternoon and evening.  With still births rather the reverse appears to be the case ; the proportion during the night is somewhat low, while in the morning and afternoon the number is rather high, though the differences are not very uniform.  Are these differences between the numbers recorded at the various hours of the

TABLE XXIV

DISTRIBUTION OF LIVE AND STILL BIRTHS OVER THE DAY *

| Time Interval | Number of Live Births Observed | Observed Number— Expected Number | Number of Still Births Observed | Observed Number— Expected Number |
|---|---|---|---|---|
| Midnight– . . | 4,064 | + 36 | 126 | – 33 |
| 3 A.M.– . . | 4,627 | +599 | 157 | – 2 |
| 6 A.M.– . . | 4,488 | +460 | 142 | – 17 |
| 9 A.M.– . | 4,351 | +323 | 195 | +36 |
| 12 noon– . . | 3,262 | – 766 | 150 | – 9 |
| 3 P.M.– . . | 3,630 | – 398 | 178 | +19 |
| 6 P.M.– . . | 3,577 | – 451 | 144 | – 15 |
| 9 P.M.–midnight . | 4,225 | +197 | 180 | +21 |
| Total | 32,224 | 0 | 1272 | 0 |

* From J. V. Deporte: *Maternal Mortality and Stillbirths in New York State, 1915–25·* (Slightly adapted.)

day likely to have occurred merely by chance in samples of the observed size ?  On the hypothesis that they have occurred by chance, that live and still births are both distributed evenly over the day, the number of live births in each three-hourly period should be 4028 and the number of still births 159, *i.e.* (32,224 ÷ 8, and 1272 ÷ 8).  These are the expected values on the hypothesis of uniformity.

For each distribution, live and still births, eight values of ((observed minus expected)$^2$ ÷ expected) have to be calculated.  Their sum is $\chi^2$.  With live births $\chi^2$ equals 413·0, with still births it is 23·8.  (It may be noted that, as the expected value is the same throughout, the quickest way of calculating $\chi^2$ is to sum the squares of the (observed minus expected) values and divide this total by the expected number, instead of making separate divisions by the expected number in each instance.) In both sets of data $n = 7$, for one value is dependent upon the total of the expected births having to equal the total of the observed births. In both cases the $\chi^2$ table shows that $P$ is less than 0·01. The differences from the uniformity that we presumed ought to be present are therefore more than would be ascribed to chance, and we conclude that neither live nor still births are distributed evenly over the twenty-four hours in these records. The differences of the live births from uniformity are more striking than those of the still births, for they show a systematic excess during the hours between 9 P.M. and 12 noon and a deficiency between 12 noon and 9 P.M. ; with the still births there is some change of sign from one period to another which makes the differences from uniformity less clearly marked—perhaps due to the relatively small number of observations. Inspection of these differences themselves adds considerably to the information provided by $\chi^2$. The latter value tells us that the differences are not likely to be due to chance ; the differences themselves show in what way departure from uniformity is taking place, and may suggest interpretations of that departure.

## The Larger Contingency Table

As an example of a larger table, known as a contingency table, to which the $\chi^2$ test can be applied, we may take the hypothetical figures given in Table XXV. In this the observed persons have been divided into five broad social classes and have then been classified according to the number of colds they experienced during a calendar year. We may regard 0 or 1 cold as a very favourable experience, 2, 3, or 4 as fair, 5, 6, or 7 as poor, and 8 or 9 as excessive. Is there any evidence in these figures that the number of persons suffering (or enjoying) these experiences varies from one social class to another ? From the absolute figures in the top half of Table XXV we are quite unable to detect whether there is any such variation, since the numbers of people seen in the different social classes are not the same. As a first step we must turn them into percentage distributions. *This is an essential step quite irrespective of the test of significance,* since without it we cannot see what is, in fact, happening. Looking at these percentages in the lower half of Table XXV, it becomes clear that there is extremely little difference between the social classes. There is no consistent trend as we pass down the social scale, and it seems that persons with good, fair, poor, and very poor experiences are proportionately equally present in each class. (Again it may be noted that the figures are hypothetical and not drawn from real life.) Whether, however, social class and the incidence of colds are independent, as the figures suggest, we may test by $\chi^2$.

TABLE XXV

NUMBER OF COLDS REPORTED BY PERSONS OF DIFFERENT SOCIAL CLASS (HYPOTHETICAL FIGURES)

| Number of Colds reported | Number of Persons in each Social Class with given Number of Colds | | | | | |
|---|---|---|---|---|---|---|
| | Class I, Professional Occupations | Class II, Intermediate | Class III, Skilled Workmen | Class IV, Intermediate | Class V, Unskilled Workmen | Total |
| 0 or 1 | 15 | 15 | 30 | 15 | 14 | 89 |
| 2, 3, or 4 | 28 | 29 | 46 | 26 | 25 | 154 |
| 5, 6, or 7 | 20 | 35 | 46 | 27 | 25 | 153 |
| 8 or 9 | 17 | 21 | 28 | 22 | 16 | 104 |
| Total | 80 | 100 | 150 | 90 | 80 | 500 |
| Percentage Values in each Cell | | | | | | |
| 0 or 1 | 19 | 15 | 20 | 17 | 18 | 17·8 |
| 2, 3, or 4 | 35 | 29 | 31 | 29 | 31 | 30·8 |
| 5, 6, or 7 | 25 | 35 | 31 | 30 | 31 | 30·6 |
| 8 or 9 | 21 | 21 | 19 | 24 | 20 | 20·8 |
| Total | 100 | 100 | 101 | 100 | 100 | 100·0 |

As our evidence of the distribution of colds in the "universe" of all persons we must use the right-hand marginal totals, which give as follows :—

M

17·8 per cent. with 0 or 1 cold
30·8    ,,        ,,    2, 3, or 4 colds
30·6    ..        ,,    5, 6, or 7 colds
20·8              ,,    8 or 9 colds.

If there is no relationship between social class and incidence of colds, then we should expect this percentage distribution to be repeated in each of the 5 classes of 80, 100, 150, 90, and 80 persons. By simple proportion we can, therefore, find the expected numbers, *e.g.* for Class I, 17·8 per cent. of 80 = 14·2, 30·8 per cent. of 80 = 24·6, 30·6 per cent. of 80 = 24·5, and 20·8 per cent. of 80 = 16·6.

Alternatively, we may regard the table this way. According to its marginal totals, the chance of belonging to Social Class I is 80/500 and the chance of having 0 or 1 cold is 89/500. *If* the two events are independent, the chance of being so fortunate as to belong to Class I *and* to have only 0 or 1 cold is the product of these two independent probabilities $\left(\dfrac{80}{500} \times \dfrac{89}{500}\right)$. With a sample of 500 persons the number of times that so fortunate an individual would be expected to occur is $500\left(\dfrac{80}{500} \times \dfrac{89}{500}\right)$ = 14·2 as before. All the " expected " values, on the hypothesis of independence, can thus be calculated. They are set out in Table XXVI, together with the differences between observation and expectation and the square of each difference divided by the corresponding expected number. It may be noted for checking purposes that (*a*) the sum of the expected values must equal the sum of the observed values in each row and column, and (*b*) that the sum of the differences, taking sign into account, must be zero. $\chi^2$ equals the sum of the values of $(O - E)^2/E$ and is found to be 4·069. The number of cells for which an expected value must be calculated independently is 12, for the remaining 8 are then fixed by the marginal totals (or $n = (c - 1)(r - 1)$ = (5 − 1)(4 − 1) = 12). Looking at Fisher's table for $n = 12$ and $\chi^2 = 4·069$, it will be seen that $P$ is nearly 0·98. In other words, observation and expectation, on the hypothesis of independence, are so alike that if we made 100 trials of this size and type, in as many as 98 of them we should expect to get by chance *more* disparity than this between observation and hypothesis.

TABLE XXVI

| Number of Colds reported | | Social Class of Persons observed | | | | | |
|---|---|---|---|---|---|---|---|
| | | I | II | III | IV | V | Total |
| 0 or 1 | Observed | 15 | 15 | 30 | 15 | 14 | 89 |
| | Expected | 14·2 | 17·8 | 26·7 | 16·0 | 14·2 | 88·9 |
| | O – E . | +0·8 | – 2·8 | +3·3 | – 1·0 | – 0·2 | |
| | (O – E)²/E | 0·045 | 0·440 | 0·408 | 0·063 | 0·003 | |
| 2, 3, or 4 | Observed | 28 | 29 | 46 | 26 | 25 | 154 |
| | Expected | 24·6 | 30·8 | 46·2 | 27·7 | 24·6 | 153·9 |
| | O – E . | +3·4 | – 1·8 | – 0·2 | – 1·7 | +0·4 | |
| | (O – E)²/E | 0·470 | 0·105 | 0·001 | 0·104 | 0·007 | |
| 5, 6, or 7 | Observed | 20 | 35 | 46 | 27 | 25 | 153 |
| | Expected | 24·5 | 30·6 | 45·9 | 27·5 | 24·5 | 153·0 |
| | O – E . | – 4·5 | +4·4 | +0·1 | – 0·5 | +0·5 | |
| | (O – E)²/E | 0·827 | 0·633 | 0·000 | 0·009 | 0·010 | |
| 8 or 9 | Observed | 17 | 21 | 28 | 22 | 16 | 104 |
| | Expected | 16·6 | 20·8 | 31·2 | 18·7 | 16·6 | 103·9 |
| | O – E . | +0·4 | +0·2 | – 3·2 | +3·3 | – 0·6 | |
| | (O – E)²/E | 0·010 | 0·002 | 0·328 | 0·582 | 0·022 | |
| Total | Observed | 80 | 100 | 150 | 90 | 80 | 500 |
| | Expected | 79·9 | 100·0 | 150·0 | 89·9 | 79·9 | 499·7 |

Far, therefore, from there being any evidence of an association between social class and the incidence of colds, there is in these figures a close similarity between the class distributions. This similarity was indeed to be expected, for the basic figures were derived from the " cold " figures used in earlier chapters, that is by extracting 80 random sampling numbers to represent Social Class I, another 100 to represent Social Class II, etc. The number of 0's and 1's and 2's, 3's, and 4's, etc., ought, therefore, to be identical in the five social classes, and the differences observed are merely sampling fluctuations. A point, however, to be noted is that in " real " life so high a $P$ as this might fairly be regarded with suspicion. The suspicion arises in this way. A very wide departure of observation from expectation gives a very low $P$, and, as has been noted, this means that it is very unlikely that chance is the explanation of that difference. But it is also unlikely in real life that an *exceedingly* close concordance will be revealed—*some* variation is much more frequent. Therefore if observation and expectation are almost identical, we may reasonably pay further attention to the data (or the arithmetic)—the result is too good to be true. As Yule and Kendall ask, should we believe an investigator who says that he threw a die 600 times and got exactly 100 of each number from 1 to 6 ? ($\chi^2=0$, $P=1$.) " We might, if we knew him very well, but we should probably regard him as rather lucky, which is only another way of saying that he has brought off a very improbable event." That view of $\chi^2$, and of other tests of significance, is a useful one to bear in mind.

By a rather similar process of reasoning we may sometimes use the $\chi^2$ test as a test of the uniformity with which different observers are making observations in the same field. For instance, suppose observers A and B each see 100 cases of cancer of the cervix uteri and grade them according to the stage of disease. If there is no reason at all to suppose that they are likely to see different types of patients (*i.e.* they are sampling the same universe), we should expect them to see the same numbers in stages 1, 2, 3, and 4 apart from sampling fluctuations.

We can then test whether the differences they report are within chance limits and, if not, query whether they are using identical definitions for the stages.

### Interpretation of the Associations found

It must be fully realised that $\chi^2$ gives no evidence whatever of the *meaning* of the associations found. For instance in Table XXII the value of $\chi^2$ was such that we concluded that the intelligence and the state of nutrition of a group of children were not independent. The interpretation of that association is quite another matter. We cannot say offhand that the state of nutrition *affected* the level of intelligence. Possibly those children who fell in the group with low intelligence had more instances of subnormal nutrition because intelligence is an inherited characteristic and parents of low intelligence may feed their children inefficiently. Similarly one measles serum may have " prevented " measles to a greater extent than another not because of its superior efficiency but because the children to whom it was administered had, in fact, been less exposed to risk of infection. We need to be satisfied that the children were effectively equivalent in other relevant respects. The value of the $\chi^2$ test is that it prevents us from unnecessarily seeking for an explanation of, or relying upon, an " association " which may quite easily have arisen by chance. But, if the association is not likely to have arisen by chance, we are not, as with all tests of "significance," thereby exonerated from considering different hypotheses to account for it. If we use some form of treatment on mild cases and compare the fatality experienced by those cases with that shown by severe cases not given that treatment, the $\chi^2$ value will certainly show that there is an association between treatment and fatality. But clearly that association between treatment and fatality is only an indirect one. We should have reached just the same result if our treatment were quite valueless, for we are not comparing like with like and have merely shown that mild cases die less frequently than severe cases. Having applied the sampling test, we must always consider with care the possible causes to which the association may be due.

It must be observed also that the value of $\chi^2$ does not measure the *strength* of the association between two factors but only whether they are associated at all in the observations under study. Given sufficiently large numbers of observations, the test will show that two factors are associated even though the degree of relationship may be very small and of no practical importance whatever.

## The " Fourfold " Table

With what is known as a fourfold table—*i.e.* one with four groups in it—$\chi^2$ may be calculated by means of the expected numbers, in the way previously illustrated, or alternatively from the formula :—

$$\chi^2 = \frac{(ad - bc)^2(a + b + c + d)}{(a + b)(c + d)(a + c)(b + d)},$$

where $a$, $b$, $c$, and $d$ are the numbers falling in the groups and the additions are the totals in the margins, as in the table below :—

|  | Number of Individuals | | Total |
|---|---|---|---|
|  | Inocu-lated | Not Inocu-lated |  |
| Number of { attacked . | $a$ | $c$ | $a+c$ |
| individuals { not attacked | $b$ | $d$ | $b+d$ |
| Total   .   .   . | $a+b$ | $c+d$ | $a+b+c+d$ |

$n$ in this case is only 1, since, when one expected value has been found, the remainder can be found by subtraction. The $\chi^2$ table is therefore consulted with $n = 1$ and the value of $\chi^2$ as found from the observations.

If the numbers involved are small the value of $\chi^2$ will be more accurately given by the formula :—

$$\chi^2 = \frac{\{ad - bc - \frac{1}{2}(a + b + c + d)\}^2(a + b + c + d)}{(a + b)(c + d)(a + c)(b + d)},$$

where $ad$ is the bigger of the two cross products (a correction due to F. Yates).

For instance, suppose the table is as follows :—

|  | Inoculated | Not Inoculated | Total |
|---|---|---|---|
| Attacked   .   . | 10 | 65 | 75 |
| Not attacked   . | 30 | 95 | 125 |
| Total   .   . | 40 | 160 | 200 |

The larger cross product is $30 \times 65$. For $\chi^2$ we, therefore, have

$$\frac{\{65 \times 30 - 10 \times 95 - \frac{1}{2}(200)\}^2 \times 200}{40 \times 160 \times 75 \times 125}$$

and $\chi^2 = 2 \cdot 7$. For $n = 1$ and $\chi^2 = 2 \cdot 7$, $P$ is $0 \cdot 10$, so that the difference between the inoculated and uninoculated is not more than might be expected to occur by chance (10 times in 100 tests would we reach so large a difference by chance). Without the correction $\chi^2 = 3 \cdot 33$ and $P$ is $0 \cdot 07$, which rather exaggerates the association. This is the value we should also reach if we made the calculation by means of the expected values. In this case we should argue that, according to these figures, the chance of being attacked is 75/200. The chance of being inoculated is 40/200. The chance of being an inoculated *and* an attacked person, if the two characteristics are independent (our null hypothesis), is then $(75/200 \times 40/200)$. This is the chance for each of the 200 individuals observed. Therefore the number we should expect to see in the " inoculated-attacked " cell on this hypothesis of independence is 200 times the probability, or $200(75/200 \times 40/200) = 15$. It will be noted that the actual number (10) is rather less than the expected number. The difference between these observed and expected values is 5, its square is 25, and dividing by the expected number the contribution of this cell to $\chi^2$ is $1 \cdot 66$. The other expected values can be similarly calculated (or by subtraction from the marginal totals), and their contributions to $\chi^2$ computed. $\chi^2$ then equals $1 \cdot 66 + 1 \cdot 00 + 0 \cdot 42 + 0 \cdot 25 = 3 \cdot 33$ and $P$ is $0 \cdot 07$, as above.

These results could, of course, be equally well tested by means of the formula for the standard error of the difference of two proportions ; 25 per cent. of the inoculated and 40·6 per cent. of the uninoculated were attacked, a difference of 15·6 per cent. The standard error of this difference is, as previously shown, $\sqrt{\dfrac{37 \cdot 5 \times 62 \cdot 5}{40} + \dfrac{37 \cdot 5 \times 62 \cdot 5}{160}} = 8 \cdot 6$ (where 37·5 is the percentage attacked in the total group). The difference is not twice its standard error and therefore cannot be regarded as an unlikely event to occur by chance. (The difference is $1\cdot81$ times its S.E., viz. $15\cdot6/8\cdot6 = 1\cdot81$, and from a table of the normal curve it can be found that the probability of such a difference, or a larger one, occurring is $0\cdot07$. The $\chi^2$ test, without Yates' correction, and the use of the S.E. of the difference between two proportions are, in fact, identical tests.)

### The Additive Characteristic of $\chi^2$

One further characteristic of $\chi^2$ is useful in practice. Suppose we had three such tables as the above showing the incidence of attacks upon different groups of inoculated and uninoculated persons, observed, say, in different places, and each table suggests an advantage to the inoculated, but in no case by more than could fairly easily have arisen by chance— e.g. the $\chi^2$ values are $2\cdot0$, $2\cdot5$, and $3\cdot0$, and, with $n$ equal to 1 in each case, the $P$'s are $0\cdot157$, $0\cdot114$, and $0\cdot083$. The systematic advantage of the inoculated suggests that some protection is conferred by inoculation. We can test this uniformity of result, whether taken together these tables show a " significant " difference between the inoculated and uninoculated, by taking the sum of the $\chi^2$ values and consulting the $\chi^2$ table again with this sum and the sum of the $n$ values—namely, $\chi^2 = 2\cdot0 + 2\cdot5 + 3\cdot0 = 7\cdot5$ and $n = 3$. $P$ in this case is slightly larger than $0\cdot05$, so that we must still conclude that the three sets of differences, though very suggestive, are not quite beyond what might fairly frequently arise by chance in samples of the size observed.

It may finally be noted that the $\chi^2$ test in the forms so far discussed, does not, in effect, answer the second part of the question originally posed on p. 153. The observation was there made that, as one passed up the scale of intelligence, the proportion of children with unsatisfactory nutrition declined from $11\cdot6$ per cent. of those with the lowest I.Q. to $10\cdot6$ per cent. of those in the next I.Q. group, and then to $6\cdot8$ per cent. in the third group, and finally to $4\cdot4$ per cent. of those with the highest I.Q. The question at issue was then put as, " Is it likely that the magnitude of the differences between these percentages, and also their orderly progression, could arise merely by chance in taking samples of the size given ? " The $\chi^2$ test as applied gives an answer as to whether the *magnitude of the differences* could easily have arisen by chance, but it clearly takes no account whatever of the *orderly progression* observed. We should have reached precisely the same value for $\chi^2$ if the four columns had been transposed in any way, *e.g.* so that the proportions (based upon the same numbers as are given in Table XXI) read 11·2, 6·8, 10·6, and 4·4.

If the test shows that the differences, whatever may be their order, are *unlikely* to have arisen by chance, no serious difficulty arises in its use. One has then to interpret the figures, which are unlikely to be due to chance, and the only difference between the two situations is that often it will be easier to reach a plausible explanation with an orderly progression than with a " disorderly " one. In short, one has significant departures of one kind or another from expectation and they have to be interpreted.

If, on the other hand, the $\chi^2$ test shows that the results do *not* differ significantly from the uniformity assumed, *i.e.* that the observed differences between the groups may well be due to chance, then it is sometimes argued, very properly, that, since the orderly progression " makes sense " and the " disorderly " does not, the order should be brought into the picture.

To take order into account some other test of significance (see below) must be applied. Without such a test in the two situations it is, however, reasonable to argue thus : (1) In cases of disorder. The $\chi^2$ test has shown that these differences might easily be due to chance ; further, their order is not systematic, so even if they were real differences no sensible explanation of their meaning would be easy to develop ; it is therefore preferable to accept them as due to chance. (2) In cases of order. The $\chi^2$ test has shown that these differences might easily be due to chance ; their order is, however, systematic and a rational explanation of the trend is simple ; it is therefore reasonable to argue somewhat cautiously from them, and well worth while pursuing further data.

## A Test of Order in Proportions

A very commonly occurring problem arises from this order of a series of proportions (such as those of Table XIX) and the application of a test, which is not difficult to use, is therefore important and worth illustrating.

Taking once again the figures of Table XXI (p. 153) let us suppose that the data are not in terms of measured intelligence quotients but relate to a teacher's qualitative assessments of intelligence, so that the table now reads :—

|  | Assessment of Intelligence | | | | Total |
|---|---|---|---|---|---|
|  | Very Poor | Poor | Good | Very Good |  |
| (i) Number of children with satisfactory nutrition . . | 245 | 228 | 177 | 219 | 869 |
| (ii) Number of children with unsatisfactory nutrition . | 31 | 27 | 13 | 10 | 81 |
| (iii) Total number of children observed . . . . | 276 | 255 | 190 | 229 | 950 |
| (iv) Percentage in each intelligence group that had unsatisfactory nutrition (and the difference of the group from the mean value for all groups) | *11·2* (+2·7) | *10·6* (+2·1) | *6·8* (−1·7) | *4·4* (−4·1) | *8·5* |
| (v) Intelligence " score " assigned to each group . . | −1 | 0 | +1 | +2 |  |
| (vi) Difference of intelligence score of the group from mean intelligence score . . | (−1·39) | (−0·39) | (+0·61) | (+1·61) |  |

To calculate a $\chi^2$ value which takes into account the *progression* of the percentages, the qualitative assessment of intelligence must first be placed upon a quantitative scale, as shown in line (v). Such scores are, clearly, to some extent subjective and arbitrary and, as Cochran has pointed out, " some scientists may feel that the assignment of scores is slightly unscrupulous, or at least they are uncomfortable about it. Actually," he adds, " any set of scores gives a *valid* test, provided that they are constructed without consulting the results of the experiment. If the set of scores is poor, in that it badly distorts a numerical scale that really does underlie the ordered classification, the test will not be sensitive. The scores should therefore embody the best insight available about the way in which the classification was constructed and used" (*Biometrics*, 1954, *10*, 417).

Having adopted this quantitative scale we can calculate in its terms the mean intelligence of all the children observed, namely the sum of $(276 \times -1) + (255 \times 0) + (190 \times 1) + (229 \times 2) = +372$, divided by the total number of children, 950, $= +0.39$. The position of each group can then be determined in relation to this mean, as in line (vi). Similarly the proportion with poor nutrition in each group can be calculated as an excess, or defect, in relation to the figure of 8·5 per cent. for the observed population as a whole (see line (iv)).

From the data in this form we can calculate (*a*) a measure of the degree of relationship of intelligence to nutrition and (*b*) the $\chi^2$ value associated with that degree of relationship (in terms of the following Chapter XV we can calculate the regression coefficient of intelligence upon nutrition and the $\chi^2$ for that regression). The measure of the degree of relationship of intelligence to nutrition (the regression coefficient) is calculated as follows. For each intelligence group separately the difference between its own intelligence score and the mean intelligence score for all children is multiplied by the corresponding difference between its own percentage with unsatisfactory nutrition and the mean percentage in the whole population with unsatisfactory nutrition ; the resulting product must be " weighted," or multiplied, by the number of children in that particular group, *i.e.* to whom this product applies. These sums for the four intelligence groups are then added together to form the numerator of the required measure of relationship.

Its denominator requires for each intelligence group the *square* of the difference between its own intelligence score and the mean intelligence of all children, again weighted by the number of children in that particular group, and then the sum of these values for all the four groups.

Thus we have as the measure of relationship :—

Sum of all group values of
$$\{(\text{Score} - \text{Mean Score}) \, (\% - \text{Mean}\%) \, (\text{Total number in group})\}$$
Sum of all group values of
$$\{(\text{Score} - \text{Mean Score})^2 \, (\text{Total number in group})\}$$

Tabulating gives as follows :—

| Intelligence Group | No. in Group (a) | Score − Mean Score (b) | % − Mean % (c) | (a) × (b) × (c) | (b)² | a × (b)² |
|---|---|---|---|---|---|---|
| Very poor | 276 | − 1·39 | + 2·7 | − 1035·8 | 1·9321 | 533·3 |
| Poor    . | 255 | − 0·39 | + 2·1 | − 208·8 | 0·1521 | 38·8 |
| Good    . | 190 | + 0·61 | − 1·7 | − 197·0 | 0·3721 | 70·7 |
| Very good | 229 | + 1·61 | − 4·1 | − 1511·6 | 2·5921 | 593·6 |
| Total   . | 950 | | | − 2953·2 | | 1236·4 |

The fraction giving the measure of relationship is $-\dfrac{2953\cdot2}{1236\cdot4}$.

Calling it in general terms numerator/denominator, the $\chi^2$ value to test its significance is $\dfrac{(\text{Numerator})^2}{(\text{Denominator}) \times (pq)}$ where $p$ is the percentage of marked persons in the total observations (*i.e.* with unsatisfactory nutrition) and $q$ is the percentage of unmarked persons (*i.e.* with satisfactory nutrition).

$\chi^2$ therefore equals $\dfrac{(2953\cdot2)^2}{(1236\cdot4)(8\cdot5)(91\cdot5)} = \dfrac{8{,}721{,}390}{961{,}610} = 9\cdot07$

and it has *one degree of freedom*. Consulting the table gives $P$ considerably less than 0·01, or highly significant.

Since the original example of Table XXI had already a numerical scale of intelligence, the test could have been applied in those terms. More often, however, in a contingency table the scale is not quantitative and the demonstration of the procedure was therefore made for such an example and also to illustrate the requirement of an assigned numerical scale.

## Summary

The $\chi^2$ test is particularly useful for testing the presence, or absence, of association between characteristics which cannot be quantitatively expressed.   It is not a measure of the strength of an association, though inspection of the departure of the observed values from those expected on the no-association hypothesis will often give some indication, though not a precise numerical measure, of that degree. As with all tests of " significance," the conclusion that a difference has occurred which is not likely to be due to chance does not exonerate the worker from considering closely the various ways in which such a difference may have arisen. In other words, a difference due to one special factor is not a corollary of the conclusion that a difference is not due to chance.   There are a number of ways in which the value of $\chi^2$ can be calculated, some speedier than others.   An alternative method is given for fourfold tables and a correction in such instances for small samples.   The calculation of $\chi^2$ must always be based upon the absolute numbers.   In this discussion the mathematical development of the test and the foundation of the table by means of which the value of $\chi^2$ is interpreted in terms of a probability have been ignored. The test can be applied intelligently without that knowledge, provided the rules for calculation of the values of $\chi^2$ and $n$ are followed, and the usual precautions taken in interpreting a difference observed.   It must also be borne in mind that with small expectations the probability derived from the test may be inaccurate and must therefore be cautiously used (or some other method of analysis applied).

(*For exercises see p. 317.*)

# XV

# THE COEFFICIENT OF CORRELATION

A PROBLEM with which the scientific worker is frequently faced is the measurement of the *degree* of relationship between two, or more, characteristics of a population. For instance in a particular area the air temperature is recorded at certain times and the mean air temperature of each week is computed ; the number of deaths registered as due to bronchitis and pneumonia is put alongside it. Suppose the following results are reached :—

| Mean Temperature of Week in °F. | Number of Weeks with Given Mean Temperature | Mean Number of Deaths Registered as due to Bronchitis and Pneumonia in these Weeks | Range in Weekly Deaths |
|---|---|---|---|
| 35– | 5 | 253 | 186–284 |
| 38– | 7 | 205 | 147–238 |
| 41– | 10 | 130 | 94–180 |
| 44–47 | 4 | 87 | 69–112 |

There is clearly some relationship between these two measurements. As the mean weekly temperature rises there is a decrease in the average weekly number of deaths from bronchitis and pneumonia, which fall from an average of 253 in the 5 coldest weeks to an average of 87 in the 4 warmest weeks. On the other hand there is at the same mean temperature a considerable variability in the number of deaths registered in each week, as shown in the ranges given in the right-hand column. In individual weeks there were sometimes, for instance, more deaths registered when the temperature was 38°–41° than when it was 35°–38°. In measuring the closeness of the relationship between temperature and registered deaths this variability must be taken into

180

account.  The declining number of deaths as the mean temperature rises, and also the variability of this number in weeks of about the same temperature, are shown clearly in Fig. 13—known as a *scatter diagram*.  It appears from the distribution of the points (each of which represents the mean temperature of and the deaths registered in one week) that the relationship between the temperature and the deaths could be reasonably described by a straight line, such as the

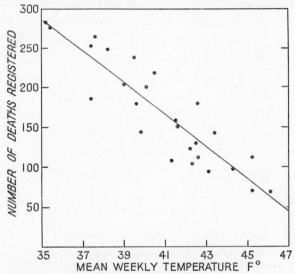

Fig. 13.—Number of deaths registered in each week with varying mean temperatures.  A scatter diagram.

line drawn through them on the diagram.  The points are widely scattered round the line in this instance but their downward trend follows the line and shows no tendency to be curved.  The means in the table above very nearly fall on the line.  As one aspect of the association we could calculate the fall in the mean number of deaths for each 1° fall in the temperature.  We can, however, also calculate a useful measure of relationship known as the *coefficient of correlation*, the advantage of which is that it gives in a single figure an assessment of the degree of the relationship between the two characteristics which is more vaguely shown in the table and diagram (both of which are, however, perfectly valid and valuable ways of showing associations).

## Dependent and Independent Characteristics

There are various ways of considering this coefficient. The following (based upon the " regression " of one character upon the other, see pp. 186 to 187) is perhaps the simplest :—

(i) Let us suppose first that deaths from pneumonia and bronchitis are dependent upon the temperature of the week

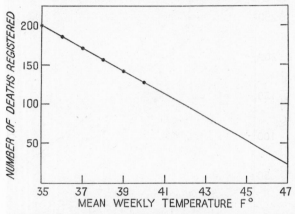

Fig. 14.—Number of deaths registered in each week with varying mean temperatures.    Hypothetical case of complete correlation.

and upon no other factor and also follow a straight line relationship—*i.e.* for each temperature there can be only one total for the deaths and this total falls by the same amount as the temperature increases each further degree.    Then our scatter diagram reduces to a series of points lying exactly upon a straight line.    For instance, in Fig. 14 the deaths total 200 at 35°, 185 at 36°, 170 at 37°.    For each weekly temperature there is only a single value for the deaths, the number of which falls by 15 as the temperature rises one degree.    If we know the temperature we can state precisely the number of deaths.    No error can be made for there is no scatter round the line.

(ii) Now let us suppose that the deaths are completely

independent of the temperature, but fluctuate from week to week for quite other reasons. When the temperature is low there is then no reason why we should observe a larger number of deaths than when the temperature is high, or vice versa. If we had a very large number of weekly records we should observe at each temperature all kinds of totals of deaths. The scatter diagram would take the form shown in Fig. 15 (only roughly, of course, in practice). At 35° there were, for example, weeks in which were recorded 50, 75, 100,

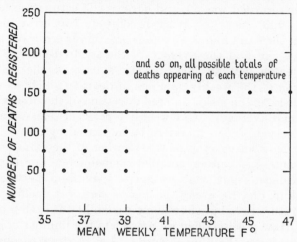

FIG. 15.—Number of deaths registered in each week with varying mean temperatures. Hypothetical case of complete absence of correlation.

125, 150, 175, and 200 deaths ; at 36° we see the same totals, and similarly at each higher temperature. The average of the weekly totals of deaths observed is the same at each temperature and is equal to the average of all the weekly observations put together, for the two characteristics being independent there is no tendency for these averages to move up or down as the temperature changes. If we know the temperature of the week we obviously cannot state the number of deaths in that week with any accuracy. We can, however, attempt to do so and we can measure the amount of our error. The best estimate of the deaths we can make at any weekly temperature is the average number of deaths

N

taking place in all the weeks put together—for, as pointed out, we have no reason to suppose that the deaths recorded in a specified week will be more or less numerous than the average merely because the temperature was high or low. Our error in a specified week is therefore the difference between the mean number of deaths in all weeks and the number of deaths that actually occurred in that particular week ; *e.g.* the mean number of deaths in all the weeks recorded in Fig. 15 was 125 ; in one week with a mean temperature of 36° the number recorded was 50, and our error of estimation for this week is $125 - 50 = 75$. We can compute this error for each week in turn and find the average size of our error, or, preferably, we can find the average of the squared errors. This latter value will, in fact, be the square of the standard deviation of the weekly numbers of deaths (which, as shown previously, is the mean squared deviation of the observations from their average). Our weekly errors between estimation and observation can therefore be measured by $\sigma^2$.

(iii) Now let us suppose that neither of the extreme cases is present—*i.e.* neither complete dependence nor complete independence—but that we have something between the two, as in Fig. 13, where the deaths certainly decline as the temperature rises but show some variability at each temperature. How precisely can we now state the number of deaths when we know the temperature ? Let us draw through the points a line which represents, broadly, their trend. From that line we can read off the expected number of deaths at each temperature and compare it with the observed number in that week. The difference will be the error we make in using this line. We can calculate this error for each week and the average of these squared errors we can call $S^2$.

Are we any better off in our estimations of the actual weekly deaths by the use of this line than when we say that in each week we expect to see the average number of deaths that took place in all the weeks ? We can measure our relative success by comparing $\sigma^2$ with $S^2$. If the two characteristics are entirely *independent* of one another (as in Fig. 15) the line we draw can have no slope at all and will pass at each temperature through the average number of deaths in all the weeks (there is nothing to make it higher or lower than the average at different temperatures). $S^2$ and $\sigma^2$ will then be the same. If the two characteristics are completely *dependent*, as in Fig. 14, then there is no scatter round the line at all and $S^2$ becomes 0. In practice, we use as a measure of the degree of association $\sqrt{1 - \dfrac{S^2}{\sigma^2}}$ which is known as $r$ or the correlation coefficient. If no association at all exists, $S^2$ and $\sigma^2$ are, as pointed out, equal and $r$ equals 0. If there is complete dependence, $S^2$ is 0 and $r$ equals 1. For any other degree of association $r$ must lie between 0 and 1, being low as its value approaches 0 and high as it approaches 1.

### The Use and Meaning of the Correlation Coefficient

The actual mode of calculation of the correlation co-efficient is described in the next chapter, and attention will be confined here to its use and meaning. It is calculated in such a way that its value may be either positive or negative, between $+1$ and $-1$. Either plus or minus 1 indicates complete dependence of one characteristic upon the other, the sign showing whether the association is direct or inverse ; a positive value shows that the two characteristics rise and fall together—*e.g.* age and height of school-children—a negative value that one falls as the other rises, as in our example of deaths and temperature. In the latter instance the value of the coefficient is, in fact, $-0.90$. This figure shows that there is in this short series of observations a very high degree of relationship between the temperature and the deaths, but, as it and the graph make obvious, not a complete relationship. Other factors are influencing the number of deaths as well as the temperature. If we knew the equation to the line we could certainly predict the number of deaths that would take place in a particular week with a given mean temperature with more accuracy than would be possible without that information ; but the diagram shows that in individual weeks we might still be a long way out in our prediction in spite of the very high correlation coefficient. It is the original variability in the number of deaths at *each* temperature that makes it impossible for the prediction to be accurate for an individual week, though we might be able to predict very closely the *average* number of deaths in a group of weeks of the same temperature. The advantage of the coefficient is, as previously pointed out, that it gives in a single figure a measure of the amount of relationship. For instance, we might calculate two such coefficients between, say, mean weekly temperature and number of deaths from bronchitis and pneumonia at ages 0–5, and between mean weekly temperature and number of these deaths at ages 65 and over, and thus determine in which of the two age-groups are deaths from these causes more closely associated with temperature level. We can also pass beyond the coefficient of correlation and find the equation to the straight line that we have drawn through the points. Reading from the diagram the straight line shows that at a weekly temperature of 39° F. the estimated number of deaths is about 205 ; at a weekly temperature of 40° F. the deaths become about 185 ; at a temperature of 41° F. they become 165. For each rise of 1° F. in the mean weekly temperature the deaths will fall, according to this line, by some 20 deaths. In practice, the method of calculating the coefficient of correlation ensures that this line is drawn through the points in such a way as to make the sum of the squares of the differences between the actual observations at given temperatures and the corresponding values predicted from the line for those temperatures have the smallest possible value. No other line drawn through the points could make the sum of the squared errors of the estimates have a smaller value, so that on this criterion our estimates are the best possible.

### THE REGRESSION EQUATION

The equation to the line can be found from the following formula :—

Deaths minus Mean number of deaths

$$= \frac{\text{Correlation}}{\text{coefficient}} \times \frac{\text{Standard deviation of deaths}}{\text{Standard deviation of temperature}}$$

× (Temperature minus Mean of the weekly temperatures),

where the two means and standard deviations are those of all the weekly values taken together.

Writing in the values obtained from the data under study this becomes—

$$\text{Deaths} - 167{\cdot}038 = -0{\cdot}9022 \,\frac{64{\cdot}310}{2{\cdot}867}\,(\text{Temperature} - 40{\cdot}908).$$

The fraction on the right-hand side of the equation equals $-20{\cdot}24$, so that we have—

Deaths $= -20{\cdot}24$ (Temperature $-40{\cdot}908$) $+167{\cdot}038$.

Removing the parentheses and multiplying the terms within by $-20{\cdot}24$ this becomes—

Deaths $= -20{\cdot}24$ Temperature $+827{\cdot}978+167{\cdot}038$

or, finally,

Deaths $= -20{\cdot}24$ Temperature $+995{\cdot}02$.

The figure $-20{\cdot}24$ shows, as we saw previously from the diagram, that for each rise of $1°$ F. in the temperature the deaths decline by about 20. (For when the temperature is, say, $40°$ F., the deaths estimated from the line are $995{\cdot}02 - (20{\cdot}24) \times 40 = 185{\cdot}4$, and when the temperature goes up $1°$ F. to $41°$ F., the estimated deaths are $995{\cdot}02 - (20{\cdot}24) \times 41 = 165{\cdot}2$.)

The figure $-20{\cdot}24$ is known as the *regression coefficient* ; as seen above it shows the change that, according to the line, takes place in one characteristic for a unit change in the other. The equation is known as the *regression equation*. As far as we have gone our conclusions from the example taken are that deaths from bronchitis and pneumonia are in a certain area closely associated with the weekly air temperature and that a rise of $1°$ F. in the latter leads, on the average, to a fall of 20 in the former.


### Precautions in Use and Interpretation

In using and interpreting the correlation coefficient certain points must be observed.

(1) In calculating this coefficient we are, as has been shown, presuming that the relationship between the two factors with which we are dealing is one which a straight line adequately describes. If that is not approximately true then this measure of association is not an efficient one. For instance, we may suppose the absence of a vitamin affects some measurable characteristic of the body. As administration of the vitamin increases, a favourable effect on this body measurement is observed, but this favourable effect may continue only up to some optimum point. Further administration leads, let us suppose, to an unfavourable effect. We should then have a distinct *curve* or relationship between vitamin administration and the measurable characteristic of the body, the latter first rising and then falling. The graph of the points would be shaped roughly like an inverted U and no straight line could possibly describe it. Efficient methods of analysing that type of curvilinear relationship have been devised and the correlation coefficient should not be used. Plotting the observations, as in Fig. 13 relating to temperature and deaths from bronchitis and pneumonia, is a rough but reasonably satisfactory way of determining whether a straight line will adequately describe the observations. If the number of observations is large it would be a very heavy test to plot the individual records, but one may then plot the *means of columns* in place of the individual observations—*e.g.* the mean height of children aged 6–7 years was so many inches, of children aged 7–8 years so many inches—and see whether those means lie approximately on a straight line.

THE LINE MUST NOT BE UNDULY EXTENDED

(2) If the straight line is drawn and the regression equation found, it is dangerous to extend that line beyond the range of the actual observations upon which it is based. For example, in school-children height increases with age

in such a way that a straight line describes the relationship reasonably well.   But to use that line to predict the height of adults would be ridiculous.   If, for instance, at school ages height increases each year by an inch and a half, that increase must cease as adult age is reached.   The regression equation gives a measure of the relationship between certain observations ;  to presume that the same relationship holds beyond the range of those observations would need justification on other grounds.

## ASSOCIATION IS NOT NECESSARILY CAUSATION

(3) The correlation coefficient is a measure of *association*, and, in interpreting its meaning, one must not confuse association with causation.   Proof that A and B are associated is not proof that a change in A is directly responsible for a change in B or vice versa.   There may be some common factor C which is responsible for their associated movements. For instance, in a series of towns it might be shown that the phthisis death-rate and overcrowding were correlated with one another, the former being high where the latter was high and vice versa.   This is not necessarily evidence that phthisis is due to overcrowding.   Possibly, and probably, towns with a high degree of overcrowding are also those with a low standard of living and nutrition.   This third factor may be the one which is responsible for the level of the phthisis rate, and overcrowding is only indirectly associated with it.   It follows that the meaning of correlation coefficients must always be considered with care, whether the relationship is a simple direct one or due to the interplay of other common factors.   In statistics we are invariably trying to disentangle a chain of causation and several factors are likely to be involved.   Time correlations are particularly difficult to interpret but are particularly frequent in use as evidence of causal relationships—*e.g.* the recorded increase in the death-rate from cancer is attributed to the increase in the consumption of tinned foods.   Clearly such concomitant movement might result from quite unrelated causes and the two characteristics might actually have no relationship what-

ever with one another except in time. Merely to presume that the relationship is one of cause and effect is fatally easy ; to secure satisfactory proof or disproof, if it be possible at all, is often a task of very great complexity.

## THE STANDARD ERROR

(4) As with all statistical values, the correlation coefficient must be regarded from the point of view of sampling errors. In taking a sample of individuals from a universe it was shown that the mean and other statistical characteristics would vary from one sample to another. Similarly if we have *two* measures for each individual the correlation between those measures will differ from one sample to another. For instance, if the correlation between the age and weight in all school-children were 0·85, we should not always observe that value in samples of a few hundred children ; the observed values will fluctuate around it. We need a measure of that fluctuation, or, in other words, the standard error of the correlation coefficient. Similarly if two characteristics are not correlated at all so that the coefficient would, if we could measure all the individuals in the universe, be 0, we shall not necessarily reach a coefficient of exactly 0 in relatively small samples of those individuals. The coefficient observed in such a sample may have some positive or negative value. In practice, we have, then, to answer this question : could the value of the coefficient we have reached have arisen quite easily by chance in taking a sample, of the size observed, from a universe in which there is no correlation at all between the two characteristics ? For example, in a sample of 145 individuals we find the correlation between two characteristics to be + 0·32. Is it likely that these two characteristics are not really correlated at all ; that if we had taken a very much larger sample of observations the coefficient would be 0 or approximately 0 ? It can be proved that if the value of the correlation coefficient in the universe is 0, then (*a*) the *mean* value of the coefficients that will be actually observed if we take a series of samples from that universe will be 0, but (*b*) the separate coefficients

will be scattered round that mean, with a standard deviation, or standard error, of $1/\sqrt{n-1}$, where $n$ is the number of individuals in each sample. In the example above, the standard error will, therefore, be $1/\sqrt{144} = 0\cdot083$. Values which deviate from the expected mean value of 0 by more than twice the standard deviation are, we have previously seen, relatively rare. Hence if we observe a coefficient that is more than twice this standard error we conclude that it is unlikely that we are sampling a universe in which the two characters are really not correlated at all. In the present case the coefficient of $0\cdot32$ is nearly four times its standard error ; with a sample of 145 individuals we should only very rarely observe a coefficient of this magnitude if the two characters are not correlated at all in the universe. We may conclude that there is a " significant " correlation between them—*i.e.* more than is likely to have arisen by chance due to sampling errors. If, on the other hand, the size of the sample had been only 26, the standard error of the coefficient would have been $1/\sqrt{25} = 0\cdot2$. As the coefficient is only $1\cdot6$ times this standard error we should conclude that a coefficient of this magnitude might have arisen merely by chance in taking a sample of this size, and that, in fact, the two characters may not be correlated at all. We should need more evidence before drawing any but very tentative conclusions. This test of " significance " should be applied to the correlation coefficient before any attempt is made to interpret it. (This is a large-sample test but it is not seriously in error for as few as 10 pairs of observations.)

## Summary

The correlation coefficient is a useful measure of the degree of association between two characteristics, but only when their relationship is adequately described by a straight line. The equation to this line, the regression equation, allows the value of one characteristic to be estimated when the value of the other characteristic is known. The error of this estimation may be very large even when the correlation is very high. Evidence of association is not necessarily evidence of causation, and the possible influence of other common factors must be remembered in interpreting correlation coefficients. It is possible to bring a series of characteristics into the equation, so that, for instance, we may estimate the weight of a child from a knowledge of his age, height, and chest measurement, but the methods are beyond the limited scope of this book.

# XVI

## CALCULATION OF THE CORRELATION COEFFICIENT

THE correlation coefficient, $r$, can also be described by means of the formula $r$ = mean of all the values of {(observation of $x$ minus mean of the observations of $x$) ÷ standard deviation of $x$ × (corresponding observation of $y$ minus mean of the observations of $y$) ÷ standard deviation of $y$}.   In other words, if a particular value of $x$ lies a long (or a short) way from the mean of all the $x$'s, does the corresponding value of $y$ lie a long (or a short) way from the mean of all the $y$'s, the two distances being measured in terms of the standard deviations of the observations ?   Put in these terms it can be most easily calculated from the following formula :—

$$r_{xy} = \frac{Sum\ \{(x - \bar{x})(y - \bar{y})\}}{\sqrt{Sum\ (x - \bar{x})^2\ Sum\ (y - \bar{y})^2}}.$$

Using the *sums* of the various values in this way avoids having to divide both the numerator and the denominator by the actual number of observations, a division which applies to each sum concerned.   Its omission simplifies the arithmetic.

### The Ungrouped Series

Suppose, for instance, we have measured on twelve persons their pulse-rate and their stature, and wish to measure the degree of relationship, if any, between the two by means of the correlation coefficient.   The twelve observations are given in columns (2) and (3) of Table XXVII.

The sums of the squared deviations, and the two standard deviations, can be found, as previously shown in Chapter VIII, by means of the formula

$$Sum\ (x - \bar{x})^2 = Sum\ (x^2) - (Sum\ x)^2/n.$$

Thus for the pulse-rate the sum of the squared deviations of

193

the observations round their mean is $62,980 - (864)^2/12 = 772$ and their standard deviation is therefore $\sqrt{772/11} = 8{\cdot}38$.

For the height of the twelve individuals the sum of the squared deviations round their mean is $57,194 - (828)^2/12 = 62$ and their standard deviation is therefore $\sqrt{62/11} = 2{\cdot}37$.

We now need the numerator to the formula for $r$ given above, viz. the sum of the values of {(observation of $x$ minus

TABLE XXVII

| Individual No. | Resting Pulse-rate in Beats per Minute | Height in Inches | $x^2$ | $y^2$ | $x -$ Mean $x$ | $y -$ Mean $y$ | (6)×(7) | $x \times y$ or (2)×(3) |
|---|---|---|---|---|---|---|---|---|
| (1) | $x$ (2) | $y$ (3) | (4) | (5) | (6) | (7) | (8) | (9) |
| 1 | 62 | 68 | 3,844 | 4,624 | − 10 | − 1 | +10 | 4,216 |
| 2 | 74 | 65 | 5,476 | 4,225 | + 2 | − 4 | − 8 | 4,810 |
| 3 | 80 | 73 | 6,400 | 5,329 | + 8 | +4 | +32 | 5,840 |
| 4 | 59 | 70 | 3,481 | 4,900 | − 13 | +1 | − 13 | 4,130 |
| 5 | 65 | 69 | 4,225 | 4,761 | − 7 | 0 | 0 | 4,485 |
| 6 | 73 | 66 | 5,329 | 4,356 | + 1 | − 3 | − 3 | 4,818 |
| 7 | 78 | 69 | 6,084 | 4,761 | + 6 | 0 | 0 | 5,382 |
| 8 | 86 | 70 | 7,396 | 4,900 | +14 | +1 | + 14 | 6,020 |
| 9 | 64 | 72 | 4,096 | 5,184 | − 8 | +3 | − 24 | 4,608 |
| 10 | 68 | 71 | 4,624 | 5,041 | − 4 | +2 | − 8 | 4,828 |
| 11 | 75 | 68 | 5,625 | 4,624 | + 3 | − 1 | − 3 | 5,100 |
| 12 | 80 | 67 | 6,400 | 4,489 | + 8 | − 2 | − 16 | 5,360 |
| Total 12 | 864 | 828 | 62,980 | 57,194 | 0 | 0 | − 19 | 59,597 |
| Mean values | 72 | 69 | 5248·33 | 4766·17 | .. | .. | − 1·58 | 4966·42 |

mean of the observations of $x$) × (corresponding observation of $y$ minus mean of the observations of $y$)}. For this purpose the deviation of each individual's pulse-rate from the mean pulse-rate of the twelve persons is given in column (6) and of each height from the mean height in column (7). If there is any substantial (and direct) correlation between the two measurements, then a person with a pulse-rate below the mean pulse-rate ought to have a stature below the mean height, one with a pulse-rate above the mean rate ought to have a stature above the mean height. (If the association is inverse, positive signs in one will be associated with negative signs in the other.) Inspection of the figures suggests very little correlation between the characteristics. For the numerator of the correlation coefficient formula we need the product of the two deviations shown by each person. These are given in column (8) and their sum is $-19$. The coefficient of correlation is, therefore, $-19/\sqrt{772 \times 62}$, which gives a value of $-0.09$. In other words, in these twelve individuals the pulse-rate and stature are not related to one another, since $r$ is nearly zero.

In the example taken this is a satisfactory mode of calculation because the mean pulse-rate and the mean height are whole numbers and also the original measurements are whole numbers ; it is, then, easy to calculate the deviation of each observation from its mean. But if decimals had been involved the deviations would have been troublesome to calculate. In that case it is easier to avoid altogether using deviations and to multiply directly the pulse-rate of each person by his stature, as in column (9), applying a correction at the end to the resulting sum of the values. The correction is given by the formula : $Sum\ (x - \bar{x})(y - \bar{y}) = Sum\ (xy) - Sum\ (x)\ Sum\ (y)/n$. Thus in the example taken this gives $59{,}597 - (864)(828)/12 = -19$, or the same value as was previously reached by working with the real deviations from the means.

This is the simplest and best method of calculating the two standard deviations and the correlation coefficient between the characteristics in anything up to 50–60 observations. With a larger series of observations, finding the individual squares and products becomes progressively more laborious and it is better to construct a grouped correlation table.

### The Grouped Series

As an example, let us presume that we have data for each of a number of large towns, viz. (1) a measure of the amount of overcrowding present in a given year, and (2) the infant mortality-rate in the same year ; we wish to see whether in towns with much overcrowding the infant mortality-rate tends to be higher than in towns with less overcrowding.  We must first construct a table which shows not only how many towns there were with different degrees of overcrowding but also their associated infant mortality-rates.

Table XXVIII gives this information.  The town with least overcrowding had only 1·5 per cent. of its population living more than 2 persons to a room (this being used as the criterion of overcrowding) ; the percentage for the town with

TABLE XXVIII

OVERCROWDING AND INFANT MORTALITY.  EXAMPLE
OF CORRELATION TABLE

| Infant Mortality-rate | Percentage of Population in Private Families Living more than Two Persons per Room | | | | | | Total |
|---|---|---|---|---|---|---|---|
| | 1·5– | 4·5– | 7·5– | 10·5– | 13·5– | 16·5–19·5 | |
| 36– | 5 | .. | .. | .. | .. | .. | 5 |
| 46– | 9 | 1 | .. | .. | .. | .. | 10 |
| 56– | 10 | 4 | 1 | .. | .. | 1 | 16 |
| 66– | 4 | 7 | 5 | 2 | .. | .. | 18 |
| 76– | 2 | 5 | 4 | 1 | 1 | .. | 13 |
| 86– | .. | 2 | 2 | 2 | .. | 1 | 7 |
| 96– | .. | 1 | 2 | 2 | 1 | 1 | 7 |
| 106–116 | .. | 1 | .. | 1 | .. | .. | 2 |
| Total | 30 | 21 | 14 | 8 | 2 | 3 | 78 |

most overcrowding was 17·5.  The lowest infant mortality-rate was 37 deaths under 1 per 1000 live births and the highest was 110.  Reasonably narrow groups have been adopted to include those maximum and minimum values and each town is placed in the appropriate " cell "—e.g. there were 5 towns in which the overcrowding index lay between 1·5 and 4·5 and in which the infant mortality-rates were between 36 and 46, there were 2 in which the overcrowding index lay between 10·5 and 13·5 and in which the infant mortality-rates were between 86 and 96.  (If a very large number of observations is involved it is best to make a separate card for each town, person, or whatever may have been measured, putting the observed measurements on the card always in the same order ; the cards are first sorted into their proper groups for one characteristic (overcrowding), and then each of those packs of different (overcrowding) levels is sorted into groups for the other characteristic (infant mortality). The cards in each small pack then relate to a particular cell of the table.)

Table XXVIII shows at once that there is some association between overcrowding and the infant mortality-rate, for towns with the least overcrowding tend, on the average, to show relatively low mortality-rates, while towns with much overcrowding tend to show high mortality-rates. The table is, in fact, a form of scatter diagram.

To calculate the coefficient of correlation we need (1) the squared deviations of the observations from their mean for the overcrowding index ; (2) similar figures for the infant mortality-rate ; and (3) for each town the product of its two deviations from the means—*i.e.* (overcrowding index in town A minus mean overcrowding index) × (infant mortality-rate in town A minus mean infant mortality-rate). In other words, we wish to see whether a town that is abnormal (far removed from the average) in its level of overcrowding is also abnormal in the level of its infant mortality-rate. In calculating the means and the deviations from them we can entirely ignore the centre of the table ; we have to work on the totals in the horizontal and vertical margins. The method is shown in Table XXIX.

For instance, we see from the right-hand totals that in 5 towns the infant mortality-rate was between 36 and 46, in 10 between 46 and 56, in 16 between 56 and 66, and so on. For this distribution we want the mean and squared deviations. As shown previously, these sums are more easily carried out in " working units " instead of in the real, and larger, units. In these units we have 5 towns with a mortality-rate of $-3$, 10 with a rate of $-2$, and so on. In working units the sum of the rates is thus found to be $+5$ and the mean rate is therefore $+5/78 = +0\cdot06$. The mean in real units is, then, 71 (the centre of the group opposite 0) $+0\cdot06 \times 10$ (10 being the unit of grouping) $= 71\cdot6$. To reach the squared deviations from the mean we continue to work in these units. Measuring the deviations from the 0 value instead of from the mean there are 5 towns with a squared deviation of $(-3)^2$ and these contribute 45 to the sum of squared deviations ; there are 10 towns with a squared deviation of $(-2)^2$ and these contribute 40 to the sum of squared deviations.

In working units the sum of squared deviations from 0 is thus found to be 237. Their sum when measured around the mean will therefore be $237 - (5)^2/78$, *i.e. Sum* $(x^2) - (Sum\ x)^2/n$, which equals 236·68.

TABLE XXIX

OVERCROWDING AND INFANT MORTALITY.   CALCULATION
OF CORRELATION COEFFICIENT

| Infant Mortality-rate | | Percentage of Population in Private Families Living more than Two Persons per Room | | | | | | Total |
|---|---|---|---|---|---|---|---|---|
| | | R.U. : 1·5– W.U. –2 | 4·5– –1 | 7·5– 0 | 10·5– +1 | 13·5– +2 | 16·5– 19·5 +3 | |
| R.U. | W.U. | | | | | | | |
| 36– | – 3 | 5 ( +30) | .. | .. | .. | .. | .. | 5 |
| 46– | – 2 | 9 ( +36) | 1 ( +2) | .. | .. | .. | .. | 10 |
| 56– | – 1 | 10 ( +20) | 4 ( +4) | 1 (0) | .. | .. | 1 ( – 3) | 16 |
| 66– | 0 | 4 (0) | 7 (0) | 5 (0) | 2 (0) | .. | .. | 18 |
| 76– | +1 | 2 ( – 4) | 5 ( – 5) | 4 (0) | 1 ( +1) | 1 ( +2) | .. | 13 |
| 86– | +2 | .. | 2 ( – 4) | 2 (0) | 2 ( +4) | .. | 1 ( +6) | 7 |
| 96– | +3 | .. | 1 ( – 3) | 2 (0) | 2 ( +6) | 1 ( +6) | 1 ( +9) | 7 |
| 106–116 | +4 | .. | 1 ( – 4) | .. | 1 ( +4) | .. | .. | 2 |
| Total | .. | 30 | 21 | 14 | 8 | 2 | 3 | 78 |

R.U. = Real units ;   W.U. = Working units.

We can now work in just the same way on the distribution of overcrowding—there are 30 towns whose overcrowding index in working units was – 2, 21 whose index was – 1, and so on. This gives a sum of – 60, a mean of – 0·77, and a sum of squared deviations of 137·85, all in working units. In this there is nothing new ; the process was given in full in Chapter VIII.

We now need the product of the deviations from the means for the numerator of the correlation coefficient. This is easily reached by continuing to measure the deviations in working units from the 0 values and making a correction as usual at the end.

For instance, there are 5 towns the deviation of which is − 2 in overcrowding and − 3 in infant mortality. The product deviation is therefore + 6, and as there are 5 such towns the contribution to the product deviation sum is + 30. Each of these values can be written in the appropriate cell (they are the figures in parentheses in Table XXIX). Their sum is + 107. These deviations in working units were measured from the two 0 values whereas they ought to have been measured from the two mean values. The correction formula, as already given above, is $Sum\ (xy) - (Sum\ x)$ $(Sum\ y)/n$. Thus we have $+ 107 - (5)(-60)/78 = 110·85$ so that

$$r = \frac{+110·85}{\sqrt{236·68 \times 137·85}} = +0·61.$$

It may be noted that no conversion to true units is necessary since, whatever units are used, they apply to both numerator and denominator of the fraction.

There is, we see, a fair degree of correlation between overcrowding and the infant mortality-rate, but at the same time Table XXVIII shows that with towns of the same degree of overcrowding there are considerable differences between the infant mortality-rates. The standard error of the coefficient is $1/\sqrt{n-1} = 1/\sqrt{78-1} = 0·11$; as the coefficient is more than five times its standard error it may certainly be accepted as " significant."

The calculation is very much speedier with the observations thus grouped, and little change has been made in the values reached, as the following figures show :—

|  | Grouped Series of Table XXVIII | Same 78 Observations Ungrouped |
|---|---|---|
| Means— |  |  |
| Overcrowding . | 6·7 | 6·6 |
| Infant mortality . | 71·6 | 71·0 |
| Standard deviations— |  |  |
| Overcrowding . | 3·99 | 3·74 |
| Infant mortality . | 17·4 | 17·3 |
| Correlation coefficient | +0·61 | +0·59 |

O

The regression equation is :

$$\text{Infant Mortality} - 71 \cdot 6 = + 0 \cdot 61 \frac{17 \cdot 4}{3 \cdot 99} (\text{overcrowding index} - 6 \cdot 7)$$

which reduces to Infant Mortality $= 2 \cdot 66$ Overcrowding Index $+ 53 \cdot 78$. (It must be noted that the values in *real* units must be inserted in this equation.) In other words, on the average the infant mortality rises, according to these data, by $2 \cdot 66$ per 1000 as the percentage of the population overcrowded increases by 1.

(*For exercises see pp. 318-319*)

# XVII

## STANDARDISED DEATH-RATES AND INDICES

In using death-rates in comparison with one another, or as a measure of the success attending some procedure, it must be remembered that such rates are usually affected considerably by the age and sex constitution of the population concerned. The fact that the death-rate of Bournemouth, an attractive seaside resort, was, in a given year, 13·3 per 1000, while the rate in Bethnal Green, an unattractive East London borough, was only 10·3, is no evidence of the salubrity of the latter. The greater proportion of old persons living in Bournemouth *must* lead to a higher death-rate there, since old persons, however well-housed and fed, die at a faster rate than young persons. The appropriate census shows that there were at the time 2½ times as many persons in Bournemouth as in Bethnal Green at ages over 75 years, 70 per cent. more at ages 50–74, and 10 per cent. less at ages 10–40. Any population containing many persons round about the ages of 5 to 20, where the death-rate is at its minimum, must have a lower *total* death-rate than that of a population containing many infants or old people, at which points of life the death-rate is relatively high, even though comparisons at every age show an advantage to the latter. The fictitious figures of Table XXX may be taken as an example.

Comparison of the two districts shows that B has *in every age-group* a lower death-rate than A. Yet its death-rate at all ages, the *crude* death-rate, is more than double the rate of A. The fallacy of the crude rates lies in the fact that like is not being compared with like : 72 per cent. of B's population is over age 45 and only 26 per cent. of A's population ; in spite of B's relatively low death-rates at these ages over 45, the *number* of deaths registered must be higher than in A's smaller population and therefore its total death-rate must be high.

Comparison of the rates at ages is the most satisfactory procedure, for then like is being placed against like, at least

TABLE XXX

A COMPARISON OF DEATH-RATES

| Age-group (years) | District A | | | District B | | |
|---|---|---|---|---|---|---|
| | Population | Deaths | Death-rate per 1000 | Population | Deaths | Death-rate per 1000 |
| 0– | 500 ⎫ | 2 | 4 | 400 ⎫ | 1 | 2·5 |
| 15– | 2000 ⎬ 74% | 8 | 4 | 300 ⎬ 28% | 1 | 3·3 |
| 30– | 2000 ⎭ | 12 | 6 | 1000 ⎭ | 5 | 5 |
| 45– | 1000 ⎫ | 10 | 10 | 2000 ⎫ | 18 | 9 |
| 60– | 500 ⎬ 26% | 20 | 40 | 2000 ⎬ 72% | 70 | 35 |
| 75+ | 100 ⎭ | 15 | 150 | 400 ⎭ | 50 | 125 |
| All ages | 6100 | 67 | 11·0 | 6100 | 145 | 23·8 |

in respect of age (so long as the age-groups are not too wide ; in the above example they were made unduly wide for the sake of compression and clarity). No single figure can fully replace them and succinctly summarise the contrasts.

### The Standardised Rate

At the same time a legitimate desire is often felt for a single mortality-rate, summing up the rates at ages and enabling satisfactory comparisons to be made between one rate and another. For this purpose the standardised death-rate is generally used. For its calculation (by what is known as the *direct* method) the mortality-rates at ages in the different districts are applied to some common standard population, to discover what would be the total death-rate in that standard population if it were exposed first to A's rates and then to B's rates at each age. These total rates are clearly fictitious, for they show what *would* be the mortality in A and B if they had populations which were equivalent in their age-distributions instead of their actual differing populations.

But these fictitious rates are more comparable with one another, and show whether B's rates at ages would lead to a better—or worse—total rate than A's rates if they had populations of the same age type.

For example, if the standard population taken for A and B consisted of 500 persons in each of the age-groups under 15 and 75 and over, 2500 in each of the age-groups 15–29 and 60–74, and 3000 in each of the age-groups 30–44 and 45–59, then in this standard population A's death-rates would lead to a total of 235 deaths and B's rates to 201 deaths, giving standardised rates at all ages of 19·6 and 16·8 per 1000. Taking a population of the same age-distribution thus shows the more favourable mortality experience of B, and the fallacy of the crude rate is avoided.

This example is, of course, a very exaggerated one and such gross differences in population are unlikely to occur in practice. On the other hand, the differences that do occur in practice are quite large enough to make the use of crude rates seriously misleading.

For instance, the crude death-rate, in England and Wales, of women from cancer was 103 per 100,000 in 1901–10 and 139 in 1921–30, a very appreciable rise being shown during that time. The corresponding standardised rates were 94 and 99 ; clearly the larger number of women living in the older age-groups (where cancer is more frequent) in 1921–30 compared with the number in 1901–10 was largely responsible for the increase in the crude rates, and no more subtle factor need be looked for.

With the present increasing proportion of persons living at later ages (owing to the fall in birth- and death-rates) it is certain that the *crude* death-rate from all causes in England and Wales will in time begin to rise, in spite of the fact that the death-rates at each age may continue to decline.

Comparison of death-rates may also be affected by the sex proportions of the populations considered, for at most ages and from most causes females suffer a lower mortality-rate than males. Standardisation, therefore, is sometimes made for both sex and age. The methods in general use will now be illustrated in detail.

## The Direct Method

In columns (2) and (3) of Table XXXI are given for males and females separately the Registrar-General's estimated populations for mid-1936 for (a) all the County

### TABLE XXXI

MORTALITY IN THE COUNTY BOROUGHS AND RURAL DISTRICTS OF ENGLAND AND WALES IN 1936 (EXCLUDING AREAS WITHIN GREATER LONDON)

#### COUNTY BOROUGHS

| Age-group | Estimated Population of County Boroughs in 1936 (to nearest hundred) | | Number of Deaths from all Causes in County Boroughs in 1936 | | Death-rates per 1000 in County Boroughs in 1936 | |
|---|---|---|---|---|---|---|
| | Males | Females | Males | Females | Males | Females |
| (1) | (2) | (3) | (4) | (5) | (6) | (7) |
| 0– | 461,000 | 447,300 | 10,101 | 7,704 | 21·9 | 17·2 |
| 5– | 998,400 | 988,900 | 1,916 | 1,691 | 1·9 | 1·7 |
| 15– | 1,011,600 | 1,071,100 | 2,706 | 2,674 | 2·7 | 2·5 |
| 25– | 1,030,700 | 1,104,800 | 3,271 | 3,193 | 3·2 | 2·9 |
| 35– | 845,500 | 980,300 | 4,689 | 4,269 | 5·5 | 4·4 |
| 45– | 727,900 | 864,300 | 9,265 | 7,241 | 12·7 | 8·4 |
| 55– | 590,900 | 680,800 | 16,504 | 12,317 | 27·9 | 18·1 |
| 65– | 313,100 | 396,200 | 20,030 | 18,867 | 64·0 | 47·6 |
| 75+ | 95,400 | 159,800 | 15,588 | 21,935 | 163·4 | 137·3 |
| All ages | 6,074,500 | 6,693,500 | 84,070 | 79,891 | 13·8 | 11·9 |
| All ages, both sexes | 12,768,000 | | 163,961 | | 12·8 | |

#### RURAL DISTRICTS

| Age-group | Estimated Population of Rural Districts in 1936 (to nearest hundred) | | Number of Deaths from all Causes in Rural Districts in 1936 | | Death-rates per 1000 in Rural Districts in 1936 | |
|---|---|---|---|---|---|---|
| | Males | Females | Males | Females | Males | Females |
| 0– | 255,900 | 246,000 | 4,308 | 3,180 | 16·8 | 12·9 |
| 5– | 598,100 | 575,600 | 861 | 745 | 1·4 | 1·3 |
| 15– | 595,000 | 517,200 | 1,452 | 1,100 | 2·4 | 2·1 |
| 25– | 587,400 | 566,400 | 1,683 | 1,571 | 2·9 | 2·8 |
| 35– | 481,500 | 529,400 | 2,023 | 1,929 | 4·2 | 3·6 |
| 45– | 422,300 | 470,100 | 3,608 | 3,396 | 8·5 | 7·2 |
| 55– | 366,800 | 398,200 | 7,222 | 5,918 | 19·7 | 14·9 |
| 65– | 243,300 | 259,900 | 11,498 | 10,162 | 47·3 | 39·1 |
| 75+ | 94,500 | 123,700 | 13,763 | 14,901 | 145·6 | 120·5 |
| All ages | 3,644,800 | 3,686,500 | 46,418 | 42,902 | 12·7 | 11·6 |
| All ages, both sexes | 7,331,300 | | 89,320 | | 12·2 | |

Boroughs and (*b*) all the Rural Districts of England and Wales (excluding in both instances any such areas falling within the radius defined as Greater London). The deaths that these populations experienced in 1936 are given in columns (4) and (5). Combining these two items of information leads to the death-rates of columns (6) and (7). In Fig. 16 the death-rates of the Rural Districts are plotted as

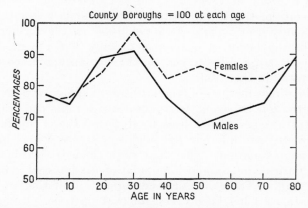

FIG. 16.—The death-rates in 1936 in the Rural Districts of England and Wales, at different ages, expressed as percentages of the corresponding death-rates in the County Boroughs (excluding in both groups areas within Greater London).

percentages of the rates in the County Boroughs and it is clear that the former group had an advantage at all ages and for both sexes, and usually a substantial advantage. Returning to Table XXXI two things will be observed. First, in both groups of areas and in every one of the age-groups the death-rate of females is less than the death-rate of males. Clearly the population that contains the greater number of females will benefit in its total death-rate. In fact, 52 per cent. of the population are females in the County Boroughs against 50 per cent. in the Rural Districts. Secondly, the death-rate is relatively high at ages 0–5 and rises steeply after age 55. The population that contains the smaller number of persons at these ages will thereby benefit in its total death-rate. In fact, both have 7 per cent. of their total population at ages 0–5 but in the County Boroughs only 17·6 per cent. of the population is of age 55 and over compared with 20·3 per cent. in the Rural Districts. Correspondingly, more of the population of the County Boroughs belongs to the age-groups 5–35, when the death-rate is relatively low, than is the case in the Rural Districts.

As a result of these age and sex differences the crude death-rate of the Rural Districts is very little below that of the County Boroughs — 12·2 per 1000 in the former and 12·8 in the latter, a difference of only 5 per cent. The relatively large advantages in the age-groups have been obliterated in the total.

The direct method of standardisation endeavours to meet this situation by seeing what total death-rates the two sets of rates at ages would lead to if they existed *not* in two populations of different age and sex constitution, but in *identical* populations. The first step, then, is the choice of the identical, or standard, population to be used. In the upper half of Table XXXII the population of England and Wales in 1901 has been taken for that purpose. By simple proportion it is an easy matter to determine the number of deaths that would occur in this population, first at the death-rates of the County Boroughs and then at the rates of the Rural Districts (as given in Table XXXI). For instance, in the County Boroughs in 1936, 21·9 per 1000 males died at ages 0–5 ; the number of males living at these ages in England and Wales in 1901 was 1,855,361 ; therefore the number of deaths that would occur in the standard population at the County Boroughs' rate is $\dfrac{1{,}855{,}361 \times 21 \cdot 9}{1000} = 40{,}632$ (column (4), Table XXXII). Proceeding in this way throughout the age-groups for both sexes it is found that at the rates of the County Boroughs the standard population would have experienced a total of 336,109 deaths, and at the rates of the Rural Districts a total of 269,047 deaths (columns (4), (5), (6), and (7)). As the standard population amounts in all to 32,527,843 persons (columns (2) and (3)), the rates of the County Boroughs would, therefore, lead to a rate at all ages

TABLE XXXII

STANDARDISATION OF THE MORTALITY IN THE COUNTY BOROUGHS
AND RURAL DISTRICTS OF ENGLAND AND WALES IN 1936.
DIRECT METHOD ON THE POPULATION OF ENGLAND AND
WALES IN (1) 1901, (2) 1931

| EXAMPLE (1) Age-group | Standard Population, England and Wales, 1901 | | Deaths that would occur in Standard Population at Mortality-rates of County Boroughs | | Deaths that would occur in Standard Population at Mortality-rates of Rural Districts | |
|---|---|---|---|---|---|---|
| | Males | Females | Males | Females | Males | Females |
| (1) | (2) | (3) | (4) | (5) | (6) | (7) |
| 0– | 1,855,361 | 1,861,347 | 40,632 | 32,015 | 31,170 | 24,011 |
| 5– | 3,409,963 | 3,419,068 | 6,479 | 5,812 | 4,774 | 4,445 |
| 15– | 3,080,166 | 3,286,899 | 8,316 | 8,217 | 7,392 | 6,902 |
| 25– | 2,485,954 | 2,769,886 | 7,955 | 8,033 | 7,209 | 7,756 |
| 35– | 1,931,943 | 2,064,062 | 10,626 | 9,082 | 8,114 | 7,431 |
| 45– | 1,396,209 | 1,505,982 | 17,732 | 12,650 | 11,868 | 10,843 |
| 55– | 907,945 | 1,035,305 | 25,332 | 18,739 | 17,887 | 15,426 |
| 65– | 477,868 | 598,138 | 30,584 | 28,471 | 22,603 | 23,387 |
| 75+ | 183,204 | 258,543 | 29,936 | 35,498 | 26,675 | 31,154 |
| All ages | 15,728,613 | 16,799,230 | 177,592 | 158,517 | 137,692 | 131,355 |
| All ages, both sexes | 32,527,843 | | 336,109 | | 269,047 | |
| Standardised death-rate per 1000 | .. | | 10·3 | | 8·3 | |

| EXAMPLE (2) Age-group | Standard Population, England and Wales, 1931 | | Deaths that would occur in Standard Population at Mortality-rates of County Boroughs | | Deaths that would occur in Standard Population at Mortality-rates of Rural Districts | |
|---|---|---|---|---|---|---|
| | Males | Females | Males | Females | Males | Females |
| 0– | 1,510,214 | 1,480,083 | 33,074 | 25,457 | 25,372 | 19,093 |
| 5– | 3,298,276 | 3,231,625 | 6,267 | 5,494 | 4,618 | 4,201 |
| 15– | 3,408,653 | 3,520,335 | 9,203 | 8,801 | 8,181 | 7,393 |
| 25– | 3,062,282 | 3,350,104 | 9,799 | 9,715 | 8,881 | 9,380 |
| 35– | 2,512,356 | 2,954,236 | 13,818 | 12,999 | 10,552 | 10,635 |
| 45– | 2,302,873 | 2,632,703 | 29,246 | 22,115 | 19,574 | 18,955 |
| 55– | 1,765,509 | 1,959,919 | 49,258 | 35,475 | 34,781 | 29,203 |
| 65– | 954,450 | 1,186,971 | 61,085 | 56,500 | 45,145 | 46,411 |
| 75+ | 318,397 | 503,391 | 52,026 | 69,116 | 46,359 | 60,659 |
| All ages | 19,133,010 | 20,819,367 | 263,776 | 245,672 | 203,463 | 205,930 |
| All ages, both sexes | 39,952,377 | | 509,448 | | 409,393 | |
| Standardised death-rate per 1000 | .. | | 12·8 | | 10·2 | |

in this standard population of $(336,109 \div 32,527,843) \times 1000$
$= 10 \cdot 3$ per 1000. Similarly the rates of the Rural Districts
would lead to a rate at all ages of $(269,047 \div 32,527,843) \times$
$1000 = 8 \cdot 3$ per 1000. These are the two standardised death-
rates, using the 1901 population as standard.

## The Choice of the Standard Population

It will be noted, however, that different standardised
rates must result if a different population is chosen as the
standard. For instance, in the lower half of Table XXXII
the population of England and Wales in 1931 has been used
and the two standardised rates on that basis are 12·8 and
10·2 per 1000 in place of the previous 1·03 and 8·3. In
consequence the question that immediately arises is what
standard population ought to be adopted. The standardised
death-rate is, it will be realised, a fiction. It is not the total
death-rate that actually exists in an area but the rate that
the area would have if, while retaining its own rates at ages,
it had instead of its real population one of some particular
chosen type. The fiction is useful because, as already seen,
it enables summary comparisons to be made between places
or between epochs, and these comparisons are free from the
distortion which arises from age and sex differences in the
existing populations. The object throughout is, therefore,
*comparison* ; a standardised death-rate alone has no meaning. Accordingly it does not really matter if by the use of a
different standard population the standardised death-rates
of the areas under study are changed, *so long as their relative
position is not changed materially*. In the example of Tables
XXXI and XXXII it is seen that the crude rate of the
Rural Districts is 95 per cent. of the crude rate of the County
Boroughs, a very poor expression of the differences at ages
revealed in Fig. 16. Using the 1901 population of England
and Wales, the standardised rates are 10·3 in the County
Boroughs and 8·3 in the Rural Districts. The latter is 81
per cent. of the former, a very much better expression of
the differences at ages. Changing to the 1931 population of
England and Wales changes the standardised rates to 12·8 in

the County Boroughs and 10·2 in the Rural Districts. The latter is 80 per cent. of the former, so that *relative* position in this example is practically unchanged by the alteration in the standard.

In practice, the comparative position between the standardised rates of two areas, or between two points of time, will not, when the standard population is changed, invariably be as close as is given in this example, and sometimes, indeed, serious differences can result, though probably not very frequently.

## The Equivalent Average Death-rate

In the particular example used above, the same *relative* answer is reached if merely the arithmetic average is taken of the 18 death-rates at ages in each of the two groups of areas. Adding the death-rates in the County Boroughs (21·9 + 1·9 + 2·7, etc.) gives a total of 543·3 and, dividing by 18, the number of rates contributing to the total, an average rate of 30·2 per 1000. In the Rural Districts the total is 453·2 and the average 25·2. The latter is 83 per cent. of the former, so again no material change has taken place in the relative position. This method, in effect, it will be noted, adopts a standard population with an equal number of persons in every age-group. It is not to be commended, for such a population, in fact, never exists, and it is hardly justifiable to attach equal importance to the high death-rates in old age, at which relatively few people survive, and to the lower death-rates at other ages, at which many persons exist. The method may, however, be used effectively over a more restricted span of life and has been adopted by the Registrar-General of England and Wales for some comparisons at ages 0–64. His procedure is to calculate the arithmetic mean of the rates at quinquennial groups of ages, *i.e.* at 0–4, 5–9, 10–14, up to 60–64. If rates at all the quinquennial age-groups are not available, twice the rate for the decennial group can be substituted without appreciable error (two, of course, being added to the denominator in working the average). The resulting figure, being equivalent to calculating a standardised death-rate at ages under 65 based upon a population equally distributed over the 13 age-groups, is called the *Equivalent average death-rate*. The information given by it needs to be supplemented by rates at 65–75 and 75 and over to give a fairly complete picture of mortality (R.-G.'s *Statistical Review for 1934*, Text, pp. 2-3).

## The Direct Method Applied to a Specific Cause of Death

A further example of the direct method of standardisation is given in Table XXXIII, where a comparison is made

### TABLE XXXIII

MORTALITY FROM CANCER OF THE UTERUS IN ENGLAND AND WALES IN (1) 1911–20 AND (2) 1931–35. STANDARDISATION BY THE DIRECT METHOD

| Age-group | Death-rates from Cancer of the Uterus per Million Females | | Standard Population: England and Wales, Persons 1901 | Deaths that would occur in Standard Population at Rates of | | Standard Population: England and Wales, Females 1931 | Deaths that would occur in Standard Population at Rates of | |
|---|---|---|---|---|---|---|---|---|
| | 1911–20 | 1931–35 | | 1911–20 | 1931–35 | | 1911–20 | 1931–35 |
| (1) | (2) | (3) | (4) | (5) | (6) | (7) | (8) | (9) |
| 0– | 1 | 1 | 16,912,804 | 17 | 17 | 8,232,043 | 8 | 8 |
| 25– | 37 | 27 | 5,255,840 | 194 | 142 | 3,350,104 | 124 | 90 |
| 35– | 225 | 176 | 3,996,005 | 899 | 703 | 2,954,236 | 665 | 520 |
| 45– | 574 | 426 | 2,902,191 | 1666 | 1236 | 2,632,703 | 1511 | 1122 |
| 55– | 817 | 602 | 1,943,250 | 1588 | 1170 | 1,959,919 | 1601 | 1180 |
| 65– | 890 | 771 | 1,076,006 | 958 | 830 | 1,186,971 | 1056 | 915 |
| 75– | 832 | 804 | 393,248 | 327 | 316 | 437,872 | 364 | 352 |
| 85+ | 572 | 584 | 48,499 | 28 | 28 | 65,519 | 37 | 38 |
| All ages | 209 | 209 | 32,527,843 | 5677 | 4442 | 20,819,367 | 5366 | 4225 |
| Standardised rate | } .. | .. | .. | 175 | 137 | .. | 258 | 203 |

between the mortality-rates from cancer of the uterus experienced in England and Wales in 1911–20 and 1931–35. The rates at ages in these two periods are given in columns (2) and (3) and it will be seen that between ages 25 and 85 the mortality-rates are lower in 1931–35 than in 1911–20. Only at ages 85 and over has there been a slight rise. The two crude rates are, however, identical. The ageing of the female population conceals in this rate the real improvement in mortality that has taken place throughout nearly the whole of life. In columns (5) and (6) the rates are standardised against the population of persons in England and Wales in 1901 (given in column (4)). The resulting standardised rates are 175 per million in 1911–20 and 137 in 1931–35. In other words, the rate of mortality at all ages, when the change in age-distribution is allowed for, shows a decline of 22 per cent. (*i.e.* 175–137 as a percentage of 175).

In columns (8) and (9) the same rates are standardised against the female population of England and Wales in 1931 (column 7). The resulting standardised rates are much higher, namely 258 and 203 per million, but the relative decline is 21 per cent. so that to all intents and purposes both standard populations give the same answer.

## The Comparative Mortality Index

For students of the reports of the Registrar-General of England and Wales a brief reference may be made to a special form of direct standardisation used by him between the years 1941 and 1958. Taking 1938 as a base year he proceeded to compare the mortality experience of each subsequent (or previous) year with that of 1938. The best standard population for each such comparison was, he concluded, the arithmetic mean of the proportionate age distributions of the populations of 1938 and each year in question (not the mean of the absolute numbers in the age-groups but of the *proportions* of the total population in the age-groups). To this specially constructed standard population he then applied the observed death-rates at ages in (1) 1938 and (2) in the year in question, in the ordinary way. From the expected deaths thus reached the two standardised death-rates could at once be calculated. But since the whole object of the procedure is their *relative* magnitude, it was decided to convert them immediately into an index. Thus the total deaths expected at the rates of the year under study can be expressed as a ratio to the deaths expected at the rates of 1938. For instance, comparison of 1932 with the base year 1938 gave 11·161 deaths (per 1000 of the standard population) in 1938 and 12·484 in 1932 : the *comparative mortality index* is, therefore, $12·484/11·161 = 1·119$. Similarly the index for 1952 can be calculated to be 0·806. In other words, standardised for age and sex, mortality in 1932 was about 12 per cent. above that of 1938 while mortality in 1952 was 20 per cent. below.

All these indices relate, it will be observed, to a comparison of one given year, 1938. To compare two given years one with another one ought, on a strict application of this technique, to use the mean proportional population of those two years as the standard. Such a comparison could, however, be made with sufficient accuracy, it was concluded, by using the ratio of the two comparative mortality indices based on 1938. Thus, as shown above, the index for 1932 was 1·119 and for 1952 it was 0·806. The mortality ratio of 1952 to 1932 could then be computed as 0·806/1·119, or 0·72. In other words, allowing for changes in the age and sex constitution of the population, mortality fell by about one-quarter during these 20 years. An objection to the method is that it uses not a fixed standard population but a constantly varying one and the precision of these mortality ratios can, therefore, be questioned.

### The Indirect Method

The direct method of standardisation requires, it has been seen, a knowledge for each age-group of (1) the numbers of persons, and (2) the number of deaths in the population for which a standardised death-rate is needed. Sometimes all that information is not available, or sometimes the populations at the different ages are so small that the death-rates are subject to large fluctuations through the presence or absence of merely a few deaths. In such instances the indirect method can be applied. The first step in this method is the selection of a series of standard death-rates at ages. In Table XXXIV the rates in England and Wales in 1901–10 have been chosen (columns (4) and (5)). These rates are then applied (by simple proportion) to the population at ages in the area the standardised rate of which is sought, to determine what deaths would have occurred in that area if it had had the standard rates. For example, column (2) shows that in the County Boroughs there were 461,000 males at ages 0–5. The death-rate of males of these ages in England and Wales in 1901–10 was 50 per 1000. Therefore, at this rate, there would have been $\dfrac{461,000 \times 50}{1000}$ deaths $= 23,050$ in the County Boroughs. This procedure is carried out for each age-group for each sex and the deaths expected at the standard rates are totalled. It is thus found that if these standard rates had been operative in both groups of areas there would have been 216,950 deaths in the County Boroughs and 139,949 in the Rural Districts, or rates of mortality at all ages of 16·99 and 19·09 per 1000 inhabitants (dividing the " expected " deaths by the total populations of the two sets of areas). These rates are called the *index death-rates*, for their level is an index of the type of population from which they have been derived. For instance, if the population contains a large proportion of old persons its index death-rate will be greater than that of a population composed more of young persons. In the particular example taken, the index rates show, in fact, that the rural population is of a type to produce, under standard conditions of mortality, a higher death-rate at all ages than the urban population. In other words, their crude rates cannot be safely compared, and some adjustment of them is necessary to allow for the difference in population type revealed by their index rates.

The adjustment consists of increasing or diminishing the recorded crude mortality-rate to compensate for the advantage or disadvantage disclosed by the index rate ; the next step, therefore, is to determine how much compensation must be made in each case. The standard rates of 1901–10 are, of course, derived from the deaths and the mean population in England and Wales in those years, and with that type of population they lead to a total death-rate of 15·36 per 1000. If the populations of the County Boroughs and Rural Districts in 1936 had also been of exactly that type then their index death-rates would naturally have come out as 15·36 as well. In that case no correction to their crude rates would be necessary, for under standard conditions of mortality their populations give the same total death-rates as that which exists in the standard population. But, in fact, their index death-rates have come out to be 16·99 and 19·09, and therefore under the selected standard conditions of mortality both areas have populations which lead to too

TABLE XXXIV

STANDARDISATION OF THE MORTALITY IN THE COUNTY BOROUGHS AND RURAL DISTRICTS OF ENGLAND AND WALES IN 1936.  INDIRECT METHOD WITH DEATH-RATES OF ENGLAND AND WALES IN 1901–10 AS STANDARD RATES

| Age-group | Estimated Population of County Boroughs in 1936 (to nearest hundred) | | Standard Death-rates per 1000, England and Wales, 1901–10 | | Number of Deaths that would occur in County Boroughs at Standard Rates | |
|---|---|---|---|---|---|---|
| | Males | Females | Males | Females | Males | Females |
| (1) | (2) | (3) | (4) | (5) | (6) | (7) |
| 0– | 461,000 | 447,300 | 50·0 | 41·9 | 23,050 | 18,742 |
| 5– | 998,400 | 988,900 | 2·8 | 2·9 | 2,796 | 2,868 |
| 15– | 1,011,600 | 1,071,100 | 3·6 | 3·2 | 3,642 | 3,428 |
| 25– | 1,030,700 | 1,104,800 | 5·6 | 4·7 | 5,772 | 5,193 |
| 35– | 845,500 | 980,300 | 9·2 | 7·5 | 7,779 | 7,352 |
| 45– | 727,900 | 864,300 | 16·2 | 12·5 | 11,792 | 10,804 |
| 55– | 590,900 | 680,800 | 31·8 | 24·9 | 18,791 | 16,952 |
| 65– | 313,100 | 396,200 | 64·9 | 53·9 | 20,320 | 21,355 |
| 75+ | 95,400 | 159,800 | 152·5 | 136·2 | 14,549 | 21,765 |
| All ages | 6,074,500 | 6,693,500 | .. | .. | 108,491 | 108,459 |
| All ages, both sexes | } 12,768,000 | | 15·36 | | 216,950 | |

| Age-group | Estimated Population of Rural Districts in 1936 (to nearest hundred) | | Standard Death-rates per 1000, England and Wales, 1901–10 | | Number of Deaths that would occur in Rural Districts at Standard Rates | |
|---|---|---|---|---|---|---|
| | Males | Females | Males | Females | Males | Females |
| 0– | 255,900 | 246,000 | 50·0 | 41·9 | 12,795 | 10,307 |
| 5– | 598,100 | 575,600 | 2·8 | 2·9 | 1,675 | 1,669 |
| 15– | 595,000 | 517,200 | 3·6 | 3·2 | 2,142 | 1,655 |
| 25– | 587,400 | 566,400 | 5·6 | 4·7 | 3,289 | 2,662 |
| 35– | 481,500 | 529,400 | 9·2 | 7·5 | 4,430 | 3,971 |
| 45– | 422,300 | 470,100 | 16·2 | 12·5 | 6,841 | 5,876 |
| 55– | 366,800 | 389,200 | 31·8 | 24·9 | 11,664 | 9,915 |
| 65– | 243,300 | 259,900 | 64·9 | 53·9 | 15,790 | 14,009 |
| 75+ | 94,500 | 123,700 | 152·5 | 136·2 | 14,411 | 16,848 |
| All ages | 3,644,800 | 3,686,500 | .. | .. | 73,037 | 66,912 |
| All ages, both sexes | } 7,331,300 | | 15·36 | | 139,949 | |

high a death-rate. To allow for this the crude rates of each must be lowered. The precise degree to which they must be lowered is measured by the ratio of the death-rate at all ages in the standard to the index rates in the areas, namely 15·36/16·99 and 15·36/19·09.

The basis of those ratios can be seen more clearly in a simpler example. Suppose the death-rate at all ages in the selected standard is 12 per 1000 and the index death-rate of the area for which standardisation is required is found to be 15. Then 12 units in this index rate are what would be expected in a standard population exposed to standard rates at ages, and 3 units must be due to the peculiar age- and sex-distribution of the population of the area. In other words, one-fifth of the rate in the area is due to its age- and sex-distribution, and to allow for this its crude rate must be reduced by one-fifth. If, on the other hand, the index rate was found to be 9, then the population of the area is of a type to lead to a total mortality 3 units, or one-third, *below* the standard rate of 12. To allow for that its crude mortality-rate must therefore be increased by one-third.

In short, we find by means of the index rates what kind of populations exists in different areas—favourable or un-favourable to mortality—and then apply a " handicap " to each crude rate to compensate for the advantage or dis-advantage disclosed. These handicaps are known as the *standardising factors*. The factor in the County Boroughs is, accordingly, 15·36/16·99 = 0·9041, and in the Rural Districts 15·36/19·09 = 0·8046. The crude death-rate of the County Boroughs is 12·8 and of the Rural Districts 12·2, and there-fore, applying to them their respective factors, the standard-ised rates are 12·8 × 0·9041 = 11·6 and 12·2 × 0·8046 = 9·8. According to this result the rural mortality is 84 per cent. of the urban.

## The Choice of the Standard Rates

As with the direct method, the standardised rates will depend in part upon the standard rates that are used, and the question arises whether their relative positions will be materially changed by the change in the standard. For

P

instance, in England and Wales in 1936 both the death-rate at all ages (12·1 per 1000) and the death-rates at different ages were substantially below the rates prevailing in 1901–10. If, now, they be used in place of the latter as the standard rates in Table XXXIV the following results are reached :—

|  | County Boroughs | Rural Districts |
|---|---|---|
| Index death-rate . . . | 11·50 | 13·53 |
| Standardising factor . . . | 1·0522 | 0·8943 |
| Standardised rate . . . | 13·5 | 10·9 |

It will be seen that in comparison with this standard the population of the County Boroughs favours a relatively low death-rate and its handicap is therefore now greater than one. The population of the Rural Districts continues to favour rather a high death-rate and its handicap remains less than one. The standardised rates are both higher than those reached on the basis of the rates in 1901–10 but their ratio is very little changed. The mortality in the Rural Districts is, in fact, 81 per cent. of that in the County Boroughs. However, such equality in results will not always occur.

### Other Aspects of the Indirect Method

One advantage of the indirect method is that if we have calculated the standardising factor for a particular population as registered in the census year, then we can continue to apply that factor to its annual crude death-rate so long as we have reason to suppose that the age- and sex-distribution of its population has remained unchanged. The method then involves merely the multiplication of the crude rate by the factor already determined, and is particularly rapid. The continued use of the factor is, of course, unjustified if the population type is changing, e.g. by migration inwards or outwards.

It will also be observed that if different causes of death are being studied, then a standardising factor must be calculated specifically for each cause. For example, if an area has a population which favours a relatively high death-rate from cancer then its population is of an old-age type, for it is at these old ages that cancer mainly prevails. Its factor for cancer will be less than one to allow for its *unfavourable* population in this respect. On the other hand, this type of population will favour a relatively low death-rate from diphtheria, for that cause of death mainly prevails in childhood. Its factor for diphtheria must therefore be greater than one to allow for its *favourable* population in this respect.

## The Standardised Mortality Ratio

In some circumstances it will be possible, with the indirect method, to dispense with the fictitious standardised rates and to proceed immediately to some comparative index. Thus using as standard rates the mortality by sex and age in England and Wales in 1961 we might calculate the number of deaths that would have occurred at these rates in the population of the country as it was constituted 50 years ago. The expected total number of deaths we would compare immediately with the number that actually occurred to give an index of the change in mortality that has taken place, while allowing for the concurrent changes that have occurred in the sex and age distribution of the population. Thus we have a *standardised mortality ratio* (or S.M.R.) to express the rise or fall in mortality. Similarly the rates for all England and Wales in 1961 could be applied to the population of a particular area of the country, *e.g.* London. The number of deaths expected at these rates can be immediately compared with the number that actually occurred in London, in 1961, to give, again, an easily understood standardised mortality ratio of observation to expectation.

This index has been used extensively in the study of occupational mortality.

Here the Registrar-General takes the mortality-rates of all males as the standard rates. Applying these to the population of a particular occupational group, he finds the number of deaths that would have occurred in that group if it had had the standard rates. These expected deaths he compares with the observed deaths, expressing the latter as a percentage of the former. For instance, in 1930–32 the number of deaths from all causes of farmers and their relatives (males) was 5693 at ages 20–65. If they had experienced the death-rates of all males in those years they would have had 7803 deaths. This group, therefore, experienced 73 per cent. of their expected mortality at the standard

TABLE XXXV

CALCULATION OF THE STANDARDISED MORTALITY RATIO

| Age-group | Death-rates of All Males per 1000 | Census Population of Farmers | Expected Deaths of Farmers in 1930, 1931, and 1932 at Rates of All Males* | Observed Deaths of Farmers in 1930, 1931, and 1932 |
|---|---|---|---|---|
| (1) | (2) | (3) | (4) | (5) |
| 20– | 3·284 | 23,399 | 230 | 162 |
| 25– | 3·461 | 53,761 | 558 | 404 |
| 35– | 5·589 | 58,296 | 977 | 637 |
| 45– | 11·141 | 61,115 | 2043 | 1453 |
| 55–65 | 23·552 | 56,536 | 3995 | 3037 |
| Total . | .. | .. | 7803 | 5693 |
| Standardised mortality ratio | .. | .. | .. | 5693 ÷ 7803 = 73 per cent. |

* Death-rate of all males applied to the census population of farmers to give the expected annual deaths and multiplied by 3 to give the expected deaths for 3 years.

rates, differences in age-distribution having been allowed for. On the other hand, the observed deaths amongst dockers were 137 per cent. of their expected mortality at the standard rates. The procedure is demonstrated in detail for farmers in Table XXXV.

The underlying reasons for observed differences between occupations is, of course, another matter, outside the scope of this chapter. They may be related, it may be said in short, to such features as specific occupational hazards or absence of hazards, the general living conditions consequent upon an occupation (through, for example, low or high rates of pay), and—of considerable importance—selective factors influencing the entry of the physically fit or unfit to a particular occupation and leading also to the withdrawal from it of the fit or unfit to take up some other occupation.

## Summary

Rates of mortality and morbidity are usually affected considerably by the age, and to a slighter extent by the sex, constitution of the populations concerned.  The comparison of crude rates at all ages is therefore likely to be misleading as a measure of the mortality, or morbidity, experiences prevailing in relation to such features as the sanitary environment.  Some form of average of the death-rates at ages is required which allows for the fact that populations differ in their structure.  This average is customarily reached by a process of standardisation, a process which leads to a weighted average and thereby to more comparable indices. But it should be remembered that a standardised rate, or index, *is* only an *average*.  The basic death-rates at ages which contribute to it are likely to be very much more informative than any single summary figure that can be derived from them.

(*For exercises see pp. 320-321*)

# LIFE TABLES AND SURVIVAL AFTER TREATMENT

IN the assessment of the degree of success attending a particular treatment given to patients over a series of years the life-table method is sometimes an effective procedure. Before illustrating its application to such data, consideration of the national (and local) life tables and their use in public health work will be of value. A life table, it must be realised, is only a particular way of expressing the death-rates experienced by some particular population during a chosen period of time. For instance, the English Life Table, No. 11, was based upon the mortality of the population of England and Wales in the three years 1950–52. It contains six columns as shown in the following extract from it :—

ENGLISH LIFE TABLE. NO. 11. MALES

| Age $x$ | $l_x$ | $d_x$ | $p_x$ | $q_x$ | $\overset{o}{e}_x$ |
|---|---|---|---|---|---|
| 0 | 100,000 | 3266 | ·96734 | ·03266 | 66·42 |
| 1 | 96,734 | 233 | ·99759 | ·00241 | 67·66 |
| 2 | 96,501 | 136 | ·99859 | ·00141 | 66·82 |
| 3 | 96,365 | 98 | ·99898 | ·00102 | 65·91 |
| 4 | 96,267 | .. | .. | .. | .. |
| .. | .. | .. | .. | .. | .. |
| .. | .. | .. | .. | .. | .. |
| .. | .. | .. | .. | .. | .. |
| .. | .. | .. | .. | .. | .. |
| 102 | 7 | 3 | ·53989 | ·46011 | 1·58 |
| 103 | 4 | 2 | ·53136 | ·46864 | 1·53 |
| 104 | 2 | 1 | ·52364 | ·47636 | 1·50 |

The essence of the table is this : suppose we observed 100,000 infants all born on the same day and dying as they passed through each year of life at the same rate as was experienced at each of these ages by the population of

England and Wales in 1950–52, in what gradation would that population disappear ? How many would be still left alive at age 25, at age 56, etc. ? How many would die between age 20 and age 30 ? What would be the chance of an individual surviving from age 40 to age 45 ? What would be the average length of life enjoyed by the 100,000 infants ? Such information can be obtained from these different columns. The basis of the table is the value known as $q_x$, which is the probability, or chance, of dying between age $x$ and age $x + 1$, where $x$ can have any value between 0 and the longest observed duration of life. For instance, $q_{25}$ is the chance that a person who has reached a twenty-fifth birthday will die before reaching the twenty-sixth birthday. These probabilities, one for each year of age, are calculated from the mortality-rates experienced by the population in 1950–52. This probability of dying is the ratio of those who fail to survive a particular year of life to those who started that year of life (to take an analogy, if 20 horses start in the Grand National steeplechase and 5 fail to survive the first round of the course the probability of " dying " on that round is 5/20 ; 15 horses are left to start on the second round and if 3 fail to survive, the probability of " dying " on the second round is 3/15).

## The Probability of Dying

As pointed out above, the basic element of the life table is the probability of dying between one age and the next. Once those values are known throughout life the construction of the remainder of the table is a simple, though arithmetically laborious, process. To calculate these probabilities requires a knowledge, for the population concerned, of the numbers living and dying in each single year of life. Let us suppose that such detailed data are available and, to make it specific, that in the County Borough of A there were 1500 persons enumerated (or estimated) at the middle of the year 1946 whose age was 22 years last birthday, *i.e.* their age was between 22 and 23. During the calendar year there were, say, 12 deaths between ages 22 and 23. Then the *death-rate* at ages 22–23, as customarily calculated, is the ratio of the deaths observed to the mid-year population, *i.e.* 12 in 1500, which equals 8 per 1000, or 0·008 per person. In symbols $m_x = D \div P$, which gives the death-rate per person. This mid-year population does not indicate precisely how many persons *started* the year of life 22 to 23, as it is an enumeration of those who were *still alive* at the middle of the calendar year. On the average they were at that point of time $22\frac{1}{2}$ years old, since some would have just passed their 22nd birthday, some would be just on the point of having their 23rd birthday, and all intermediate values would be represented. If we may reasonably presume that the deaths occurring between ages 22 and 23 are evenly spread over that year of life, then we may conclude that half of them would have occurred before the mid-year enumeration (or estimation) and half would have occurred after it. In other words, the population that *started* out from age 22 is the 1500 survivors plus a half the recorded deaths, or 1500 + 6, this half of the deaths being presumed to have taken place before the mid-year point. The *probability of dying* is, by definition, the ratio of the deaths observed in a year of life to the number who set out on that year of life, *i.e.* 12 in 1506. In symbols, therefore, $q_x = D \div (P + \frac{1}{2}D)$.

If, then, we know the mid-year population at each age and the deaths taking place between each age and the next, the probabilities of dying can be readily calculated from this formula. (It is, however, not very accurate in the first 2 or 3 years of life and particularly in the first year. In the first year the deaths fall more frequently in the first 6 months of life than in the second 6 months and a more appropriate is fraction $D \div (P + \frac{7}{10}D)$.)

It is clear that there must be a simple relationship between $m_x$, the death-rate, and $q_x$, the probability of dying. It may be demonstrated as follows :—

$$m_x = \frac{D}{P}, \text{ so that } Pm_x = D.$$

$$q_x = \frac{D}{P + \frac{1}{2}D}. \text{ Substituting } Pm_x \text{ for } D \text{ gives } q_x = \frac{Pm_x}{P + \frac{1}{2}Pm_x}.$$

But $P$ occurs in both numerator and denominator, so it may be ermoved to give $q_x = \dfrac{m_x}{1 + \frac{1}{2}m_x}$ ; and, finally multiplying top and bottom by 2 to get rid of the half, gives $q_x = \dfrac{2m_x}{2 + m_x}$.

In other words, the probability of dying may be calculated from the formula (twice the death-rate) ÷ (the death-rate plus 2), where the death-rate is calculated not as usual per 1000 persons but as per person ; or from the formula (deaths) ÷ (population plus half the deaths).

### The Construction of the Life Table

Having thus calculated, by one or other formula, these values of $q_x$ for each year of life, the life table is started with an arbitrary number at age 0, e.g. 1000, 100,000, or 1,000,000. By relating the probability of a new-born infant dying before its first birthday ($q_0$) to this starting number, we find the number who will die in the first year of life. By subtracting these deaths from the starters we have the number of survivors that there will be at age 1. But for these survivors at age 1 we similarly know the probability of dying between age 1 and age 2 ; by relating this probability to the survivors we can calculate how many deaths there will be between age 1 and age 2. By simple subtraction of these deaths we must reach the survivors at age 2. And so on throughout the table till all are dead. Thus the figures on p. 220 show that for males in English Life Table No. 11 the probability of dying in the first year of life is 0·03266, or in other words, according to the infant mortality-rate of 1950–52, 3·266 per cent. of our 100,000 infants will die before they reach their first birthday. The actual number of deaths between age 0 and age 1 will therefore be 3·266 per cent. of 100,000, or 3266. Those who *survive* to age 1 must be 100,000 less 3266 = 96,734. According to this table, the probability of dying between age 1 and age 2 is 0·00241, or in other words 0·241 per cent. of these 96,734 children aged 1 year old will die before reaching their second birthday. The actual number of deaths between age 1 and age 2 will therefore be 0·241 per cent. of 96,734 = 233 ; those who survive to age 2 must therefore be 96,734 less 233 = 96,501. From these $q_x$ values the $l_x$ and $d_x$ columns can thus be easily constructed, $l_x$ showing the number of individuals out of the original 100,000 who are still alive at each age, and $d_x$ giving the number of deaths that take place between each two adjacent ages. $p_x$ is the probability of living from one age to the next. $p_x + q_x$ must equal 1, since the individuals must either live or die in that year of life (to return to our analogy if 5 out of 20 horses do not complete the round, clearly 15 out of 20 do survive the round). $p_x$, therefore, equals $1 - q_x$ ; for example, of the 96,501 children aged 2, 0·141 per cent. die before reaching age 3, and it follows that 99·859 per cent. must live to be 3 years old.

Finally, we have the column headed $\overset{\circ}{e}_x$ which is the " expectation of life " at each age. This value is not, in a sense, an " expectation " at all, for it is the *average* duration of life lived beyond each age. For example, if we added up all the ages at death of the 100,000 male infants and took the average of these durations of life we should reach the figure 66·42 years. If, alternatively, we took the 96,734 infants who had lived to be 1 year old, calculated the *further* duration of life that they enjoyed, and then found the average of those durations, we should reach the figure 67·66 years. At age 102 there are only 7 persons still surviving, and the average duration of life that they will enjoy after that age is only 1·58 years. The so-called expectation of life is thus only the average length of life experienced after each age. We thus have the complete life table.

## Calculation of the Expectation of Life

The expectation of life, or average length of life given by a life table, can be calculated from the column of deaths $(d_x)$ or from the column of survivors $(l_x)$. Using the former, we have an ordinary frequency distribution. Thus of the males in English Life Table No. 11 there were 3266 who died between age 0 and 1. We may presume they lived on the average half a year (some exaggeration, in fact). Their contribution to the total years lived by the original 100,000 is therefore $(3266 \times \frac{1}{2})$. Between ages 1 and 2 there were 233 deaths, and we may presume for these that the average length of life was $1\frac{1}{2}$ years. Their contribution to the total years lived by the original 100,000 is therefore $(233 \times 1\frac{1}{2})$. Between ages 2 and 3 there were 136 deaths, and we may presume for these that the average length of life was $2\frac{1}{2}$ years. Their contribution to the total years lived by the original 100,000 is therefore $(136 \times 2\frac{1}{2})$. And so on until at the far end of the table we reach 3 deaths between ages 102 and 103. Presuming their average length of life was $102\frac{1}{2}$, they contribute to the total years $(3 \times 102\frac{1}{2})$. Proceeding to the final point, we then have the total years of life lived by the whole population of 100,000 :—

$$(3266 \times \tfrac{1}{2}) + (233 \times 1\tfrac{1}{2}) + (136 \times 2\tfrac{1}{2}) + \dots + (3 \times 102\tfrac{1}{2})$$
$$+ (2 \times 103\tfrac{1}{2}) + (1 \times 104\tfrac{1}{2}).$$

The expectation of life is the mean number of years lived, and so this sum is divided by the 100,000 persons starting at age 0 to whom it relates. In short, $\overset{\circ}{e}_x$ at birth equals the sum of all values of $d_x \times (x + \frac{1}{2})$ divided by 100,000, and in this table for males is, as previously stated, 66·42 years.

Using the survivor column $(l_x)$, we may proceed as follows. The 96,734 survivors at age 1 have all lived a whole year of life, between age 0 and age 1. They give a contribution therefore of 96,734 whole years of life to the total years lived. But the survivors at age 2, who were 96,501 in number, have all lived another whole year of life—from age 1 to age 2. They therefore give a further 96,501 whole years of life to the total years lived. Similarly the survivors at age 3, who are 96,365, are contributing that extra number of whole years of life lived. Thus by summing the $l_x$ column from age 1 to the final entry we have the number of whole years of life lived by the 100,000 (clearly the 100,000 must not be included in the sum, for they are the starters at 0 and at that point have lived no duration). 

There is, however, a small error involved if we stop at that sum. In it we have made no allowance for the period each person lives in the year of his, or her, death. We have considered only the survivors at ages 1, 2, 3, etc. But we may presume that the 3266 who died between 0 and 1 had half a year's life before their death, that the 233 who died between 1 and 2 also had half a year's life in the year 1–2 in which they died, that the 136 who died between 2 and 3 also had half a year's life in the year 2–3 in which they died (it will be noted that their whole years of life up to age 2 have already been counted in the survivorship column and it is only the half-year in the year in which they died that has been omitted). We must therefore add to the sum of whole years lived, derived from the $l_x$ column, these half-years lived by those dying in the precise year in which they died. In other words, we have to add in $(3266 \times \frac{1}{2}) + (233 \times \frac{1}{2}) + (136 \times \frac{1}{2}) + \ldots$ to the end of the table. But this implies, as everyone is dead by the end of the table, adding in $(100,000 \times \frac{1}{2})$. The final sum of years required is, therefore, given by the sum of the $l_x$ column from 1 to the end of the table plus 100,000 times a half. The average, or expectation of life, is then this sum divided by the 100,000 at the start, which may be expressed as

$$\frac{\text{Sum of } l_x \text{ column (excluding } l_0)}{100,000} + \frac{1}{2}.$$

As stated previously, the expectation of life at a later age than 0, say age 25, is the average length of life lived beyond that age by the survivors at age 25. It can be calculated by either of the above methods (the use of the $l_x$ column being the simpler), the sum of years lived relating only to the entries beyond age 25, and the denominator, to give the average, being, of course, the survivors at age 25.

### Practical Aspects of the Life Table

In using the life table as a method of comparison of the mortality experience between place and place or epoch and epoch various values may be chosen. For example, we may take—

(a) The probability of dying between any two selected ages (the ratio of the total deaths between the two ages to the number alive at the first age).

(b) The number of survivors at any given age out of those starting at age 0 (the $l_x$ column).

(c) The probability of surviving from one age to another (the ratio of the survivors at a given age to the survivors at a previous age).

(d) The expectation of life (which suffers from the limitation inherent in any average that it takes no cognisance of the variability around it).

In practice, however, it is not often possible to construct a life table by the methods described above since they require, it was seen, a knowledge of the population and deaths in single years of life. More often than not the numbers available relate to 5- or 10-yearly age-groups, and some device has then to be adopted for estimating from these grouped data the appropriate numbers at single years of life. Alternatively there are available for public-health work excellent short methods of making a life table from the actual death-rates observed in different age-groups. To describe these methods fully is outside the scope of this chapter, the object of which has been not to show how best to construct a life table in practice, but to clarify the general principles underlying its construction so that the values given by it may be understood. Taking the example given above, it shows, to reiterate, how a population would die out if it experienced as it passed through life the same death-rates as were prevailing in England and Wales in 1950–52. It does not follow, therefore, that of 100,000 male children born in those years in reality only 96,365 would be alive at age 3 ; if the death-rate were, in fact, declining below its 1950–52 level, then more than that number would survive ; if it were rising, less than that number would survive. The life table can show only what would happen under *current conditions of mortality*, but it puts those current conditions in a useful form for various comparative purposes and for estimating such things as life insurance risks (inherent in the questions that were propounded above).

### The Measurement of Survival-rates after Treatment

We turn now to the application of the method to groups
of patients treated over a period of calendar years whose
subsequent after-history is known. Let us suppose that
treatment was started in 1954, that patients were treated in
each subsequent calendar year and were followed up to the
end of 1959 on each yearly anniversary after their treatment
had been started (none being lost sight of). Of those treated
in 1954 we shall know how many died during the first year

TABLE XXXVI

RESULTS OF TREATMENT (HYPOTHETICAL FIGURES)

| Year of Treatment | No. of Patients Treated | Number Alive on Anniversary of Treatment in | | | | |
|---|---|---|---|---|---|---|
| | | 1955 | 1956 | 1957 | 1958 | 1959 |
| 1954 | 62 | 58 | 51 | 46 | 45 | 42 |
| 1955 · | 39 | .. | 36 | 33 | 31 | 28 |
| 1956 | 47 | .. | .. | 45 | 41 | 38 |
| 1957 | 58 | .. | .. | .. | 53 | 48 |
| 1958 | 42 | .. | .. | .. | .. | 40 |

after treatment, how many died during the second year after
treatment, and so on to the fifth year after treatment. Of
those treated in 1955 we shall know the subsequent history
up to only the fourth year after treatment, in 1956 up to only
the third year after treatment, and so on. Our tabulated
results will be, let us suppose, as in Table XXXVI.

Calculation of the survival-rates of patients treated in
each calendar year becomes somewhat laborious if the
number of years is extensive and has also to be based upon
rather small numbers. If the constitution of the samples
treated yearly and their fatality-rates are not changing with
the passage of time there is no reason why the data should
not be amalgamated in life-table form. Indeed the great
advantage of the life-table method is that we can utilise *all*
the information to hand at some moment of time. In computing, say, a 5-year survival-rate we make *all* the patients
contribute to the picture and do not restrict ourselves to
only those who have been observed for the full five years.

For clarity we can write Table XXXVI in the form given in Table XXXVII.

All the patients have been observed for at least one year and their number is $42 + 58 + 47 + 39 + 62 = 248$. Of these there were alive at the end of that first year of observation $58 + 36 + 45 + 53 + 40 = 232$. The probability of surviving the first year after treatment is, therefore, $232/248 = 0.94$, or, in other words, 94 per cent. of these patients survived the first year after treatment. Of the 40 patients who were

TABLE XXXVII

RESULTS OF TREATMENT (HYPOTHETICAL FIGURES)

| Year of Treatment | No. of Patients Treated | Number Alive on Each Anniversary (none lost sight of) | | | | |
|---|---|---|---|---|---|---|
| | | 1st | 2nd | 3rd | 4th | 5th |
| 1954 | 62 | 58 | 51 | 46 | 45 | 42 |
| 1955 | 39 | 36 | 33 | 31 | 28 | .. |
| 1956 | 47 | 45 | 41 | 38 | .. | .. |
| 1957 | 58 | 53 | 48 | .. | .. | .. |
| 1958 | 42 | 40 | .. | .. | .. | .. |

treated during 1958 and were still surviving a year later, no further history is yet known. (If the year's history happens to be known for some of them these data cannot be used, for the history would tend to be complete more often for the dead than for the living, and thus give a bias to the results.) As the exposed to risk of dying during the second year we therefore have the 232 survivors at the end of the first year minus these 40 of whom we know no more—viz. 192. Of these there were alive at the end of the second year of observation $51 + 33 + 41 + 48 = 173$. The probability of surviving throughout the second year is therefore $173/192 = 0.90$. Of the 48 patients who were treated in 1957 and were still surviving in 1959 no later history is yet known. As the exposed to risk of dying in the third year we therefore have the 173 survivors at the end of the second year minus these 48 of whom we know no more—viz. 125. Of these there were alive at the end of the third year of observation $46 + 31 + 38 = 115$. The probability of surviving the third year is therefore $115/125 = 0.92$. We know no further history of the 38 patients first treated in 1956 and still surviving on the third anniversary. The number exposed to risk in the fourth year becomes $46 + 31 = 77$, and of these $45 + 28 = 73$ are alive at the end of it. The probability of surviving the fourth year is therefore $73/77 = 0.95$. Finally, during the fifth year we know the history only of those patients who were treated in 1954 and still survived at the end of the fourth year—namely, 45 persons. Of these 42 were alive on the fifth anniversary, so that the probability of surviving the fifth year is $42/45$, or $0.93$.

CONSTRUCTION OF THE LIFE, OR SURVIVORSHIP, TABLE.
ANNIVERSARY DATA

Tabulating these probabilities of surviving each successive year, we have the values denoted by $p_x$ in column (2) of Table XXXVIII. The probability of not surviving in each

TABLE XXXVIII
RESULTS OF TREATMENT IN LIFE-TABLE FORM

| Year after Treatment | Probability of Surviving Each Year | Probability of Dying in Each Year | Number Alive on Each Anniversary out of 1000 Patients | Number Dying during Each Year |
|---|---|---|---|---|
| $x$ (1) | $p_x$ (2) | $q_x$ (3) | $l_x$ (4) | $d_x$ (5) |
| 0 | ·94 | ·06 | 1000 | 60 |
| 1 | ·90 | ·10 | 940 | 94 |
| 2 | ·92 | ·08 | 846 | 68 |
| 3 | ·95 | ·05 | 778 | 39 |
| 4 | 93 | ·07 | 739 | 52 |
| 5 | .. | .. | 687 | .. |

year after treatment, $q_x$, is immediately obtained by subtracting $p_x$ from 1. The number of patients with which we start the $l_x$ column is immaterial, but 100 or 1000, or some such number is convenient. Starting with 1000, our observed fatality-rate shows that 94 per cent. would survive the first year and 6 per cent. would die during that year. The number alive, $l_x$, at the end of the first year must therefor be 940 and the number of deaths, $d_x$, during that year must be 60. For these 940 alive on the first anniversary the probability of living another year is $0.90$, or in other words

there will be 90 per cent. alive at the end of the second year—
*i.e.* 846—while 10 per cent. will die during the second year—
*i.e.* 94. Subsequent entries are derived in the same way.
(The order of the columns in the table is immaterial. The
order given in Table XXXVIII is the most logical while
the table is being constructed, because $p_x$ is the value first
calculated and the others are built up from it. In the final
form the order given in the English Life Table No. 11, of
which an extract was previously given, is more usual.)

By these means we have combined all the material we
possess for calculating the fatality in each year of observation
after treatment, and have found that according to those
fatality-rates approximately 69 per cent. of treated patients
would be alive at the end of 5 years. Having found from the
available material the probability of surviving each of the
separate years 1 to 5 we are, in effect, finding the probability
of surviving the whole 5 years by multiplying together these
probabilities, viz. $p_1 \times p_2 \times p_3 \times p_4 \times p_5$.

If we want the average duration of life so far lived by the
patients, it is easily obtained. 687 patients of our imaginary
1000 live the whole 5 years. If we presume that those who
died lived half a year in the year in which they died (some
will have lived less, some more, and we can take, usually
without serious error, the average as a half), then 60 lived
only half a year after treatment, 94 lived a year and a half,
68 lived two years and a half, 39 lived three years and a
half, and 52 lived four years and a half. The average length
of after-life is, therefore, so far as the experience extends,
$(687 \times 5 + 60 \times 0 \cdot 5 + 94 \times 1 \cdot 5 + 68 \times 2 \cdot 5 + 39 \times 3 \cdot 5 + 52 \times 4 \cdot 5)$
$\div 1000 = 4 \cdot 15$ years.

The percentage alive at different points of time makes a
useful form of comparison. For instance, of patients with
cancer of the cervix treated between 1925 and 1934, we find,
by summarising some published figures in life-table form,
roughly the following number of survivors out of 100 in each
stage of disease :—

| | Stage | | | |
|---|---|---|---|---|
| | 1 | 2 | 3 | 4 |
| At end of 5 years . | 86 | 70 | 33 | 11 |
| ,, 9 ,, . | 78 | 57 | 27 | 0 |

Q

## EXCLUSION OF PATIENTS

If some of the patients have been lost sight of, or have in a few instances died from causes which we do not wish to include in the calculation (accidents, for example), these must be taken out of the exposed to risk at the appropriate time—*e.g.* an individual lost sight of in the fourth year is included in the exposed to risk for the first three years but cannot be included for the complete fourth year. If he is taken out of the observations from the very beginning, the fatality in the first three years is rather overstated, for we have ignored an individual who was exposed to risk in those years and did not, in fact, die. If patients are being lost sight of at different times during the year or dying of excluded causes during the year, it is usual to count each of them as a half in the exposed to risk for that year. In other words, they were, on the average, exposed to risk of dying of the treated disease for half a year in that particular year of observation.

## CONSTRUCTION OF THE LIFE, OR SURVIVORSHIP, TABLE.
### DATA AT A SPECIFIED DATE

Sometimes in putting data into the life-table form we have patients observed not on anniversaries, as above, but to a specified date. Let us suppose, for instance, that patients have been treated in the years 1954 to 1958 and have been followed up to December 31st, 1959 (and thus not, as in the previous example, to the yearly anniversaries of their treatment). The data may be put in life-table form according to the technique set out in Table XXXIX.

The total number of patients treated in the 5 years and to be followed up was 194. During the first year of the follow-up 4 were lost sight of and 2 died of violence and these deaths it is proposed to exclude as irrelevant. Since the last patient was treated in 1958 and the follow-up was to December 31st, 1959, all the patients had been observed for at least one full year. The exposure to risk of dying during the first year will, therefore, be computed as 194 less

TABLE XXXIX

CONSTRUCTION OF LIFE TABLE OF PATIENTS UNDERGOING A CERTAIN TREATMENT
(HYPOTHETICAL FIGURES)

| Year after Treatment | Number Alive at Beginning of the Year | Number lost sight of During the Year | Number Dying of Violence During the Year | Number Alive Observed for only Part of the Year | Number Exposed to Risk of Dying During the Year * | Number Dying During the Year | Proportion Dying During the Year $q_x$ | Proportion Surviving the Year $p_x$ | Proportion Surviving from Start of Treatment to End of each Year † |
|---|---|---|---|---|---|---|---|---|---|
| (1) | (2) | (3) | (4) | (5) | (6) * | (7) | (8) | (9) | (10) † |
| 0 – | 194 | 4 | 2 | 0 | 191 | 24 | 0·126 | 0·874 | 0·874 |
| 1 – | 164 | 3 | 0 | 35 | 145 | 12 | 0·083 | 0·917 | 0·801 |
| 2 – | 114 | 0 | 1 | 42 | 92·5 | 6 | 0·065 | 0·935 | 0·749 |
| 3 – | 65 | 1 | 0 | 23 | 53 | 3 | 0·057 | 0·943 | 0·706 |
| 4 – | 38 | 2 | 1 | 21 | 26 | 2 | 0·077 | 0·923 | 0·652 |
| etc. | | | | | | | | | |

* Col. 6 = Col. 2 minus half Cols. 3, 4, and 5.

† Col. 10 = the products of the values of Col. 9, $i.e.$ $p_1 \times p_2 \times p_3 \ldots \ldots$

half the number lost sight of and less half the number of
deaths from violence, *i.e.* 191. In other words, we give only
half a year's exposure to those who passed out of observation
for these reasons during the year. During these 191 person-
years of exposure there were 24 deaths, giving a probability
of dying of 24/191 = 0·126. The probability of surviving the
first year is, therefore, 0·874.

The number of patients entering the second year of
follow-up is the original 194 less all those who have died or
who have been lost sight of during the first year, *i.e.* 194 –
24 – 2 – 4 = 164. Of these 164 exposed during the second
year there were 3 lost sight of during the year who must
be allowed only a half-year's exposure, and there were also
35 *who were still alive at December 31st, 1959*, but who had
not been exposed to risk over the *whole* of that second year.
These are the patients who were treated in 1958 and who,
therefore, by the end of 1959, have been exposed for one
year and some fraction of a year. As usual we shall take
the fraction to be, on the average, one-half. The number
exposed to risk of dying during the full second year is,
accordingly, 164 – ½ of 3 lost sight of – ½ of 35 alive at
December 31st, 1959, and not exposed for the whole of the
second year = 145. During that second year the number of
patients dying was 12 so that the probability of dying was
0·083 and the probability of surviving 0·917.

The number entering the third year of exposure is 164
minus the 3 lost sight of, the 12 who died and the 35 who
passed out of observation alive at December 31st, 1959,
which equals 114. Of these 114 patients, 1 died of violence
during the third year and 42 were seen for only part of that
year (*i.e.* those who were treated in 1957 and by December
31st, 1959, had been observed for 2 full years and some
fraction of a year). The number exposed to risk of dying is,
accordingly, 114 less ½ of 1 and ½ of 42 = 92·5. With 6 deaths
during the year the probability of dying is 0·065 and the
probability of surviving is 0·935. And so on.

Taking the probabilities of dying and applying them to
the customary hypothetical 1000 patients at start of treatment we can calculate the number alive at the end of each

year as in Table XXXVIII. Alternatively if we require only the percentage of the total who will be surviving at the end of each year (*i.e.* the $l_x$ column), the answer can be obtained by multiplying together the $p_x$ values in column 9 of Table XXXIX. Thus the probability of surviving one year is, according to these data, 0·874 ; the probability of surviving two years is $0·874 \times 0·917 = 0·801$ ; of surviving three years $0·874 \times 0·917 \times 0·935 = 0·749$ ; of surviving four years $0·874 \times 0·917 \times 0·935 \times 0·943 = 0·706$ ; and of surviving five years $0·874 \times 0·917 \times 0·935 \times 0·943 \times 0·923 = 0·652$. In other words, these data give a 5-year survival-rate of 65 per cent.

As a general rule the exclusion of deaths regarded as irrelevant is undesirable, *e.g.* from violence in a follow-up of patients operated upon for some form of cancer. If the number of such deaths is few their inclusion (or omission) can have little effect upon the results. If the number is large it may be difficult to interpret the results when they are omitted. It is probably better to compute the survival-rate with such deaths included and to compare this rate with the figure normally to be expected amongst persons at those ages.

### PATIENTS LOST TO SIGHT

Finally, if a relatively large number of patients is lost sight of we may be making a serious error in calculating the fatality-rates from the remainder, since those lost sight of may be more, or less, likely to be dead than those who continue under observation.

For instance, if 1000 patients were observed, 300 are dead at the end of 5 years, 690 are alive, and 10 have been lost sight of, this lack of knowledge cannot appreciably affect the survival-rate. At the best, presuming the 10 are all alive, 70 per cent. survive ; at the worst, presuming the 10 are all dead, 69 per cent. survive. But if 300 are dead, 550 are alive, and 150 have been lost sight of, the corresponding upper and lower limits are 70 per cent. surviving and 55 per cent. surviving, an appreciable difference. To measure the survival-rate on those patients whose history is known, or, what comes to the same thing, to divide the 150 into alive and dead according to the proportions of alive and dead in the 850 followed up, is certainly dangerous. The characteristic " lost sight of " *may* be correlated with the characteristics " alive or dead " ; a patient who cannot be traced may be more likely to be dead than a patient who can be traced (or *vice versa*), in which case the ratio of alive to dead in the untraced cases cannot be the same as the ratio in the traced cases. Calculation of the possible upper rate shows at least the margin of error.

## Summary

Life tables are convenient methods of comparing the mortality-rates experienced at different times and places. The same methods may be usefully applied to the statistics of patients treated and followed up.

*(For exercises see pp. 321-322)*

# XIX

## MEASURES OF MORBIDITY

In many countries with highly developed vital-statistical systems, the death-rate, from all causes or from specific causes, has been for more than a century the principal measure of sanitary progress—or lack of progress—and one of the main instigators of epidemiological research. In Great Britain it has, for instance, revealed the disappearance of cholera and the great decline in the typhoid fevers ; it has shown the dramatic reduction of diphtheria, and, in the last twenty years, the spectacular fall in the mortality-rates of childhood. While these, and other striking gains, have at some ages been offset by new and serious problems, *e.g.* the rise in cancer of the lung and the incidence of diseases of the heart in men of middle life, it has, nevertheless, become increasingly apparent that such low rates of mortality need to be supplemented by measures of morbidity. How much *sickness* is there in the population and in its many component groups, sickness which does not necessarily end fatally but which nonetheless calls for investigation and preventive measures (*e.g.* rheumatism in its various aspects) ? It is this situation which is leading in a number of countries to the development of a system of morbidity statistics. (Throughout this chapter morbidity, sickness, and illness are used synonymously.) On the one hand such statistics are required for the purposes of medical administration, to indicate the population's requirements for medical care in hospitals, etc. ; on the other hand they should serve the needs of research into the factors that influence the incidence of illness of different kinds and into the steps that may contribute to prevention and cure.

237

## Special Problems of Morbidity Statistics

Compared with the statistics of death, statistics of sickness present some very substantial problems.  Thus (a) death is a unique event whereas illness may occur repeatedly in the same person from the same or different causes ;  (b) death occurs at one precise point of time whereas illness exists over a duration of time ;  (c) death is simply and precisely defined whereas illness varies very greatly in its severity, ranging from negligible effects to a condition which is completely disabling.  In the measurement of morbidity it is clear that all these aspects have to be taken into account.

Under (a) we shall have to consider whether in computing the amount of morbidity that occurred in a given period we should add the *number of persons* ill or the *number of illnesses*. For some persons will be ill more than once.

Under (b) we shall have to consider whether we wish to know the number of *new illnesses that arise* in a given period or the number that were *extant* in that period, whether they first arose in it or extended into it from a previous period.

Under (c) we shall have closely to consider what we *intend to count* as morbidity in any given circumstances.  Thus we may, perhaps, categorise sickness broadly as (1) congenital or acquired defects, injuries or impairments (such as a residual paralysis from a past attack of poliomyelitis, visual and auditory defects) ;  (2) latent or incipient diseases usually not recognised by the person affected but revealed by laboratory or other tests, *e.g.* diabetes or tuberculosis ;  the question arises as to the point at which they are to be regarded as clinically manifest diseases, and variations in the answer to that question must influence the incidence of that disease (thus respiratory tuberculosis will increase considerably, though, in a sense, artificially, with the introduction of mass radiography) ;  (3) manifest disease recognised by the patient or by his medical attendant.  Which of these various components we intend to count will obviously depend upon the circumstances and upon our needs but, if false comparisons are not to be made, the inclusions and exclusions on each occasion must be made perfectly clear in publishing our results.

## Sources of Morbidity Statistics

The usual sources of morbidity statistics, and the principal special problems arising in each, are as follows :—

*The survey of sickness* in which a sample of a population is interviewed by social workers. The definition of sickness is usually based on subjective rather than objective criteria and the accuracy of the records depends very much upon the memories of the participants for relatively minor events in their lives (one to two months is usually the limit) as well as upon their knowledge of the true cause of their illness. On the other hand, no other method can bring to light *all* the sickness, major and minor, experienced by a population.

*General practitioner statistics* of visits and consultations. If fully maintained these records are more reliable in amount and kind than those obtained by survey, but they are necessarily limited to those sick persons who choose to consult their doctors. Many minor illnesses will thus go unobserved and the amount unobserved will undoubtedly vary with such characteristics as sex, age, social class, etc.

*Hospital in-patient statistics* are usually complete within their own field, but it is often very difficult to define the population from which they are drawn. Who are the exposed to risk who would go to such-and-such a hospital in the event of a major sickness ? They can also be influenced materially from time to time by changes in medical practice, *e.g.* many cases of primary pneumonia are today treated at home and a generation ago would have inevitably found their way to hospital.

*Sickness absence records* reveal, as their title shows, who was absent from work and, usually, why in terms of a doctor's diagnosis of the cause of the illness. However, since the certificate is often an open one, the diagnosis will not invariably reflect the doctor's real opinion. It is important to note that the incidence of sick absence must vary according to the nature of the sick person's job. Thus a fractured radius or a mild gastro-enteritis may not keep a clerk from work but make it impossible for an omnibus driver to report for duty. The statistics are, of course,

limited to those employed in industry, etc., and therefore
exclude large sections of the population.  The durations of
illness will be affected by the tendency to return to work on
particular days of the week, *e.g.* a Monday.  The statistics
will also be influenced by the workers themselves—how
readily they choose to absent themselves or not for minor
complaints.  In other words, we are inevitably dealing with
the frequency and durations of *absences* and not with the
frequency and durations of pathological conditions ; the
former may overstate or understate the latter and may do
so differentially between persons, jobs, etc.

*Notifications of disease* are usually limited to infectious
diseases and, in spite of known omissions and imperfections,
can be important as indicators to the medical officer of health
of the presence of disease in the community and of the need
for preventive action.

In spite of the problems outlined above, all these sources
of data have their own value and, in their proper sphere,
can contribute to research and knowledge.

### Rates of Morbidity

In deciding upon appropriate rates of morbidity, the illnesses that exist in a population during a given time interval
may first be classified as follows :—

(1) Illnesses beginning during the interval and ending
during the interval.
(2) Illnesses beginning during the interval and still existing at the end of the interval.
(3) Illnesses existing before the beginning of the interval
and ending during the interval.
(4) Illnesses existing before the beginning of the interval
and still existing at the end of the interval.

For each of these categories we shall need to decide whether
we take as our measure the number of persons sick or the
number of spells of illnesses occurring, *e.g.* if in a given time
interval a patient has three attacks of bronchitis, do we
count one person or three attacks ?  (Maybe we shall need
both.)

The most useful morbidity rates will, then, be these :—

I. The *Incidence Rate* defined as the number of illnesses (spells or persons as applicable) *beginning* within a specified period of time (categories 1 and 2 above) and related to the average number of persons exposed to risk during that period (or at its mid-point). In short, the object is to show the number of cases of sickness *arising* in a given interval.

II. The *Period Prevalence Rate* defined as the number of illnesses (spells or persons as applicable) *existing at any time* within a specified period (all 4 categories above) and related to the average number of persons exposed to risk during that period (or at its mid-point). In short, the object is to show the total number of cases of sickness which *existed* during a given interval.

III. The *Point Prevalence Rate* defined as the number of illnesses *existing at a specified point of time* (all 4 categories above) and related to the number of persons exposed to risk at that point of time. In short, the object is to show how many cases of sickness were in existence *on this day*.

IV. The *Average Duration of Sickness* (and the frequency distribution upon which it is based). Such an average may be in terms of *the total population exposed to risk* (the average duration of sickness per person), in terms of *the number of persons sick* (the average duration of sickness per sick person), or in terms of the *number of illnesses* (the average duration of sickness per illness). In all these measures of duration, consideration must be paid to the circumstances of the four categories set out on p. 240. Is it intended to limit the duration to that experienced *within* the defined period or is any note to be taken of the durations *preceding* the period but extending into it (categories 3 and 4) or of durations *following* the interval of illnesses that began within it (category 2) ? There can be no categorically " right " or " wrong " procedure. The decision must turn upon the nature of the circumstances and the availability of the data. As already stressed above, it is essential in publication that full details be given of the procedure actually in use.

## Summary

Statistics of morbidity are required to supplement statistics of mortality, but in definition and analysis present much greater difficulties than the latter. As the English proverb says, stone dead has no fellow. In view of these difficulties it is essential in publication that full detail be given of the definitions used, the method of collection of the data, and of the analyses applied to it. The most useful measures comprise the incidence rate showing the frequency with which new cases of disease arise and the prevalence rate showing the frequency with which established cases exist, either during a specified interval of time or at one specific point of time. Measures illustrating the duration of sickness can also be usefully employed.

# XX

## CLINICAL TRIALS

" THERAPEUTICS," said Professor Pickering, in 1949, in his Presidential Address to the Section of Experimental Medicine and Therapeutics of the Royal Society of Medicine, " is the branch of medicine that, by its very nature, should be experimental. For if we take a patient afflicted with a malady, and we alter his conditions of life, either by dieting him, or by putting him to bed, or by administering to him a drug, or by performing on him an operation, we are performing an experiment. And if we are scientifically minded we should record the results. Before concluding that the change for better or for worse in the patient is due to the specific treatment employed, we must ascertain whether the result can be repeated a significant number of times in similar patients, whether the result was merely due to the natural history of the disease or in other words to the lapse of time, or whether it was due to some other factor which was necessarily associated with the therapeutic measure in question. And if, as a result of these procedures, we learn that the therapeutic measure employed produces a significant, though not very pronounced, improvement, we would experiment with the method, altering dosage or other detail to see if it can be improved. This would seem the procedure to be expected of men with six years of scientific training behind them. But it has not been followed. Had it been done we should have gained a fairly precise knowledge of the place of individual methods of therapy in disease, and our efficiency as doctors would have been enormously enhanced."

It would be difficult to put the case for the clinical trial of new (or old) remedies more cogently or more clearly. Its

243

absence in the past may well have led, to give one example, to the many years of inconclusive work on gold therapy in tuberculosis, while, as Pickering stressed, the grave dangers of much earlier and drastic methods of therapeutics, such as blood-letting, purging, and starvation, would quickly have been exposed by comparative observations, impartially made.

## The Ethical Problem

Before embarking upon any such trial there is, however, a fundamental problem that must be carefully studied and adequately met. The basic requirement of most clinical trials is concurrent " controls," in other words a group of patients corresponding in their characteristics to the specially treated group but *not* given that special treatment. The question at issue, then, is whether it is proper to withhold from any patient a treatment that might, perhaps, give him benefit. The treatment is, clearly, not proven ; if it were, there would be no need for a trial. But, on the other hand, there must be some basis for it—whether it be from evidence obtained in test-tubes, animals, or even in a few patients. There must be some such basis to justify a trial at all. The duty of the doctor to his patient and scientific requirements may then clash. The problem will clearly turn in part, and often very considerably, upon what is at stake. If, for example, it be a question of treating the common cold in young adults and seeing whether the duration of " illness " can be effectively reduced, then the morality of a rigidly controlled trial would not be seriously in doubt—and any other form of trial probably be uninformative and a waste of time and money. At the other extreme it might be quite impossible to withhold, even temporarily, an established treatment for a disease in which life or death, or serious after-effects, are at stake.

The problem is eased more often than not by the state of our ignorance. Frequently we have no acceptable evidence that a particular established treatment does benefit patients and, whether we like it or no, we are then experimenting upon them. As F. H. K. Green has pointed out, " Where the value of a treatment, new or old, is doubtful, there may be a higher moral obligation to test it critically than to continue to prescribe it year-in-year-out with the support merely of custom or wishful thinking." Further, in withholding a new treatment it is well to remember that all the risks do not lie on one side of the balance. What is new is certainly not always the best and, as the history of antibiotics and hormones has shown, it is by no means always devoid of serious danger to the patient. It may, therefore, be far more ethical to use a new treatment under careful and designed observation, in comparison with patients not so treated, than to use it widely and indiscriminately before its dangers as well as its merits have been determined. It should be realised, too, that *no special treatment* does not, necessarily, imply *no treatment*. Constantly the question at issue is : Does this particular form of treatment offer more than the usual orthodox treatment of the day ?

However that may be, every proposed trial must be exhaustively weighed in the ethical balance—each according to its own circumstances and its own problems. Sometimes a scientifically imperfect trial must be accepted, sometimes it may be impossible to carry out a trial at all (*e.g.* it is doubtful whether anyone would to-day withhold the established treatment of a person bitten by a rabid dog. Yet the evidence in its favour is unconvincing). The result of this situation in clinical medicine, unique, perhaps, in scientific work, is that second-best or even more inferior " controls " are often adopted and, sometimes, though certainly not invariably, may have to be adopted.

## Imperfect Comparisons

Thus the following ways and means have been used from time to time, and are still used :—

(i) The treatment of patients with a particular disease is unplanned but naturally varies according to the decision of the physicians in charge. To some patients a specific drug is given, to others it is not. The progress and prognosis of these patients are then compared. But in making this comparison in relation to the treatment the fundamental assumption is made—and must be made—that the two groups are equivalent in all respects relevant to their progress, except for the difference in treatment. It is, however, almost invariably impossible to believe that this is so. Drugs are not ordered by doctors at random, but in relation to a patient's condition when he first comes under observation and also according to the subsequent progress of his disease. The two groups are therefore not remotely comparable, and more often than not the group given the specific drug is heavily weighted by the more severely ill. No conclusion as to its efficacy can possibly be drawn.

(ii) The same objections must be made to the contrasting in a trial of volunteers for a treatment with those who do not volunteer, or in everyday life between those who accept and those who refuse. There can be no knowledge that such groups are comparable ; and the onus lies wholly, it may justly be maintained, upon the experimenter to prove that they are comparable, before his results can be accepted. Particularly, perhaps, with a surgical operation the patients who accept may be very different from those who refuse (see also Chapter XXI, p. 271).

(iii) The contrast of one physician, or one hospital, using a particular form of treatment, with another physician, or hospital, not adopting that treatment, or adopting it to a lesser degree, is fraught with much the same difficulty— apart from the practicability of being able to find such a situation (with, it must be noted, the same forms of ancillary treatment). It must be proved that the patients are alike in relevant group characteristics, *i.e.* age, sex, social class, severity of illness at the start of therapy, before they can be fairly compared and their relative progress, or lack of progress, interpreted. That proof is clearly hard to come by.

(iv) The " historical " control relies upon a contrast of past records of the pre-drug days with those of the present treated patients. Of the former group 10 per cent., say, died and 90 per cent. recovered, while for the present group the ratios are 5 and 95 per cent. If everything else remained constant in time, this comparison would clearly be valid.

But does it ?  The new specific treatment may be given only
to certain patients and thus a selected group is being con-
trasted with the previous unselected group.  Or, if all
patients are given the treatment, then we must be sure that
there has been no change in those presenting themselves
for treatment—a change that the treatment itself may
sometimes promote, *e.g.* by bringing in the intractable case
with renewed hope of cure.  We must be sure that there
has been no change in the severity of the disease itself.  We
are invariably faced with the question :  were these two
groups fundamentally similar ?  and the answer is rarely
certain.  An instructive example lies in a published study
of polyarteritis nodosa treated with cortisone.  From 1950
onwards 17 cases were thus treated.  As controls 19 cases,
all proved by biopsy, were extracted from the clinical case
records of the same hospitals during the years 1941–49.
The two groups were alike in sex and age at onset and the
severity of the constitutional illness appeared similar.  But
they were found to differ in one critical respect.  Of the
controls nearly half (8 out of the 17 patients) had hypertension, while of those treated with cortisone there was only
one single patient with hypertension (1 out of the 19 patients).
The unequal distribution of this serious complication makes
comparison impossible and also leads to doubt as to whether
the two groups may not differ in other and undetected ways.
The authors were thus led to conclude that the chief importance of their labours was " to emphasize that the assessment of therapeutic activity by the use of retrospective
controls is an inherently fallacious method" (*Brit. med. J.*,
1957, **1,** 611).

In practice, too, it is rare to find records that will allow
the comparison between present and past to be made
effectively.  Usually some features of importance are lacking
from the earlier experience or were recorded differently—at
different time intervals, etc.

(v) Lastly, the worker may have no controls at all but
may rely upon his clinical impressions and general knowledge
of the past.  Sometimes, though not often, controls are indeed
unnecessary.  If in the past a disease has invariably and

R

rapidly led to death there can be no possible need for controls to prove a change in the fatality-rate. Thus the trial of streptomycin in tuberculous meningitis needed no control group. Given a precise and certain identification of the case, the success of treatment could be measured against the past 100 per cent. fatal conclusion. Controls, too, are not essential to prove the value of a drug such as penicillin which quickly reveals dramatic effects in the treatment of a disease. Such dramatic effects occurring on a large scale and in many hands cannot be long overlooked.

Unfortunately these undeniable producers of dramatic effects are the exception rather than the rule, even in these halcyon days of the antibiotics. Also, it must be noted that the position has been reached in which we are often no longer contrasting older orthodox methods of treatment with a potent modern drug, but one modern drug with another. To prove that a fatality-rate of the order of 60 per cent. (*e.g.* meningococcal meningitis) has fallen to 15 per cent. is a very much easier task than to prove that with a new treatment the 15 per cent. can be reduced to 10 per cent. Even a poor clinical trial could hardly destroy the evidence of the former profound change ; it may take a very efficient one to prove the latter. Yet, in the saving of life, that improvement is a very important change.

### The Aim of the Controlled Trial

The first step in the controlled trial is to decide precisely what it sets out to prove. It is essential that initially its aims should be laid down in every detail. For example, the object in one of the British Medical Research Council's early trials of streptomycin was to measure the effect of this drug upon respiratory tuberculosis. This illness, may, however, denote many different things : the minimal lesions just acquired by the patient, the advanced and progressive disease that offers a poor prognosis, or the chronic and relatively inactive state. Equally, its course, its rapidity of development or the recovery of the patient, may differ with age, whether early childhood, adolescence or old age. The question, therefore must be made more precise. It was, in fact, made precise by restricting the trial to " acute progressive bilateral pulmonary tuberculosis of presumably recent origin, bacteriologically proved, unsuitable for collapse therapy, age group 15 to 25 (later extended to 30)." Thus it was ensured that all patients in the trial would have a similar type of disease and, to avoid having to make allowances for the effect of forms of therapy other than mere bed-rest, that the type of disease was one not suitable for such other forms. In such cases the chances of spontaneous regression were small, but the lesion, on the other hand, offered some prospect of action by an effective chemotherapeutic agent. In short, the questions asked of the trial were deliberately limited, and these "closely defined features were considered indispensable, for it was realised that no two patients have an identical form of the disease, and it was desired to eliminate as many of the obvious variations as possible " (*Brit. med. J.*, 1948, **2**, 769).

This planning, as already pointed out, is a fundamental feature of the successful trial. It would, of course, be possible deliberately to incorporate more and different groups in a trial, but to start out without thought and with all and sundry included, with the hope that the results can somehow be sorted out statistically in the end, is to court disaster.

As a general principle it is wise to limit the questions asked to a few and to be absolutely precise upon those few. The loss in so doing lies, of course, in the fact that the answers are limited to very specific questions and clearly cannot be generalized upon outside their field.

One difficulty may sometimes arise with a precise and exact definition of the cases to be included in a trial. In testing, for instance, the effects of different specific treatments on rheumatic fever, the Anglo-American co-operative trial wisely endeavoured to lay down criteria which had to be fulfilled before any patient was accepted. He, or she, had to have such-and-such signs and symptoms. By such means mis-diagnoses would be avoided and other illnesses simulating rheumatic fever excluded. But the exhibition of these signs and symptoms, while denoting the undoubted case of rheumatic fever, may also denote that the patient is no longer in the very early stages of the disease. The very early case with highly suspicious but still indefinite signs might under these criteria be excluded until the signs had become definite—when it is no longer in those desirable early stages. That is a situation which will sometimes need close consideration and the weighing of alternatives (and was, of course, given such in the trial quoted).

## The Construction of Groups

The next step in the setting up of the trial is the allocation of the patients to be included in the treatment and the non-treatment groups (or to more than two groups if more than one treatment is under test). The aim is to allocate them to these " treatment " and " control " groups in such a way that the two *groups* are initially equivalent in all respects relevant to the inquiry. Individuals, it may be noted, are not necessarily equivalent ; it is a group reaction that is under study. In many trials this allocation has been successfully made by putting patients, as they present themselves, alternately into the treatment and control groups. Such a method may, however, be insufficiently random if the admission or non-admission of a case to the trial turns upon a difficult assessment of the patient and if the clinician involved knows whether the patient, if accepted, will pass to the treatment or control group. By such knowledge he may be biased, consciously or unconsciously, in his acceptance or rejection ; or through fear of being biased, his judgment may be influenced. The latter can be just as important a source of error as the former but is more often overlooked. For this reason, it is better to avoid the alternating method and to adopt the use of random sampling numbers ; in addition, the allocation of the patient to treatment or control should be unknown to the clinician until *after* he has made his decision upon the patient's admission. Thus he can proceed to that decision—admission or rejection —without any fear of bias. One such technique has been for the statistician (or other associated worker) to provide the clinician with a set of numbered and sealed envelopes. After each patient has been brought into the trial the appropriately numbered envelope is opened (no. 1 for the first patient, no. 2 for the second, and so on) and the group to which the patient is to go, treatment (T) or control (C), is given upon a slip inside. Alternatively a list showing the order to be followed may be prepared in advance, *e.g.* T, T, C, T, C, C, T, T, T, C, etc., and held confidentially, the clinician in charge being instructed after each admission has been made.

A further extension of this method may be made, to ensure a final equality of the groups to be compared. Separate sets of envelopes, or of lists, are provided for sub-groups of the patients to be admitted, *e.g.* for each sex separately, for specific age-groups or for special centres of treatment, and in each sub-group the number of T cases is made equal to the number of C. Thus we may have allocation lists, or envelopes based upon them, as shown in the table below.

| Patient's Number in each Sub-group | Male | | Female | |
|---|---|---|---|---|
| | 20–29 Years | 30–39 Years | 20–29 Years | 30–39 Years |
| 1 | T | T | C | T |
| 2 | C | T | T | C |
| 3 | C | T | T | C |
| 4 | T | C | T | T |
| 5 | T | C | C | C |
| 6 | C | T | C | T |
| 7 | T | C | C | T |
| 8 | C | C | T | C |
| etc. | | | | |

It is often argued that these fine subdivisions are unwarranted, since the numbers within the sub-groups will finally be far too small to justify any comparisons. Whether that be true or no, this argument overlooks the fundamental aim of the technique ; if a trial is not being confined to a narrowly defined group, the aim is to ensure that when the *total* groups, T and C, are compared they have within them-

selves equivalent numbers of persons with given characteristics.  Thus in the above example when the T and C
experiences as a whole need to be compared, it will be found
that there are 8 males and 8 females in the T group and 8
males and 8 females in the C group ; 8 T and 8 C persons
are aged 20–29, 8 T and 8 C are aged 30–39.  The T and C
groups have been automatically equalised, a result which—
and particularly with small numbers—would not necessarily
have been achieved with a single allocation list which ignored
age, sex and place.  With large numbers, equality of characteristics in the two groups will result in the long run ; with
small numbers, it will be wise to ensure equality, or near
equality, by design.

The prescribed random order must, needless to say, be
strictly followed or the whole procedure is valueless and the
trial breaks down.  Faithfully adhered to, it offers three
great advantages : (1) it ensures that our personal feelings,
or judgments, applied consciously or unconsciously, have
not played any part in building up the various treatment
groups ;  from that aspect, therefore, the groups are unbiased ;  (2) it removes the very real danger, inherent in
any allocation which is based upon personal judgments, that
believing our judgments may be biased, we endeavour to
allow for that bias and in so doing may " lean over backwards " and thus introduce a lack of balance from the other
direction ;  (3) having used such a random allocation we
cannot be accused by critics of having set up personally
biased groups for comparison.


### The Treatment

In regard to treatment there are frequently, and obviously, an infinite number of questions that can be asked of
a trial.  We can, for instance, choose one dose of a drug out
of many ;  we can vary the interval of its administration ;
we can give it by different routes ;  we can give it for different
lengths of time ;  and so on.  In testing a new form of
treatment knowledge is at first scanty, and it may often,
therefore, be best to choose one closely defined regimen

which should, it is believed, reveal the potentialities, and perhaps some of the dangers, of the drug, or whatever may be concerned. Thus the question asked of the trial may run : " If to a closely defined type of patient 2 gr. of drug X are given daily in four divided doses by intra-muscular injection, and for three months, what is the progress of such a group of patients as compared with a corresponding group not treated with this drug ? " After the answer has been reached we may be able to extend our knowledge by experimenting with other dosages of the drug, etc. Sometimes, however, it might be more informative to allow for individual idiosyncrasies during the basic trial or, in other words, to permit the clinician to vary the dosage, etc., according to his judgment of the patient's needs as shown by the latter's responses. We have then, it is clear, deliberately changed the question asked of the trial so that it now runs : " If clinicians in charge of a closely defined type of patient administer drug X intra-muscularly in such varying amounts and for such varying durations of time, and so forth, as they think advisable for each patient, what is the progress of such a group as compared with a corresponding group not treated with this drug ? "

The moot point, that must be considered in given circumstances, is which is the better question to ask. In many trials it would certainly seem most desirable to lay down a fixed schedule which, except under exceptional circumstances, e.g. for ethical reasons, must not be varied by those taking part in the trial. (The fixed schedule can, of course, be different for patients of different ages or body-weights, etc.) If dozens of people in a co-operative trial are free to vary the dosage just as they personally think fit, and in circumstances where too little is known to give any reasonable basis for such variations, then it may be very difficult finally to extract any clear or useful answer at all from the trial. Thus, for example, in the basic trials of isoniazid in pulmonary tuberculosis it was decided to give a particular dosage for a particular length of time in comparison with a correspondingly defined schedule of streptomycin. On the other hand, when it seems clear that individuals may react very differently to some therapeutic agents, *e.g.* to treatment with a hormone, it may be wiser to design a trial that permits the clinicians to select their treatment over a range of dosages and to vary it from time to time in accordance with the responses of the patient. This was the procedure adopted in a trial of cortisone compared with aspirin in the treatment of early cases of rheumatoid arthritis. It should be clear that such a procedure does not prohibit the use of the customary measures of progress—body-weight, erythrocyte sedimentation rate, pyrexia, etc.—even though the physician may base his treatment upon their level and changes. The question asked of the trial is " what after so many months are the clinical conditions, degrees of fever, etc., of two groups of patients, one treated with, say, cortisone and the other with, say, aspirin, the treatment having varied within both groups at the will of the clinicians ? " Do they differ ? We may thereby see whether what the doctors chose to do with cortisone was any better, or worse, than what they chose to do with aspirin. No dissection of the two groups, however, can possibly be made to see how patients fared upon different régimes. The physicians have deliberately varied these régimes in accordance with the patients' responses ; it is not reasonable, then, to turn round at the end of the trial and observe the responses in relation to the régimes. That would be circular reasoning. To measure the effects of different régimes there can be no other way than the setting up of a trial to that end, randomising the patients to the different régimes. In some circumstances that may be a possible and very desirable procedure. Clearly, much might be learned about the action and value of a drug if a number of randomly constructed groups could be set up and given various amounts of it, ranging, perhaps, from none to some maximum value. The responses to these different amounts would be informative.

Consideration must also be given to the treatment of the control group. In such a trial as that of streptomycin in phthisis in young adults (quoted above), involving frequent injections of the drug, it would be quite impossible to institute any corresponding procedure for the controls. They were, therefore, treated as they would have been in the past, precautions being taken that neither those treated nor the controls knew they were part of a controlled trial.

On the other hand, in the treatment of the common cold a dummy treatment would be essential, for one cannot invite volunteers for a trial, obviously keep half as " guinea-pigs," and then hope for co-operation and good records.  The fact that they are taking part in a trial should be made clear to the participants, but they should not be told which treatment they receive.  The importance of the control treatment is shown by the results of one such trial—of colds of under one day's duration at the start of treatment, 13·4 per cent. were reported as " cured," and 68·2 per cent. " cured " or " improved," on the second day following administration of an antihistamine compound ;  but with the placebo, the corresponding figures were 13·9 and 64·7 per cent. (*Brit. med. J.*, 1950, 2, 425).

In many cases, therefore, a placebo treatment is desirable and its practicability must be considered—as well, of course, as the ethics of such a procedure in each instance.

## Measuring the Results

There is one great advantage of a placebo used in such a way that the clinician cannot recognise it—the clinical impression can be included and given full weight in the analysis.  If, in other words, two groups of patients are being treated, one T and one C, and the clinician does not know the components of these groups, then he can without fear or favour assess the progress and condition of every patient.  And thus clinical instinct and opinion, as well as more strictly objective measures, can be used, without risk of bias, to assess the result.  This may be a very valuable addition to the trial and prevent us from substituting a collection of precise quantitative, but unco-ordinated, details for a " coherent though impressionistic picture."

Such a method was used in the Medical Research Council's clinical trial of an antihistaminic drug in the treatment of the common cold (quoted above).  To make sure that no bias should enter into the assessment of the results, neither patient nor clinician must be aware whether antihistamine tablets or control tablets had been given in a particular case. To ensure this result, numbered boxes of tablets and similarly numbered record sheets were issued to the centres taking part in the trial, each box to be used in conjunction with the appropriate sheet. Box No. 1, for instance, might contain antihistamine tablets, Box No. 2 the control tablets, and so on, as determined beforehand from randomly constructed lists. Neither box had any label indicating its contents. In the final analysis, therefore, record sheet No. 1 must relate to the antihistaminic group, record sheet No. 2 to the comparative group, record sheet No. 3 to the comparative group, and so on. But neither patient nor investigator in the field could know that (nor, necessarily, the worker analysing the results).

In the adoption of other measures of the effect of treatment, detailed planning must as usual play its part. Before the trial is set under way it must be laid down, for example, precisely when and how temperatures will be taken, when full clinical examinations will be made, and what will be specifically recorded, how often and at what intervals X-rays will be taken. Standard record forms must be drawn up, and uniformity in completing them stressed. Unless these rules and regulations are well kept and observed by the clinicians in charge of the trial, many and serious difficulties arise in the final analysis of the results, *e.g.* if some X-ray pictures were not taken at the required monthly interval, or if some erythrocyte sedimentation rate (ESR) tests were not made. In fact, *every* departure from the design of the experiment lowers its efficiency to some extent ; too many departures may wholly nullify it. The individual may often think " it won't matter if I do this (or don't do that) just once " ; he forgets that many other individuals have the same idea.

It is fundamental, too, that the same care in measurement and recording be given to both groups. The fact that some are specially treated and some are not is wholly irrelevant. Unless the reactions of the two groups are equally noted and recorded, any comparisons of them must clearly break down. For the same reason, if a follow-up of patients is involved it must be applied with equal vigour to all. In some circumstances the " blind " assessment technique of the patient's condition can be applied. Thus in the trial of streptomycin in young adult phthisis the chest radiographs of all patients were viewed, and changes assessed, by three members of a special radiological panel working separately and not knowing whether the films came from treated or control patients. The setting up of a team whose members worked independently gave an increased accuracy to the final result ; the " blind " assessment removed any possibility of bias or over-compensation for bias. Similarly in another trial one worker injected the patient with a compound or with saline, and another, not knowing the nature of that injection, measured the results of compound or saline in the patient.

## Reporting the Results

In reporting the results of clinical trials it is important to describe the techniques employed and the conditions in which the investigation was conducted, as well as to give the detailed statistical analysis of results. In short, a statement must be made of the type of patient brought into the trial and of the definitions governing the selection of a case ; the process of allocating patients to treatment and control groups should be exactly defined ; the treatment should be precisely stated ; the assessments and measurements used must be clearly set out, and it must be shown whether they were made " blind " or with a knowledge of the treatment given. In other words, the whole plan and its working out should be laid before the reader so that he may see precisely what was done.

Secondly, even if a random allocation of patients has been made to the treatment and control groups, an analysis must be made to show the equality of the groups at the start of the trial. With large numbers such an equality will almost invariably be present, but with small numbers the play of chance will not invariably bring it about. It is important, therefore, to see whether there is an initial equality or an inequality for which allowance must be made (*e.g.* by subdivision of the records or by standardisation). In the trial of the antihistamine drug in the treatment of the common cold, for example, there were 579 persons given the drug and 577 a placebo. Of the former group 34·8 per cent. had had symptoms for less than a day before treatment, of the latter 30·0 per cent. ; 55·4 per cent. of the former had a blocked nose as a presenting symptom, and 53·2 per cent. of the latter ; 7·6 per cent. of the former and 8·0 per cent. of the latter said at entry that they " felt ill."

With the much smaller-scale trial of streptomycin in young adult phthisis a good degree of equality was also reached. Of 55 patients in the treatment group 54 per cent. were in poor general condition at the start of the trial ; of 52 patients in the control group 46 per cent. were in a similar condition. Twenty and 17 respectively were desperately ill, 32 and 30 had large or multiple cavities, 19 and 19 showed radiological evidence of segmental atelectasis. To such an extent can a carefully designed and deliberately limited inquiry bring about equality in even quite small groups. But that it has achieved that aim must first be shown.

## Differential Exclusions

Before analysing the results of a trial there is one other vital question to consider—have any patients *after admission* to the treated or control group been excluded from further observation ? Such exclusions may affect the validity of the comparisons that it is sought to make ; for they may *differentially* affect the two groups. For instance, suppose that certain patients cannot be retained on a drug—perhaps through toxic side-effects. No such exclusions will occur on the placebo and the careful balance, originally secured by randomisation, may thereby be disturbed. Another specific example might lie in a trial of pneumonectomy versus radiation in the treatment of cancer of the lung (supposing such a trial to be ethically possible). At operation there is no doubt that pneumonectomy would sometimes be found impossible to perform and it would seem only sensible to exclude these patients. But we must observe that no such exclusions can take place in the group treated by radiation. If we exclude such patients on the one side and inevitably retain them on the other, can we any longer be sure that we have two comparable groups differentiated only by treatment ? Unless the losses are very few and therefore unimportant, we may inevitably have to keep such patients in the comparison and thus measure the *intention to treat* in a given way rather than the actual treatment. The question of the introduction of bias through exclusions for any reason (including lost sight of) must, therefore, always be carefully studied, *not only at the end of a trial but throughout its progress*. This continuous care is essential in order that we may immediately consider the nature of the exclusions and whether they must be retained in the inquiry for follow-up, measurement, etc. It will be too late to decide about that at the end of the trial.

## Some General Principles

One advantage of a co-operative trial is that sufficient numbers of patients can be treated uniformly, though in different centres, to give a precise answer to the questions at issue. Statistically speaking, most diseases are seen relatively infrequently by any one physician working in any one centre. The personal experience is therefore frequently too slender to allow a safe passage from the particular to the general. On the other hand, the well controlled and well reported experiment does not, as is sometimes thought, necessarily demand vast numbers. Indeed, as Margaret Merrell has wisely observed : " large numbers in themselves are worse than useless if the groups are not comparable, since they encourage confidence in an erroneous opinion." If the groups are strictly comparable, then often a total of 50 to 100 cases, and sometimes very much less, will provide sufficient evidence. The actual numbers must, of course, depend upon the problem at stake and upon the magnitude of difference between the treatment and control groups that is to be expected or is actually observed.

On the other hand, it appears sometimes to be thought that there is some necessary antagonism between the clinical assessment of a few cases and the " cold mathematics " of the statistically analysed clinical trial dealing with a larger number. It is difficult to see how, in fact, there can be any such antagonism. The clinical assessment, or the clinical impression, must itself be numerical in the long run—that patients are reacting in a way different from the way the clinician believes was customary in the past. In the controlled trial an attempt is made to record and systematise those impressions (and other measurements) and to add them up. The result reached is, of course, a group result, namely, that *on the average* patients do better on this treatment than on that. No one can say how one particular patient will react. But that, clearly, is just as true of the approach via clinical impressions and two cases, as it is via a controlled and objectively measured trial and 100 cases. Also it may be noted that observation of the group does not prevent the most scrupulous and careful observation of the individual at the same time—indeed it demands it.

## The Patient as his own Control

In some instances it may be better to design the trial so that each patient provides his own control—by having various treatments in order. The advantages and disadvantages of that procedure will need careful thought.

By such means we may sometimes make the comparisons more sensitive since we have eliminated the variability that must exist *between* patients treated at the same stage of the disease in question (so far as can be judged). We have done so, however, at the expense of introducing as a factor the variability *within* patients from one time to another, *i.e.* we may be giving the patient treatment A and treatment B at *different* stages of the disease. For instance, with a disease that naturally declines in severity with the passage of time, *e.g.* the acute sore throat, a very misleading answer would be obtained if treatment A was invariably applied first and treatment B invariably applied second. The apparent advantage of treatment B would be attributable in reality to the natural history of the disease. Clearly we should have been much better off with this illness by setting up two groups of different patients, one on treatment A and one on treatment B. On the other hand we could alternatively have randomly allocated the *order* in which each patient was to receive the two treatments, so that in half the patients A preceded B and in the other half B preceded A. We would then be in a position to make a comparison of the two treatments within the same patients and at the same time, allowing for the natural progression of the disease.

In general, such comparisons within patients give no advantage and are, indeed, usually impracticable, with diseases running an acute course to death or recovery, *e.g.* pneumonia and other fevers. We cannot easily change the treatment during the illness nor measure the relative effect of doing so. Comparisons within patients are also not likely to give an advantage even with a long-protracted disease if the disease is one which shows a trend in time, *e.g.* respiratory tuberculosis. Their advantage lies rather with chronic diseases with a relatively *constant* level of disability, etc. Even here serious ethical difficulties may sometimes arise. For instance, with a patient suffering from rheumatoid arthritis and *inadequately* maintained on cortisone there would obviously be no difficulty in changing the treatment to aspirin (or vice versa) and judging the relative merits of these treatments. But suppose the patient is being *adequately* maintained on cortisone, can one then change to aspirin and perhaps persevere with it for some weeks (or months) to see whether the patient can be thus equally well maintained in good, or reasonable, health ?

A simple example of an easily and effectively conducted " within patient " trial was, however, the assessment of a rapidly acting agent in this disease, rheumatoid arthritis. Each of 43 patients (to whom the experimental nature of the trial had been explained) was injected on one occasion with the test substance and on a second occasion with normal saline. The order of injection was randomised for each patient, with the test substance given first on half the occasions and saline first on the other half. This is an essential step for, apart from the contents of the injection, it might be that the patient would react differently (subjectively or objectively) on the first or second occasion. The nature of the injection was unknown to the patient and unknown to the doctor assessing its results. There could therefore be no bias in their judgments of either. In fact, of the 43 patients 18 reported less pain in the joint after their injection of the test substance and 17 after injection of saline ; 19 with the test substance and 19 with saline reported less stiffness. The average strength of grip rose by 5 mm. of Hg after injection of the test substance and by 4 mm. after the injection of saline ; the average speed of a step test fell by 1·3 seconds after the test substance and by 1·6 seconds after saline (*Brit. med. J.*, 1950, **2**, 810).

An example of a more elaborate design in the same field has been reported by D. D. Reid. Patients were invited to take part in a trial of three ointments intended to relieve articular pain. The ointments were dispensed in identical containers and the contents were unknown to doctor and patient. They were administered on a prearranged randomised plan to the affected joint in each patient on his (or her) successive visits to the clinic. Thus the three ointments were applied to first patient in the order X, Y, and Z on his first three visits and in the reverse order, Z, Y, X, on his next three visits. With the second patient the order was Y, Z, X for his first three visits and the reverse order, X, Z, Y, for his next three visits. With the third patient the order was Z, X, Y and then the reverse, Y, X, Z. These allocations randomly allocated were repeated for each group of 3 patients. Thus, tabulating, the order of administration of the 3 ointments was as follows :—

| Patient | Order of visit to clinic | | | | | |
|---|---|---|---|---|---|---|
|  | 1 | 2 | 3 | 4 | 5 | 6 |
| 1st | X | Y | Z | Z | Y | X |
| 2nd | Y | Z | X | X | Z | Y |
| 3rd | Z | X | Y | Y | X | Z |

It will be seen that each ointment has been tested twice on every patient so that any differences in response *between patients* are equally represented. Further, each ointment has been tested once at *each order of* visit to the clinic from first to sixth ; so any tendency in the patients to a natural recovery in time affects all three ointments equally. Finally *each ointment has preceded any other* (*e.g.* X before Y) just as often as it has followed any other (X after Y) and these two sets of orders are repeated in the same patient. The tendency for a patient to make comparisons between an ointment and the one given immediately before it is thereby equalised. Possible disturbing factors in the required comparisons have thus been allowed for in this " balanced " type of design. In fact the results showed that there was very little to choose between the three ointments, which were a standard preparation in common use, the special preparation under test, and a vanishing cream used as a placebo.

## Summary

The clinical trial is a carefully, and ethically, designed experiment with the aim of answering some precisely framed question. In its most rigorous form it demands equivalent groups of patients concurrently treated in different ways. These groups are constructed by the random allocation of patients to one or other treatment ; such an allocation may sometimes preferably be made within more smaller homogeneous sub-groups composing the total groups. In some instances patients may form their own controls, different treatments being applied to them in random order and the effects compared. In principle the method is applicable with any disease and any treatment. It may also be applied on any scale ; it does not necessarily demand large numbers of patients.

S

# XXI

## COMMON FALLACIES AND DIFFICULTIES

In this and the following two chapters are set out examples of the misuse of statistics in medicine. In some of them the actual figures have been taken from published papers ; in others hypothetical figures have been used to indicate the type of error which has led the worker to fallacious conclusions. No principles are involved that have not been discussed in the previous chapters. The object is merely to illustrate, at the risk of " damnable iteration," the importance of these principles by means of simple numerical examples ; in some instances—e.g. (a) below—the figures are deliberately exaggerated to make clearer the point at issue. The fact that in practice such grossly exaggerated differences rarely occur does not lessen the importance of accurate statistical treatment of data. Differences do occur very often of a magnitude to lead to erroneous conclusions, if the data are incompetently handled in the ways set out.

### Mixing of Non-comparable Records

(a) Let us suppose that in a particular disease the fatality-rate is twice as high among females as it is amongst males, and that amongst male patients it is 20 per cent. and amongst female patients 40 per cent. A new form of treatment is adopted and applied to 80 males and 40 females ; 30 males and 60 females are observed as controls. The number of deaths observed among the 120 *individuals* given the new treatment is 32, giving a fatality-rate of 26·7 per cent., while the number of deaths observed amongst the 90 *individuals* taken as controls is 30, giving a fatality-rate of 33·3 per cent.

Superficially this comparison suggests that the new treatment is of some value ; in fact, that conclusion is wholly unjustified, for we are not comparing like with like.  The fatality-rates of the total number of individuals must be influenced by the proportions of the two sexes present in each sample ;  males and females, in fact, are not equally represented in the sample treated and in the sample taken as control.  Tabulating the figures shows the fallacy clearly (Table XL).

TABLE XL

| | Males | Females | Males and Females Combined |
|---|---|---|---|
| Normal fatality-rate . . | 20% | 40% | .. |
| Number of patients given new treatment . . | 80 | 40 | 120 |
| Deaths observed in treated group . . . . | 16 | 16 | 32 |
| Fatality-rates observed in treated group . . . | 20% | 40% | 26·7% |
| Number of patients used as controls . . . . | 30 | 60 | 90 |
| Deaths observed in control group . . . . | 6 | 24 | 30 |
| Fatality-rates observed in control group . . . | 20% | 40% | 33·3% |

The comparison of like with like—*i.e.* males with males and females with females—shows that the treatment was of no value, since the fatality-rates of the treated and untreated sex groups are identical, and equal to the normal rates. Comparison of the total samples, regardless of sex, is inadmissible, for the fatality-rate recorded is then in part dependent upon the proportions of the two sexes that are present. There are proportionately more females amongst the controls than in the treated group, and since females normally have a higher fatality-rate than males their presence in the control group in relatively greater numbers must lead to a comparatively high fatality-rate in the total sample.  Equally their relative deficiency in the treated group leads to a comparatively low fatality-rate in that total sample.  No comparison is valid which does not allow for the sex differentiation of the fatality-rates.

(b) A more extensive example of the same kind is shown in Table XLI. In this it is presumed that the fatality-rate of an illness varies with the sex of the patient (males are more vulnerable than females), with the age of the patient (the old are more vulnerable than the young), and with the severity of the attack (the severely ill are more vulnerable than the mildly ill), all very reasonable assumptions. The comparison of 800 patients in Hospital A with 800 patients in Hospital B suggests a serious state of affairs—a fatality-rate in the latter *twice* as high as that in the former (10 per cent. compared with 5 per cent.). A test of significance

TABLE XLI

| Characteristics | | | Hospital A | | | Hospital B | | |
|---|---|---|---|---|---|---|---|---|
| Sex | Age in years | Category of Disease | No. of Cases | No. of Deaths | Fatality-rate % | No. of Cases | No. of Deaths | Fatality-rate% |
| Male | 50 and over | Severe | 40 | 10 | 25% | 160 | 40 | 25% |
| ,, | ,,  ,, | Mild | 100 | 5 | 5% | 200 | 10 | 5% |
| ,, | Under 50 | Severe | 60 | 6 | 10% | 100 | 10 | 10% |
| ,, | ,,  ,, | Mild | 200 | 4 | 2% | 50 | 1 | 2% |
| Female | 50 and over | Severe | 40 | 6 | 15% | 100 | 15 | 15% |
| ,, | ,,  ,, | Mild | 100 | 4 | 4% | 50 | 2 | 4% |
| ,, | Under 50 | Severe | 60 | 3 | 5% | 40 | 2 | 5% |
| ,, | ,,  ,, | Mild | 200 | 2 | 1% | 100 | 1 | 1% |
| | | Total | 800 | 40 | 5% | 800 | 81 | 10% |

shows that the difference is highly " significant "—it is nearly four times its standard error. Yet the difference is entirely spurious and the comparison is not valid. Dissection of the data shows that Hospital B has twice as many severely ill patients as Hospital A (400 to 200), about 30 per cent. more men (510 to 400), and nearly twice as many old persons above the age of 50 (510 to 280), and these are all features associated with a high fatality-rate. Comparison of like with like in these respects shows that the hospitals have, in fact, identical fatality-rates. It is the amalgamation of the different groups in different proportions that has led to the impressively " significant " but fallacious conclusion. The importance of trying to unravel the chain of causation is apparent.

(c) One more important example of the result of mixing non-comparable records may be given. The following (hypothetical) figures show the attack-rates of a disease upon an inoculated and an uninoculated population (Table XLII).

TABLE XLII

| Year | Number of Persons | | Number of Persons Attacked | | Attack-rates per cent. | |
|---|---|---|---|---|---|---|
| | Inoc. | Uninoc. | Inoc. | Uninoc. | Inoc. | Uninoc. |
| 1953 | 100 | 1000 | 10 | 100 | 10 | 10 |
| 1954 | 500 | 600 | 5 | 6 | 1 | 1 |
| 1953 and 1954 | 600 | 1600 | 15 | 106 | 2·5 | 6·6 |

In each calendar year the attack-rate of the inoculated is equal to the attack-rate of the uninoculated. Between 1953 and 1954 there has, however, been a large change in the size of the inoculated and uninoculated populations and also a large change in the level of the attack-rate. Summation of the results for the two years leads to the fallacious conclusion that the inoculation afforded some protection. The large uninoculated population in 1953 when the attack-rate was high leads to an absolutely large number of cases—though in relation to their numbers the uninoculated are at no disadvantage compared with the inoculated. The inoculated cannot contribute an equal number of cases, for the population at risk in that year (1953) is far smaller. Thus amalgamation of the unequal numbers of persons exposed to different risks in the two years is unjustified. No fallacy would have resulted if the attack-rate had not changed or if the proportions exposed to risk had not changed, as the figures of Table XLIII show.

When the populations at risk and the attack-rates *both* vary, the calendar year becomes a relevant factor, and must be taken into account by the calculation of rates within the year.

Such a problem has arisen quite frequently in practice in assessing the incidence of various infectious diseases in immunised and unimmunised children.

TABLE XLIII

| Year | Number of Persons | | Number of Persons Attacked | | Attack-rates per cent. | |
|---|---|---|---|---|---|---|
| | Inoc. | Uninoc. | Inoc. | Uninoc. | Inoc. | Uninoc. |
| | | | Constant Attack-rates | | | |
| 1953 | 100 | 1000 | 10 | 100 | 10 | 10 |
| 1954 | 500 | 600 | 50 | 60 | 10 | 10 |
| 1953 and 1954 | 600 | 1600 | 60 | 160 | 10 | 10 |
| | | | Constant Populations | | | |
| 1953 | 500 | 600 | 50 | 60 | 10 | 10 |
| 1954 | 500 | 600 | 5 | 6 | 1 | 1 |
| 1953 and 1954 | 1000 | 1200 | 55 | 66 | 5·5 | 5·5 |

## Neglect of the Period of Exposure to Risk

(a) A further fallacy in the comparison of the experiences of inoculated and uninoculated persons lies in neglect of the time during which the individuals are exposed first in one group and then in the other.   Suppose that in the area considered there were, on January 1st, 1954, 300 inoculated persons and 1000 uninoculated persons.   The number of attacks are observed within these two groups over the calendar year and the annual attack-rates are compared. This is a valid comparison *so long as the two groups were subject during the calendar year to no additions or withdrawals.* But if, as often occurs in practice, persons are being inoculated *during* the year of observation the comparison becomes invalid unless the point of time at which they enter the inoculated group is taken into account.

Suppose on January 1st, 1954, there are 5000 persons under observation, none of whom are inoculated ; that 300 are inoculated on April 1st, a further 600 on July 1st, and another 100 on October 1st.   At the end of the year there are, therefore, 1000 inoculated persons and 4000 still uninoculated.   During the year there were registered 110 attacks amongst the inoculated persons and 890 amongst the uninoculated.   If the ratio of recorded attacks to the population *at the end of the year* is taken, then we have rates of 110/1000 = 11·0 per cent. amongst the inoculated and

890/4000 = 22·3 per cent. amongst the uninoculated, a result apparently very favourable to inoculation. This result, however, *must* be reached even if inoculation is completely valueless, for no account has been taken of the unequal lengths of time over which the two groups were exposed. None of the 1000 persons in the inoculated group were exposed to risk for the *whole* of the year but only for some fraction of it ; for a proportion of the year they belong to the uninoculated group and must be counted in that group for an appropriate length of time.

The calculation should be as follows (presuming, for simplicity, that one attack confers no immunity against another) :—

All 5000 persons were uninoculated during the first quarter of the year and therefore contribute $(5000 \times \frac{1}{4})$ years of exposure to that group.   During the second quarter 4700 persons belonged to this group—*i.e.* 5000 less the 300 who were inoculated on April 1st—and they contribute $(4700 \times \frac{1}{4})$ years of exposure to the uninoculated group.   During the third quarter 4100 persons belonged to this group—*i.e.* 4700 less the 600 who were inoculated on July 1st—and they contribute $(4100 \times \frac{1}{4})$ years of exposure.   Finally in the last quarter of the year there were 4000 uninoculated persons— *i.e.* 4100 less the 100 inoculated on October 1st—and they contribute $(4000 \times \frac{1}{4})$ years of exposure.   The " person-years " of exposure in the uninoculated group were therefore $(5000 \times \frac{1}{4}) + (4700 \times \frac{1}{4}) + (4100 \times \frac{1}{4}) + (4000 \times \frac{1}{4}) = 4450$, and the attack-rate was 890/4450 = 20 per cent.—*i.e.* the equivalent of 20 attacks per 100 persons per annum.   Similarly the person-years of exposure in the inoculated group are $(0 \times \frac{1}{4})$ $+ (300 \times \frac{1}{4}) + (900 \times \frac{1}{4}) + (1000 \times \frac{1}{4}) = 550$, for there were no persons in this group during the first three months of the year, 300 persons during the second quarter of the year, 900 during the third quarter, and 1000 during the last quarter.   The attack-rate was, therefore, 110/550 = 20 per cent., and the inoculated and uninoculated have identical attack-rates. Neglect of the durations of exposure to risk must lead to fallacious results and must favour the inoculated.   The figures are given in tabulated form (Table XLIV).

TABLE XLIV

| Inoculated at Each Point of Time | Inoculated | | Uninoculated | |
|---|---|---|---|---|
| | Exposed to Risk in Each Quarter of the Year | Attacks at 5 per cent. per Quarter | Exposed to Risk in Each Quarter of the Year | Attacks at 5 per cent. per Quarter |
| Jan. 1st,    0 | 0 | 0 | 5000 | 250 |
| April 1st,  300 | 300 | 15 | 4700 | 235 |
| July 1st,  600 | 900 | 45 | 4100 | 205 |
| Oct. 1st,  100 | 1000 | 50 | 4000 | 200 |
| Total at end of the year  .    . | 1000 | 110 | 4000 | 890 |

*Fallacious Comparison.*—Ratio of attacks to final population of group. Inoculated $110/1000 = 11 \cdot 0$ per cent. Uninoculated $890/4000 = 22 \cdot 3$ per cent.

*True Comparison.*—Ratio of attacks to person-years of exposure. Inoculated $110/(300 \times \frac{1}{4}) + (900 \times \frac{1}{4}) + (1000 \times \frac{1}{4}) =$ 20 per cent. Uninoculated $890/(5000 \times \frac{1}{4}) + (4700 \times \frac{1}{4}) + (4100 \times \frac{1}{4}) + (4000 \times \frac{1}{4}) = 20$ per cent.

This example is an exaggerated form of what may (and does) happen in practice if the time-factor is ignored. Clearly even if the time-factor is allowed for, interpretation of the results must be made with care. If the inoculated show an advantage over the uninoculated it must be considered whether at the point of time they entered that group the incidence of the disease was already declining, due merely to the epidemic swing. Strictly speaking, the experience of the vaccinated should be compared with that of the unvaccinated only from the time that the former entered the vaccinated group. It would seem necessary in these circumstances to select randomly at the proper time a comparable control person for each person vaccinated, the former to remain unvaccinated. But this procedure, while an epidemic is in progress, would be impracticable and unethical. All comparisons based upon vaccination *during* an epidemic should therefore be regarded with caution, if not scepticism.

(*b*) A cruder neglect of the time-factor sometimes appears in print, and may be illustrated as follows. In 1949 a new form of treatment was introduced and applied to patients seen between 1949 and 1954. The proportion of patients still alive at the end of 1954 is calculated. This figure is compared with the proportion of patients still alive at the end of 1954 who were treated in 1944–48, prior to the introduction of the new treatment. Such a comparison is, of course, inadmissible. The patients seen in 1944–48 have by the end of 1954 had 6 to 11 years in which to succumb, with an average exposure of $8\frac{1}{2}$ years if their attendances were equally spread over 1944–48. The patients seen in 1949–54 have had only 0 to 6 years in which to succumb, with an average exposure of 3 years if their attendances were equally spread over 1949–54. To be valid the comparison must be between the survival-rates at equal stages of time, 1, 2, 3 years, etc., after treatment.

## Volunteers for Inoculation

Another very frequent source of error in the assessment of a vaccine lies in the comparison of persons who volunteer, or choose, to be inoculated (or volunteer on behalf of their children) with those who do not volunteer or choose. The volunteers may tend to come from a different age group and thus, on the average, be older or younger ; they may tend to include more—or fewer—males than females ; they may tend to be drawn more from one social class than another. Thus, in the early days of vaccination against poliomyelitis one survey in the U.S.A. showed that the vaccinated children came more from the white families, more from mothers with a high standard of education behind them, and more from fathers in " white collar " and relatively well-paid occupations. Given adequate records these, and similar easily defined characteristics, can be identified. The comparisons of the inoculated and uninoculated can then be made within like categories. But far more subtle and undetectable differences may well be involved. The volunteers for inoculation may be persons more careful of their health, more aware of the presence of an epidemic in the community. They may on such occasions take other steps to avoid infection, *e.g.* the avoidance of crowded transport or cinemas. It may (as in the example quoted above) be the more intelligent mothers who bring their children to be inoculated ; and more intelligent mothers may also endeavour to protect their children from infection in other ways. They may too, perhaps, have smaller families so that the inoculated child is automatically less exposed to infection from siblings. Thus in one pioneer trial of vaccines against whooping cough it was found that 47 per cent. of the inoculated children were only children, *i.e.* with no sibs, compared with only 20 per cent. of the control children.

Lastly, with diseases that do not have a uniform incidence and do not themselves confer a lasting immunity, *e.g.* influenza and the common cold, there may well be in the act of volunteering a grave element of self-selection. Persons who rarely suffer from such minor illnesses are unlikely to volunteer, those who are constantly troubled by them may well seek relief through inoculation. In other words, self-selection may tend to bring the susceptibles into the inoculated class and leave the resistants as " controls." The comparison is, then, valueless. We are not comparing like with like. Such dangers are not imaginary ; they have been demonstrated often in carefully documented trials.

### Associations in Time and Space

Standing alone, associated movements in time of two characteristics may be very poor evidence of cause and effect —particularly if the trend be merely a steady upward, or downward, movement. Thus in the last 25 years the emission of exhaust gases from motor vehicles has risen in the large cities of Great Britain. There has also been a rise in the death-rate from cancer of the lung. This concurrent movement in time, together with the obvious possibility of a causal relationship, might well justify a carefully planned investigation. But without quite other evidence we have no sure basis for deduction. Many factors move together in time, *e.g.* in these 25 years the increase in television and the decline in long skirts in women. The movements of some may be directly associated, the movements of others be only indirectly associated.  The problem is to sort them out.

Associations in space may also be difficult to interpret. The fact that in areas of Scandinavia the level of the birth-rate varies directly with the prevalence of storks is not likely to mislead us.  But what of the fact that the incidence of paralytic poliomyelitis appears to be rather less in Wales than in England ?  Half a dozen factors might be thought of as relevant—genetic and environmental—but none can take us further than a useful basis for further investigation.

Even a planned investigation, or experiment, revealing an association in time or space can be quite unconvincing without the introduction of a control group.

(a) For example, a well-planned trial was made of vaccination against the common cold (*Jour. Amer. Med. Assoc.*, 1938, **2**, 1168).  University students who believed themselves to be particularly susceptible were invited to participate and were allocated at random to a vaccine or control group (vaccinated with normal saline).  An extract from the results is given in Table XLV.

TABLE XLV

A STUDY OF VACCINATION AGAINST THE COMMON COLD

|  | Vaccine Group | Control Group |
|---|---|---|
| Number of persons vaccinated . . | 272 | 276 |
| Average number of colds per person | | |
| Previous year . . . . | 5·9 | 5·6 |
| Current year . . . . | 1·6 | 2·1 |
| % reduction in current year . . | *73* | *63* |

Whatever may have been the explanation (*e.g.* exaggerated memories of the past year's experience), the most striking feature is the enormous reduction in the colds observed in the year of the trial compared with those of the previous year.  *But suppose no control group had been used* ;  would one not have been impressed by so great a reduction as 73 per cent. in the vaccinated group ?  It is only alongside the control group that it falls into its proper perspective and relieves us of the danger of deducing cause and effect merely from a time relationship.  In fact, the vaccine, it appears, achieved nothing very remarkable for its recipients. Nevertheless some of them were well satisfied, for the authors report that from time to time physicians would write to them saying, " I have a patient who took your cold vaccine and got such splendid results that he wants to continue it. Will you be good enough to tell me what vaccine you are using ? " It must have been embarrassing to reply " water," yet in that reply lies all the fallibility of the *individual* judgment *post hoc ergo propter hoc*.

(*b*) As an instance of a study in space and time, the effect of bacteriophage was measured by comparing the incidence of cholera in two areas, one in which bacteriophage was distributed, the other serving as a standard of comparison. In the former the incidence was found over an observed period of time to be at a lower level than the incidence in previous years or in the area observed as a control (the question of duration of exposure to risk, dealt with above, having been properly observed). It is clear that there is an association both in time and space between the incidence of cholera and the administration of bacteriophage. Is that association one of cause and effect ? The answer must be that the results are perfectly *consistent* with that hypothesis, but that consistency is not the equivalent of proof. The incidence of epidemic disease fluctuates both in time and space for unknown reasons, and the abnormally low attack-rates in the area in which bacteriophage was administered *may* be the result of the influence of those undetermined natural causes operating at the same time as the experiment was carried out. Repetition of the experiment in another area with equivalent results would strengthen the hypothesis that bacteriophage was beneficial. With observations of this kind, limited in time and space, it is well to reflect upon the fact that " if when the tide is falling you take out water with a twopenny pail, you and the moon together can do a great deal." The history of scarlet fever may well be remembered, in this connexion, as illustrated by the testimony of R. J. Graves (*A System of Clinical Medicine*, Dublin, 1843). In the first few years of the nineteenth century the disease " committed great ravages in Dublin " and was " extremely fatal." After the year 1804 it assumed a " very benign type " and was " seldom attended with danger until the year 1831." In 1834 it again took the form of a " destructive epidemic." The low fatality after 1804 was " every day quoted as exhibiting one of the most triumphant examples of the efficacy " of new methods of treatment. But Graves candidly admits that " the experience derived from the present [1834–35] epidemic has completely refuted this reasoning, and has proved that, in spite of our boasted improvements, we have not been more successful in 1834–5 than were our predecessors in 1801–2 " (quoted from Charles Creighton's *History of Epidemics in Britain*, Camb. Univ. Press, 1894, vol. ii., pp. 722-25).

# XXII

## FURTHER FALLACIES AND DIFFICULTIES

### Absence of Exposed to Risk or Standard of Comparison

IT often happens that an investigation is confined to individuals marked by some characteristic.

(a) For example, a detailed inquiry is made into the home conditions of each infant dying in the first year of life in a certain area over a selected period of time, and it is found that 15 per cent. of these infants lived under unsatisfactory housing conditions. Do such conditions, or factors associated with them, lead to a high rate of infant mortality ? The limitation of the inquiry to the dead makes it quite impossible to answer this question. We need information as to the proportion of *all* infants who were born in that area over that period of observation who live under unsatisfactory housing conditions. If 15 per cent. of *all* infants live under such conditions, then 15 per cent. of the deaths may reasonably be expected from those houses and unsatisfactory housing appears unimportant. If, on the other hand, only 5 per cent. of *all* infants are found in these conditions but 15 per cent. of the deaths come from such houses, there is evidence of an excess of mortality under the adverse conditions. In practice, it may be impossible for financial or administrative reasons to investigate the home conditions of all infants. It should be possible, however, to inquire into a random sample of them, say every tenth birth registered in the area over a given period of time. Without some such standard of comparison no clear answer can be reached. Such limited investigations have been made into the problems of both infant and maternal mortality.

(*b*) **After very careful inquiry** it is shown that of motor-car drivers involved in accidents a certain proportion, say three-quarters, had consumed alcohol during some period of hours previous to the accidents, and one-quarter had not. The deduction that alcohol contributes to the risk of accident is not justified from these figures alone. It is well recognised that white sheep eat more than black sheep—because there are more of them. Before the ratio of 3 " alcoholics " to 1 " non-alcoholic " amongst the accident cases can be interpreted, information is also required as to the comparable ratio amongst drivers *not involved in accidents*. Suppose, for example, there are 1000 drivers on the roads, and 48 accidents are recorded. Of the 48 drivers involved in these accidents three-quarters are found to have consumed alcohol —*i.e.* 36—and one-quarter—*i.e.* 12—have not. If three-quarters of all the 1000 drivers have consumed alcohol within a few hours of driving and one-quarter have not, then the populations " exposed to risk " of accident are 750 and 250. The accident-rates are, then, identical—namely, 36 in 750 and 12 in 250, or 4·8 per cent. in each group. A knowledge of the exposed to risk, or at least of the ratio of alcohol consumers to non-consumers in a random sample of all drivers, is essential before conclusions can be drawn from the ratio in the accident cases.

Careful inquiry into the destination of drivers involved in accidents on a Sunday morning might show that a larger proportion was driving to golf than to church. The inference that driving to golf is a more hazardous occupation is not valid until we are satisfied that there are not, in this case, more black sheep than white sheep. Lest it should be thought that undue stress is being laid upon the obvious, the following quotation from a debate in the House of Lords may be of interest. A noble Lord is reported (*Times*, February 7th, 1936) to have said that " only 4 per cent. of the drivers involved in fatal accidents were women, and that was because they drove more slowly." Without evidence of the hours of driving endured (perhaps a fitting word nowadays) by each sex—and perhaps of the type of area—that conclusion cannot be justified.

## Proportional Rates

Without a knowledge of the exposed to risk, rates of mortality, morbidity, etc., cannot be calculated. In their place refuge is often taken in *proportional* rates.

It is not uncommon for some confusion to be shown over the difference between such absolute and relative figures. For instance, take the following figures (which relate to the position in England and Wales in 1932) :—

| Age-group (years) | Estimated Population in Age-group | Number of Deaths Registered | | Death-rates per Million | |
|---|---|---|---|---|---|
| | | All Causes | Tuber-culosis (all forms) | All Causes | Tuber-culosis (all forms) |
| 5– 9 | 3,181,900 | 6601 | 774 | 2075 | 243 |
| 10–14 | 3,349,100 | 4643 | 827 | 1386 | 247 |

From the estimated populations and the numbers of deaths registered the death-rates experienced in the two age-groups can be calculated. At ages 5–9 years the death-rate from tuberculosis was 243 per million persons and at ages 10–14 it was 247, a negligible difference. In other words, the risk of dying from tuberculosis did not vary materially between these two age-groups. Suppose, however, we had no means of estimating the populations exposed to risk, and the sole information at our disposal consisted of the deaths registered from tuberculosis and from all causes. In that event the only rate that it is possible to calculate is a proportional rate—*i.e.* the deaths from tuberculosis as a percentage of the deaths from all causes. At ages 5–9 this rate is $774 \times 100 \div 6601 = 11 \cdot 7$ per cent. and at ages 10–14 it is $827 \times 100 \div 4643 = 17 \cdot 8$ per cent. The *proportional death-rate* from tuberculosis is 52 per cent. higher at ages 10–14 than at ages 5–9. It is necessary to be quite clear on the meaning of this rate. The information it gives is that *in relation to other causes of death* mortality from tuberculosis was, in these data, more frequent at ages 10–14 than at ages 5–9. This is certainly an important aspect of the figures ; it shows that any action which reduced deaths from tuberculosis (without changing the death-rate from other causes) would have more effect on the total death-rate at ages 10–14 than at ages 5–9, because more of the total deaths were attributable to tuberculosis at the higher ages. But obviously we cannot deduce from the proportional rates that the *absolute* risk of dying from tuberculosis differs in the same ratios ; we have, in fact, seen that the absolute risks were equal. The proportional rate is dependent upon the level of two factors—viz. the deaths from tuberculosis and the deaths from all causes—which form the numerator and denominator of the ratios. Differences in *either* factor will influence the ratio. In the case cited the numerators (deaths from tuberculosis) are nearly equal, 774 at ages 5–9 and 827 at ages 10–14, but the denominators (deaths from all causes) differ appreciably, 6601 at 5–9 and 4643 at 10–14. The proportion of deaths due to tuberculosis at ages 10–14 is higher than the proportion at ages 5–9, not because of a rise in the incidence of tuberculosis but because there is a fall in the incidence of other causes of death. While other causes of death—*e.g.* diphtheria, scarlet fever, measles—were declining, tuberculosis remained nearly steady. Relatively, therefore, its importance increased, absolutely it was unchanged.

## Changes in Proportional Rates

To take another example, in 1917 the deaths at age 0–1 year formed 12·9 per cent. of all the deaths registered in England and Wales, whereas in 1918 the proportion was 10·5 per cent. It does *not* follow that the infant mortality-rate of 1918 was lower than that of 1917 ; in fact, it was very slightly higher, 97 per 1000 live births compared with 96 in 1917. The lower *proportion* in 1918 is due to the great increase in deaths *at ages over* 1 as a result of the influenza pandemic. The numerator of the ratio did not change appreciably (64,483 deaths under 1 in 1917 and 64,386 deaths in 1918) ; the denominator did change appreciably (from 498,922 deaths at all ages in 1917 to 611,861 deaths in 1918).

Similarly an absence of change in a proportional rate does not necessarily denote an absence of change in the absolute

T

rate.  If in 1900 there were 5 per cent. of all deaths due
to cause X and in 1930 the proportion was still 5 per cent.,
this is not incompatible with an absolute decline in the mortality due to cause X.  If the death-rates due to cause X
and to all other causes have *both* been halved, the proportion
must remain the same.

## Proportional Death-rates in Occupations

Correspondingly a lower proportion of deaths due to
cause X amongst, say, coal-miners than amongst bank
clerks does not necessarily denote an absolutely lower death-
rate from that cause amongst the miners.  Expressing the
numbers of deaths due to each various cause as percentages
of the total number due to all causes gives a series of figures
that must add up to 100.  Differences between any one
proportion amongst miners and bank clerks must, to some
extent, influence all the other differences.  For instance,
if the proportion of deaths amongst miners which is due to
accidents is very much higher than the corresponding proportion amongst bank clerks, it follows that other causes of
deaths amongst miners must be *proportionately* decreased.
The point is clear if we suppose only two causes of death to
exist, say accidents and tuberculosis.  Amongst populations
of clerks and miners of equal size there are, let us suppose,
in the clerks 50 deaths of each kind, while amongst miners
there are 100 deaths from accidents and 50 deaths from
tuberculosis.   The actual mortality-rates from tuberculosis
(deaths divided by the number in the population) are
identical, for the populations are of equal size ; but proportionately the tuberculosis deaths form only one-third
of the total amongst miners and one-half amongst clerks.
The relative excess of tuberculosis amongst clerks is not due
to an absolutely greater risk of this disease but to a lower
risk from accidents.

*The cardinal rule in the interpretation of proportional rates
is to pay equal attention to the numerator and to the denominator
of the ratios.*   Departure from that rule may be illustrated in
one or two examples culled from published figures.

## Proportional Rates in Hospital Statistics

In hospital statistics the population at risk—*i.e.* from which the recorded cases are drawn—is usually not known. Mortality or incidence rates cannot, therefore, be calculated, and one falls back on proportional rates.

For example, cases of pernicious anaemia are expressed as a proportion of all cases of illness admitted to hospital, the hospital being situated in the United States. Of the 47,203 admissions of persons who were born in the United States, 291, or 0·62 per cent., were cases of pernicious anaemia ; of the 2814 admissions of persons who were born in England, 25 were cases of pernicious anaemia or 0·89 per cent. ; and of the 7559 admissions of persons who were born in Russia, 14 were cases of pernicious anaemia or 0·19 per cent. It is impossible to accept these figures as adequate evidence of racial differences in the liability to pernicious anaemia. The mortality from that disease is correlated both with age and with sex, the death-rate rising with age and falling more heavily on women than on men. There is no doubt that the incidence varies similarly. The numerator of the proportional ratio (the number of cases of pernicious anaemia) is therefore influenced by the sex and age composition of the population from which the cases are drawn, and it is unlikely that the composition is the same in native-born and immigrant populations.

Equally, the age and sex compositions of the populations at risk in the area may influence the admission rates for other causes of illness—*i.e.* the denominators of the ratios—since many causes of illness are correlated with age and sex. In the absence of any knowledge of the constitution of those populations it is impossible to draw reliable conclusions from these different proportions of pernicious anaemia.

It is clear that in the clinical records compiled at a hospital (or in general practice) many characteristics of sick persons can be studied—age, sex, race, occupation, family and personal history, etc. From these records much can be learned about the symptoms, the pathology, the course and the prognosis of the disease, either in the total group of sick

persons or in sub-groups.  But in the absence of a knowledge
of the exposed to risk very little can be learned of its
*epidemiology*.  We are unable to answer the basic questions,
" *who* in particular succumbs to this disease, *when, where,*
and *why* ? "  We have the numerators to the fractions but
no denominators.  Proportional rates are usually quite in-
adequate substitutes.  The fact for instance that 20 per cent.
of certain cases are aged, say, between 40 and 49 years may
mean that this age-group is particularly vulnerable to the
disease in question ;  but it may mean merely that 20 per
cent. of the population from which the hospital draws its
patients are aged 40 to 49.   In medical literature many
comparisons are annually made between the characteristics
of a series of cases collected in Hospital A by one worker
and in Hospital B by another.  Yet, the differences may
reflect no more than the characteristics of the populations
served by these two hospitals.  It is obvious, for instance,
that the occupations followed by the patients with peptic
ulcer will differ between hospitals in a Lancashire cotton
town and those in a near-by rural district of Derbyshire.  It
is not so obvious that similar, if less pronounced, differences
in the populations at risk may always underlie the contrasts
we make and the conclusions we seek to draw from an
enumeration of cases only.

### Proportional Rates in Infancy

The infant mortality experienced at different stages of
the first year of life was differentiated between urban and
rural areas and gave the following figures :—

DEATHS PER 1000 LIVE BIRTHS AT DIFFERENT MONTHS
OF AGE

| | Under 1 Month | Months | | | | Under 1 Year |
| | | 1– | 2– | 3– | 6–12 | |
|---|---|---|---|---|---|---|
| Urban | 29·67 | 12·06 | 8·73 | 22·77 | 22·14 | 95·37 |
| Rural . | 23·77 | 7·44 | 5·18 | 10·98 | 11·29 | 58·66 |

Expressing these figures as proportions, it is concluded
that " it is significant that while the proportion of infants

succumbing in the first month after birth was 31 per cent. in urban areas, it rose to 41 per cent. in rural areas, which points to the lack of institutional facilities in connexion with confinements in such districts and to the difficulty often experienced of summoning skilled medical assistance in time." Clearly that conclusion does not necessarily follow from the proportions. The *absolute* rate at under 1 month is *lower* in the rural areas than in the urban areas (23·77 to 29·67)—though possibly it might be lower still given better institutional facilities. But it will remain *proportionately* higher just as long as the urban environment shows a relatively excessive death-rate at ages 1–12 months. If 69 per cent. of the deaths are at ages 1–12 months in the urban areas and only 59 per cent. in the rural areas, then whatever the absolute rates at age 0–1 month the proportions *must* be 31 in the urban and 41 in the rural areas at that age—*i.e.* a *relatively* unfavourable state of affairs in the rural areas. Given the best possible institutional facilities, that state of affairs will prevail so long as the urban areas show higher rates during the remainder of the first year.

From the absolute rates, in fact, two arguments may be advanced. The smaller advantage in the rural areas at 0–1 month compared with later ages may be the result of inferior institutional facilities there, or it may be due to the fact that the urban environment does not exert its maximum unfavourable effects until after the age of one month.


## Statistics of Post-Mortems

Much attention has been paid in recent years to the extent to which cancer of the lung has increased. The recorded mortality statistics have been regarded doubtfully, for their rise is certainly due in part to more accurate certification of death now than in the past. The number of *post-mortems* at which this form of malignant disease is found has sometimes been held to be a more certain basis. This number can be taken as the numerator of the rate. But in the absence of a knowledge of the population from which the hospital draws its inmates, an incidence rate cannot be calculated. In its place a proportional rate is used, taking, for instance, as the denominator either the total number of *post mortems* carried out, or the total of all cases of disease admitted to the hospital. Thus we have the cases of cancer of the lung observed at *post mortems* as a proportion of all *post mortems* or of all cases admitted. Calculating this ratio year by year shows its secular trend. In interpreting this trend we have to consider possible changes both in the numerator and the denominator. The numerator—cases of cancer of the lung found at *post mortems* —may be influenced by an increasing interest in the condition; persons in whom it is now suspected may be more frequently submitted to *post mortem* than in past years. If the denominator were unchanged this would give an apparently rising incidence. But it is equally important to inquire whether the denominator has changed—*i.e.* all *post mortems* or all cases admitted. If the criteria, upon which *post-mortem* examination, or admission to hospital, are based, have changed with time, this will also inevitably influence the trend of the ratio. An addition to the denominator of cases or *post mortems* that would not have been present in earlier years must result in a declining ratio, even though the actual incidence rate of cancer of the lung on the population exposed to risk has not changed, or, indeed, has risen.

For example, suppose the incidence of cancer of the lung in the unknown population is 5 cases per annum, all of which come to the hospital, and are recognised, and this number is unchanged between 1930 and 1960. If in 1930 there were 500 *post mortems* carried out, then the proportional rate is 5 in 500 ; if in 1960 a laudable attempt to determine more accurately the causes of death of patients led to an increase of the *post-mortem* examinations to 600, the ratio falls to 5 in 600, without any change in the real incidence. Alternatively, we may suppose that the cases of cancer of the lung have actually gone up threefold, *i.e.* to 15. At the same time all *post-mortem* examinations have doubled to 1000. The proportional rates are 5 in 500, or 1 per cent., and 15 in 1000 or 1·5 per cent. The real rise in cancer of the lung is masked by the general rise.

It may, perhaps, be reiterated that the denominator needs just as much consideration as the numerator.

## The Problem of Attributes

In medical statistics subdivisions of the cases treated have often to be made in order to ensure that like is being compared with like. It is obviously idle to compare the fate of two groups of patients with cancer of the cervix uteri treated by different methods, if one group contains 50 per cent. of persons whose disease was far advanced when treatment was begun and the other had but 10 per cent. in the same category. To avoid this fallacy an attempt is made to classify the patients according to the stage, or severity, of the disease when first seen. Such a division, it is recognised, may be influenced by the different interpretation of what constitutes degrees of severity by the observers, and such statistics must always be regarded with that difficulty in mind.

For instance, one hospital classifies two-thirds of its patients to stages of disease 1 and 2 and one-third to stages 3 and 4 ; another hospital has only one-quarter of the patients at stages 1 and 2 and three-quarters at stages 3 and 4. Do patients really present themselves at these hospitals in such widely differing proportions or is the difference due to differing standards of classification ? The answer to that question is unknown, but in comparing the fatality-rates following treatment the problem must not be disregarded. It must be remembered that different standards of classification may favourably influence one hospital as compared with another at *every* stage of the disease. This may be shown diagrammatically by supposing the patients are set out in a line in order of severity, from mildest to most severe.

Hospital A  . Stage 1 | Stage 2 | Stage 3 | Stage 4 |
Hospital B  .            Stage 1 | Stage 2 | Stage 3 | Stage 4 |

Hospital B includes in Stage 1 a proportion of patients which Hospital A relegates to stage 2 ; the latter hospital, therefore, has only the very best of the patients in stage 1 and will in consequence have a more favourable result than Hospital B at that stage. In the stage 2 group Hospital A includes favourable cases which B had called stage 1, while B includes less favourable cases which A classifies to stage 3. Hospital A will again show a better result. The same difference is apparent in the subsequent stages, Hospital B having only the extreme cases in stage 4 and A including some which B would relegate to stage 3. At each stage Hospital A will, therefore, compare favourably with Hospital B, though in the total there may be no difference whatever.

In any series of statistics based upon division by attributes by different observers this possible fallacy must be considered with care. The difficulty has occurred acutely in the assessment of malnutrition amongst school-children where different observers have used different criteria of determination and placed a different meaning on such terms as " good," " fair," " poor," etc. This has led to an incidence differing unbelievably from one place to another, but so far no simple objective measure has been devised to replace the subjective assessment. In the same way, differing interpretations by different persons made the statistics of the blind and dumb collected at the census enumerations in the past of doubtful value, and led (in England and Wales) to the questions being abandoned. Faced with such statistics the reader must always ask himself : Could these classifications have been made by means of objective measurements, which, given equal skill in making those measurements, would not vary appreciably from observer to observer ? If not, how far may the presence of subjective influences affect the results and in what way ?

## Prospective and Retrospective Data

It was pointed out in Chapter IV (p. 49) that with data gathered retrospectively it may be impossible, and is always difficult, to calculate actual rates of incidence, etc. One possible and serious error is worthy of mention. Suppose, for example, 12 women all suffer during the first 3 months of pregnancy from an attack of rubella and that of the babies subsequently born to them 4 have specified congenital defects and 8 are found to be normal. Thus, tabulating, we have :—

| Mother | Baby |
|--------|------|
| A | Normal |
| B | Congenital cataract |
| C | Normal |
| D | Normal |
| E | Normal |
| F | Congenital deafness |
| G | Normal |
| H | Congenital cataract |
| I | Normal |
| J | Normal |
| K | Congenital disease of the heart |
| L | Normal |

It is clear that these data viewed *prospectively*, and correctly, give the risk of a baby suffering from a congenital defect after rubella occurring in the mother during the first trimester as 4 in 12 or, in other words, 1 in 3. But suppose that the problem is approached *retrospectively* (as is so often done with hospital data), *i.e.* by observing merely the 4 affected children and inquiring of the mother's history. *All* 4 mothers will then be found to have had rubella during the first 3 months and from this it may be quite erroneously concluded that the risk is 100 per cent. Once more the original number exposed to risk is unknown, and its paramount importance has been forgotten.

# XXIII

## FURTHER FALLACIES AND DIFFICULTIES

### Unplanned " Experiments " in Treatment

In Chapter XX emphasis was laid upon the necessity for controlled trials of a new form of treatment. The present reference is, therefore, limited to a general comment and word of warning. Owing to specific difficulties, or to a mere lack of planning, frequently the available figures relating to a mode of treatment are rather of this nature : 100 patients were seen in hospital over some specified period of time, and of these, without planning but in the course of events, 35 were treated with, say, a sulphonamide compound, 30 were treated by serum, 15 had sulphonamide and serum, and 20 had neither sulphonamide nor serum. Such indices as the fatality-rate, the complication-rate, and the speed of recovery may be calculated for each of these groups. The question is whether these resulting rates may be fairly compared one with another and, from them, conclusions drawn as to the efficacy of the modes of treatment. It is invariably *most* doubtful whether such comparisons may be made. In making them, to judge of the effect of the treatment, the implicit assumption is made that in other respects the groups of patients were, on the average, equivalent and that therefore they varied only in their treatment. Whether that is likely to be true, must, in such a case, be closely considered. In the natural course of events it is obviously possible that the physicians concerned will give both sulphonamide *and* serum to the most severely ill patients in the hope that the maximum treatment may be of benefit. They may withhold them altogether from the very mild cases which need no special help. Why, again, it may be asked, was the " method of choice " sulphonamide in one patient and serum in another ? Some feature of the clinical condition at entry may—perhaps one could say, must—have led to the decision. In other words, we have no evidence that the patients allocated initially to these four different treatment groups ever were similar in their clinical features. It is, indeed, inherently unlikely that they were, and consequently the onus lies on the worker to prove that they were before the comparisons can be accepted.

A further difficulty may lie in the transference of a patient from one treatment group to another during the course of his illness. For instance, an apparently mild case at entry may be given no special treatment at first, but if recovery is delayed or complications ensue sulphonamide treatment is started. It follows, then, that the sulphonamide group is loaded with the " no " treatment cases that were progressing unfavourably, and the advantages (if any) of the sulphonamide treatment is inevitably obscured by such selective factors, while the " no " treatment group is finally composed only of the uninterrupted recoveries, a highly selected group.

For such reasons data of this kind are extremely difficult to interpret and cannot be readily accepted.

## Duration of Treatment

A point of some interest arises in experiments to determine the most favourable duration of a form of treatment. To make the discussion specific one may take the trials of penicillin in the treatment of subacute bacterial endocarditis. One question at issue was whether it was advisable to give $x$ units to the patient within one week or the *same* number of units spaced out over four weeks. The two methods are tried and the fatality-rate (or relapse-rate) is observed over some specified period of time, say 1 year. The point at issue is, from what point of time are the deaths counted—from the *completion* of the course of treatment or from its *initiation* ? At first sight the former seems reasonable, but, in fact, it would be wrong. If the deaths are counted only from the completion of treatment, then, artificially, the treatment of the longer duration may always show an apparent advantage, even though it has no real advantage. The reason is that by such a method all the deaths (or relapses) between day 7 and day 28 must be counted against the 7 days' treatment group (the treatment of which is complete at day 7), but no such death can be counted against the 28 days' treatment group (the treatment of which is not then complete). If the number of such deaths (or relapses) is appreciable, the answer *must* favour the long duration of treatment—indeed it would seem better to give the specified number of units over a year, for the deaths will then relate only to those who survive that length of time ! The conclusion is that for a valid comparison the deaths must be counted from the *initiation* of treatment (as was indeed done in the trials upon which this comment is based). It may be argued that the specified treatment was not, in fact, then given in all cases, but the answer to that is that a specified treatment *had been chosen*. If the patient died before its completion the method of choice clearly failed, and that failure must be debited to it. We are thus led to the conclusion that the results must be measured from the initiation of treatment —though, of course, separate rates may be computed for the first month and for subsequent periods. If any exclusions are to be made, *e.g.* death after only one administration of the drug, they must be made uniformly from all groups.

## Standardisation

The principles of standardisation discussed in full in Chapter XVII are often applicable in experimental work. For instance, some form of treatment is applied to certain persons and others are kept as controls. If the two groups are not equal in their age-distribution a comparison of the total result may be misleading. A comparison in each separate age-group must be made, or to reach a total figure the two sets of rates at ages can be applied to some selected standard population. A useful method is to use the treated group as the standard and calculate how many deaths would have taken place in it if it had suffered the same fatality-rates at ages as the controls. This expected figure can then be compared with the observed figure.

In considering published rates at all ages combined—death, fatality, sickness, incidence, etc.—one must always put the questions : do the populations on which these rates are based differ in their age- or sex-distribution, and would such differences materially influence the comparability of the crude rates ? Crude rates themselves should never be accepted without careful consideration on those lines.

## Statistics of Causes of Death

In making comparisons between death-rates from different causes of death at different times or between one country and another, it must be realised that one is dealing with material which is, in Raymond Pearl's words, " fundamentally of a dubious character," though of vital importance in public health work. Although much progress has been made in international comparability the recorded incidence of a particular cause may still be influenced by differences in nomenclature, differences in tabulation, medical fashions, and the frequency with which the cause of death is certified by medically qualified persons. A few examples of the risks of comparison may be taken—though old they are by no means a thing of the past.

### MORTALITY FROM CANCER

The crude death-rate from cancer (all forms) in Eire has in the past been well below that registered in England and Wales. Part of this difference may be due to a more favourable age-distribution of the population in Eire—*i.e.* standardised rates should be used in the comparison—but it is likely that it has also arisen from differences in the certification of causes of death. In Eire considerably more deaths have been ascribed to senility than in England and Wales—for example, 15 per cent. in the former in 1932 against about 4 per cent. in the latter. Such a difference cannot inspire confidence in the death-rate from such a disease as cancer, in which the majority of deaths fall at advanced ages.  In general, in comparing the cancer death-rates of different countries or of the different areas of the same country—*e.g.* rural and urban—it is not sufficient to pay attention to the cancer rubric ; other headings such as " uncertified," " senility," and " ill-defined causes " must be taken into consideration, and an attempt made to determine whether transferences between these rubrics are likely to play a part.

The kind of indirect correlation that one may observe is this.  It is stated that the cancer death-rate is associated with the consumption of sugar, and the level of the former is compared with some measure of the latter in different countries.  It is found that the countries with a low consumption of sugar have relatively low cancer death-rates.  But it is at least possible that those countries which have a high standard of living have a relatively higher sugar consumption, and also a higher standard of vital statistics, and therefore more accurate cancer death-rates, than countries with a low standard of living and less accurate vital statistics.  Other " causes " of death—*e.g.* ill-defined and old age—would need study as well as those attributed directly to cancer.

### MATERNAL MORTALITY

It has been recognised that the maternal death-rates of different countries may be affected by varying rules of tabulation in vogue.  Some years ago a sample of deaths associated with pregnancy and childbirth that took place in the U.S.A. was assigned by different statistical offices of the world to puerperal and non-puerperal groups according to the rules of those offices (Children's Bureau Publication No. 229).  The variability was considerable.  In the U.S.A. 93 per cent. were tabulated to puerperal causes, in England and Wales 79 per cent., in Denmark 99 per cent.  Such differences may still make international comparisons difficult.

### MORTALITY FROM RESPIRATORY CAUSES

In England and Wales bronchitis and pneumonia have shown pronounced differences in their incidence in different parts of the country at certain ages.  It appears that the

" bronchitis " of one area might include deaths which would be attributed to pneumonia in another. For instance, the Registrar-General concluded that " at both extremes of life London appears to call pneumonia many cases which are elsewhere regarded as bronchitis " (Registrar-General's Annual Report, Text, p. 85, 1932). Such " internal " differences are always closely considered by the Registrar-General, and his reports are invaluable to all who are concerned with the changes in the causes of death in England and Wales.

## Infant Mortality-rates

The international comparison of mortality in infancy may be quite materially affected by the laws regulating the registration of births and deaths. In many countries, *e.g.* England and Wales, if the infant shows any signs of life but then dies within a short period of time, the law requires the registration of a livebirth and then of a death. In some countries, on the other hand, a baby born alive but dying before the end of the 2-3 days allowed for registration of the birth is not included in the statistics of infant mortality but is treated as a stillbirth. Very early infant mortality is thereby excluded from the rate and the comparison of the figures for the various countries is not strictly valid. Apart from this the comparisons will also be affected by the criteria adopted in defining a stillbirth. When is it that the infant is to be regarded as having been born alive and when as a stillbirth ? The definitions vary in different countries and affect the relative levels of their infant mortality and still-birth rates.

## The Average Age at Death

The average age at death is not often a particularly useful measure. Between one occupational group and another it may be grossly misleading. For instance, as William Farr pointed out three-quarters of a century ago, the average age at death of bishops is much higher than the corresponding average of curates. But making all the curates bishops will not necessarily save them from an early death. The average

age at death in an occupation must, of course, depend in part upon the age of entry to that occupation and the age of exit from it—if exit takes place for other reasons than death. Bishops have a higher age at death than curates because few men become bishops before they have passed middle life, while curates may die at any age from their twenties upwards.

The following misuse of this average is taken from a report on hospital patients.

It is stated that in 31 cases of renal hypertension which came to autopsy the average age of death was 45. "Thus the common fate of the renal hypertensive is to die in the fifth decade of life." This may be a true statement of fact, but it clearly cannot be deduced from the average age ; the average might be 45 years without a single individual dying in the fifth decade. The report continues : "In 86 cases of essential hypertension which came to autopsy the average age at death was found to be 60, while in 20 cases seen in private practice the average age at death was nearly 70.

"Thus, the fate of the non-renal hypertensive is very different from that of the renal. The subject of uncomplicated essential hypertension may reasonably expect to live into the seventh or even the eighth decade."

The first deduction is probably valid, though obviously information regarding the *variability* round those averages is required. The frequency distributions of the age at death for the two groups should be given. The "reasonable expectation" has no real foundation in the figures given. If the subjects of uncomplicated essential hypertension mainly live into the seventh or eighth decade one might reasonably adopt that as an expectation. But if the average age is derived from individual ages at death varying between say, 40 and 90, one has no justification for using that average as an expectation.

The author regards statistics as "dull things" and therefore refers to them as "briefly as possible"—so briefly that in his hands they are of very little use.

To take one further example, a difference in the average ages at death from, say, silicosis in two occupations may imply that in one occupation the exposure to risk is mor intense than in the other and thus leads to earlier death ; but this interpretation can only hold, as is pointed out above, so long as the employed enter the two occupations at the same ages and give up their work at the same ages and to the same extent. It is usually very difficult to secure good evidence on these points, and the average ages at death must be regarded with some caution.

## The Expectation of Life

It was stated in Chapter XVIII that the " expectation of life " is the average number of years lived beyond any age by the survivors at that age when exposed to some selected mortality-rates. For instance, at the age mortality-rates of England and Wales in 1910–12 the average length of life of males after birth was 51·5 years ; at the rates of 1950 it was 66·5. It is sometimes wrongly deduced that those figures imply an increase of some 15 more years of life to enjoy *when we reach retiring age*. Actually the expectation of life of males at age 60 was 13·78 years in 1910–12 and 15·09 years in 1950, an increase of only 16 months. Apart from the fact that the calculation involves the assumption that current mortality-rates will continue to prevail, it must be remembered that the average length of life after birth will be influenced by reductions in the death-rate at *any* stage of life. The increase in the expectation has been largely due to the fall in infant mortality and early childhood, which implies much fewer very short durations of life than formerly. Such a fall would increase the average length of life even if not a soul survived age 60 then or now. After age 60 mortality-rates did not fall sufficiently between 1910–12 and 1950 to increase the average length of survival substantially.

## Problems of Inheritance

Literally hundreds of disorders or derangements in mankind have been recorded as showing evidence of hereditary factors. The evidence mainly consists of the appearance of

U

the disease or disability in a more or less orderly fashion among related individuals. In many instances there is no doubt that hereditary factors are important, but in others their presence is difficult of proof, in the inevitable absence of controlled breeding experiments and the impossibility sometimes of distinguishing genetic from environmental influences. Cases are reported, for example, of a familial incidence of cancer; a man whose father died of cancer of the stomach died himself of cancer in the same site, while his wife died of cancer of the breast and their six children and one grandchild all died of various forms of cancer. This is a very striking family history, but it is not necessarily evidence of an inherited factor. If each of these individuals had been known to have passed through an attack of measles we should not deduce a particular family susceptibility to measles, since we know that measles in the whole population is so widespread that a familial incidence is bound to occur very frequently. Similarly we want to know the probability of observing a series of familial cases of cancer merely by chance. Even if that probability is small it must be remembered that the field of observation amongst medical men is enormously wide and a few isolated instances of multiple cases cannot be adequate evidence. Usually, too, only one part of the field is reported in medical literature, for notice is taken of the remarkable instances and no reference made to the cases in which no inheritance is apparent. The data required in such a problem are reasonably large numbers of family histories, so that, if possible, it may be seen whether the distribution of multiple cases differs from the distribution that might be expected by chance, or whether the incidence in different generations suggests a Mendelian form of inheritance. Even if the distribution of multiple cases differs from that expected on a chance hypothesis, the question of a common family environment cannot be ruled out—*e.g.* multiple cases of tuberculosis may occur more frequently in families of a low social level not through an inherited diathesis but through undernourishment.

## The Errors Balance Out

It is sometimes reasonable to suppose that errors in statistical data will balance out and therefore are of no importance. For instance, in calculating the arithmetic mean as in Chapter VI we presume that the observations in a frequency distribution are spread across each of the frequency groups in such a way that we may accept, as a sufficiently accurate approximation, the centre of the group as applying to all the observations in it. Spread over the whole of the distribution, the errors we make are likely to balance out. Similarly there may sometimes be errors in observations which will balance out. For example, deaths attributed to a form of cancer may be overstated by the attribution to it of deaths really due to other causes ; they may be understated by the omission of deaths attributed to other causes which were in fact due to it. The errors could balance out (though we should need evidence to that effect).

On the other hand, biased errors cannot possibly balance out. If in taking case histories of patients, the majority deliberately—or merely through wishful thinking—understate their normal daily consumption of alcohol, there can be no balancing out of errors. The final answer, and the figures derived from it, *must* be an understatement. Whether errors are likely to balance out or to lead to an erroneous picture therefore often requires careful thought in planning an inquiry or in analysing its results. The answer is not always so clear-cut as in the examples above.

Similar reflection may be required in the study of the *relative* position of two groups in which the observations are liable to error. To take a specific example, in measuring the incidence of influenza in a vaccinated and an unvaccinated group we are certain, owing to the difficulties of diagnosis, to be including illnesses due to other respiratory causes against which the vaccine would be expected to be powerless. We must by this dilution weaken the evidence in favour of the vaccine. Instead of comparing the two relative rates of influenza ($x_1$ against $x_2$) we are comparing the relative rates of influenza *plus in each group a constant amount of other diseases* $((x_1 + y)$ against $(x_2 + y))$. If the other diseases are relatively infrequent, as they may well be when influenza is sharply epidemic, then clearly the assessment of the vaccine will not be seriously at fault ($y$ is a small and unimportant component). But if the other diseases included are relatively frequent, as they may well be when influenza is merely sporadic, then the assessment of the vaccine may be in serious jeopardy ($y$ dominates the comparison). There can be no question of the errors balancing out.

### The " All or None Syndrome "

A widespread misconception of scientific evidence of cause and effect, that arises in even well-educated minds, lies in the argument that some personally observed exception gravely weakens, or even destroys, the more general and, often, very extensive evidence of that relationship. Exceptions to an apparent rule are, of course, important in all circumstances of observation or experiment and we must never lightly dismiss them. The fact, for instance, that a non-smoker contracts cancer of the lung, or a man who never drinks water sickens with typhoid fever, is both interesting and important. We are by such observations informed, *whatever we may believe about smoking and polluted water supplies*, that there must certainly be other means of acquiring these diseases. Similarly the fact that heavy smokers or drinkers of a contaminated water supply do *not* fall sick is also important. *However much we believe in the relationship*, we are thereby informed that there must be further undetected environmental or constitutional factors to sway the balance upwards or downwards in the individual. But, clearly, none of the exceptions is incompatible with the observation that *on the average* drinkers of polluted water may have more typhoid fever than those who have a pure supply or that those who smoke most may *on the average* die more frequently of lung cancer. Whether we deal with the *bacillus typhosus*, a carcinogenic agent, or an industrial dust hazard there are very few things in life that are 100 per cent. effective or have a simple all-or-none reaction.

# XXIV

## GENERAL SUMMARY AND CONCLUSIONS

THE aim of this book has been to make clear to the non-mathematically inclined worker some of the technique that the statistician employs in presenting and in interpreting figures. Much of that discussion has been directed to two basic problems :—

(1) The "*significance*," or reliability in the narrow sense, of a difference which has been observed between two sets of figures—be those figures averages, measures of variability, proportions, or distributions over a series of groups.

(2) The *inferences* that can be drawn from a difference which we are satisfied is not likely to be due to chance.

### A Secure Foundation for Argument

The discussion of the first problem led to the development of tests of " significance "—the standard errors of individual values, the standard errors of the differences between values, and the $\chi^2$ test. The object of such tests is to prevent arguments being built up on a foundation that is insecure owing to the inevitable presence of sampling errors. Medical literature is full of instances of the neglect of this elementary precaution. Illustration is hardly necessary, but the following is just one quotation : " a mere list of the treatments which have been tried in thrombo-angiitis obliterans would be of formidable length and there is little point in mentioning many of them—they have only too often fallen by the way after an introduction more optimistic than warranted by results " (*Lancet*, 1937, 1, 551).

In general, worker A, who is at least careful enough to

299

observe a control group, reports after a short series of observations that a particular method of treatment gives him a greater proportion of successes than he secures with patients not given that treatment, and that therefore this treatment should be adopted.  Worker B, sceptically or enthusiastically, applies the same treatment to similar types of patients and has to report no such advantage.  The application of the simple probability tests previously set out would have (or should have) convinced A that though his treatment *may* be valuable, the result that he obtained *might* quite likely have been due to chance.  He would consequently have been more guarded in his conclusions and stressed the limitations of his data.

If, however, the test satisfied worker A that the difference in reaction that he observed between his two groups was *not* likely to be due to chance, then there comes the second, and usually much more difficult, problem.  Were his two groups of patients really equivalent in all relevant characteristics except in their differentiation by mode of treatment ?  This question immediately emphasises the importance of the initial planning of clinical trials with some new treatment or procedure, a point which was discussed at length in Chapter XX.  The simple probability tests are *not* rules merely to be applied blindly at the end of an experiment, whether that experiment be well or badly carried out.  Certainly they can tell us in either case whether certain observed results are likely or not likely to be due to chance ; equally certainly they can tell us nothing beyond that.  But if the trials are well-planned then we can with reason infer that the " significant " difference observed between the groups is more likely to be due to the specific treatment than to any other factor, for such other factors are likely to be equally present in both groups in the well-planned test.  If the trials are badly planned, in the sense that the groups to be compared are allowed to differ in various important respects as well as in treatment, then we can infer nothing whatever about the advantages of the specific treatment.  The time to reach that very obvious conclusion is not at the end of the experiment, when time, labour, and money have been spent, but before the experiment is embarked upon. To argue at the end of a badly planned experiment that the statistical method is not applicable is not reasonable. The statistical method (like any other method) must fail if it has to be applied to faulty material ; but faulty material is often the product of a faulty experiment. Much thought, in fact, must be given to the devising of a good experiment, of really effective clinical trials, and the statistical aspect must be borne in mind from the start.

### Field Surveys

The same reasoning applies, and with no less strength, to the collection of data by survey methods. We are not then making an experiment to see what happens, but asking questions, in one way or another, to see what exists, and, usually, to determine what relationships may prevail in the population between its various characteristics, *e.g.* its habits of eating and its incidence of enteric fever. But asking questions, whether by clinical examination, by cross-examination, or by means of questionnaires, is often an exceedingly difficult task, though many workers still do not recognise it as such.

As stressed in Chapter IV, the first and most decisive step in a field survey is the construction of the form of record. No amount of attention to detail in this task can be misplaced. Much thought must be given also to an appropriate scheme of sampling or, if Nature presents the sample, to the dangers of selection.

### The Numbers Required

A question very frequently put to the statistician relates to the size of the sample that is necessary to give a reliable result. To that there is usually no simple answer. If two groups are to be compared, a treated and a control group, then the size of the sample necessary to " prove the case " must depend upon the magnitude of the difference that ensues.

If, to take a hypothetical example, the fatality-rate (or any other selected measure) is 40 per cent. in the control group and 20 per cent. in the treated group, then by the ordinary test of " significance " of the difference between two proportions, that difference would be more than is likely to occur by chance with 42 patients in each group (taking twice the standard error as the level).    In other words, with those fatality-rates we must have observed at least 42 patients in each group to feel at all confident in our results.    If there were 50 patients in each group and 20 died in the control group and 10 in the specially treated group, that difference is (on the criterion of " significance " adopted) more than would be likely to occur by chance.    If, on the other hand, the improvement was a reduction of the fatality-rate from 40 to 30 per cent. we should need at least 182 patients in each group.    If we had 200 in each group and 80 died in the one and 60 in the other, that difference is more than would be likely to occur by chance.    Finally, if the fatality-rate was only 4 per cent. in the control group and 2 per cent. in the treated group, we should require as many as 600 patients in each group to be able to dismiss chance as a likely explanation.    With that number in each group there would be 24 and 12 deaths, and a difference of this order on smaller numbers might well be due to chance.    (In such a case the fatality-rate, of course, might not be the best measure of the advantages of the treatment.)

The determination of the numbers required is based, it will be noted, upon the difference observed between the groups.    In practice, we often do not know what that difference is likely to be, until at least some preliminary or pilot trials have been made.    Unless there is some indication from past experience as to the kind of difference that may result, and that we would regard as important, there can be no answer given in advance to the question " how many observations must be made ? "

Even the smallest amount of data may well have its advantage, if collected on some uniform system and clearly defined.    In some instances it is only by the accumulation of such data that an answer to a problem can be reached.

For example, there is some evidence that epidemics of milk-
borne and water-borne enteric fever differ in the sex- and
age-incidence of the persons attacked, the former attacking
women and children—the larger consumers of milk—with
proportionately greater frequency. The degree to which
that occurs cannot be settled by the evidence from any one
epidemic ; it requires the accumulation of data from a series
of epidemics of the two types. The field of observation of
any one worker is insufficient, but if uniform data of the sex
and age of patients are systematically collected and published
reliable evidence can eventually be reached.

## " Not Significant "

It is also, on this point of numbers, important to keep in
mind the meaning of statistically " significant " and " not
significant." The calculation of standard errors, $\chi^2$, and
similar constants is undoubtedly of value in preventing us
from " overcalling a hand " and from attributing too freely
to some cause what might very well be due only to chance.
The calculation also has the advantage of setting a standard
of judgment which is constant from one person to another.
Beyond that it cannot go. A " significant " answer does not
*prove* that the difference is real—chance is still a possible,
though unlikely, explanation ; it certainly does not prove
that the difference is of any material importance—it could be
significant on large enough numbers but utterly negligible ;
inspection and consideration of the results themselves must
be (and *always* should be) made for that ; it never proves
(or even indicates) the cause of the difference. On the other
hand, a " not significant " answer does not tell us that Group
A does *not* differ from Group B—the figures in front of us
show, in fact, that it does, though maybe immaterially. But
it does tell us that chance is a not unlikely reason for that
difference, and it is clearly important to know that, before
we seek some more recondite explanation or before we take
action. When a material difference *is* apparent between two
groups, but, with the numbers involved, is insufficient to pass
the formal probability test, it is better (particularly in a

matter of importance) to take " statistically not significant "
as the " non-proven " of Scots law rather than as the " not
guilty " of English law.

## Common Sense and Figures

Apart from these problems of the errors of sampling, much
of the discussion of the interpretation of figures has centred,
it will have been noted, not so much on technical methods
of analysis but on the application of common sense to figures
and on elementary rules of logic.   The common errors discussed in Chapters XXI to XXIII are not due to an absence
of knowledge of specialised statistical methods or of mathematical training, but usually to the tendency of workers
to accept figures at their face value without considering
closely the various factors influencing them—without asking
themselves at every turn " what is at the back of these
figures ?  what factors may be responsible for this value ?  in
what possible ways could these differences have arisen ? "
That is constantly the crux of the matter.  Group A is
compared with Group B and a difference in some characteristic is observed.  It is known that Group A differed from
Group B in one particular way—*e.g.* in treatment.  It is
therefore concluded too readily that the difference observed
is the result of the treatment.  To reject that conclusion in
the absence of a full discussion of the data is *not* merely an
example of armchair criticism or of the unbounded scepticism
of the statistician.  Where, as in all statistical work, our
results may be due to more than one influence, there can be
no excuse for ignoring that fact.  And it has been said with
truth that the more anxious we are to prove that a difference
between groups is the result of some particular action we
have taken or observed, the more exhaustive should be our
search for an alternative and equally reasonable explanation
of how that difference has arisen.

It is also clearly necessary to avoid the reaction to
statistics which leads an author to give only the flimsiest
statement of his figures on the grounds that they are dull
matters to be passed over as rapidly as possible.  They may

be dull—often the fault lies in the author rather than in his data—but if they are cogent to the thesis that is being argued they must inevitably be discussed fully by the author and considered carefully by the reader.   If they are not cogent, then there is no case for producing them at all.   In both clinical and preventive medicine, and in much laboratory work, we cannot escape from the conclusion that they are frequently cogent, that many of the problems we wish to solve *are* statistical and that there is no way of dealing with them except by the statistical method.

# DEFINITIONS

## Common Statistical Terms

*Frequency Distribution.*—A table constructed from a series of records of individuals (whatever the characteristic measured) to show the frequency with which there are present individuals with some defined characteristic or characteristics.

*Arithmetic Mean or Average.*—The sum of the values recorded in a series of observations ÷ the number of observations.

*Weighted Mean or Average.*—The average of two or more means, or rates, each mean, or rate, being weighted by the number of observations upon which it is based. Thus if the mean of 150 observations is 10·5 and of another 200 observations it is 8·3, the weighted average is {(150 × 10·5) + (200 × 8·3)} ÷ (150 + 200).

*Median.*—The centre value of a series of observations when the observations are ranged in order from the lowest value to the highest (with an even number of observations the mean of the two central observations is usually taken). In the frequency distribution it is calculated as the mid-point which divides the distribution into two halves. The median is a useful form of average when the arithmetic mean is unduly affected by very large or very small outlying observations.

*Mode.*—The maximum point on the curve which most closely describes an observed frequency distribution, *i.e.* the measurement which occurs most frequently. It can be calculated approximately from the formula Mode = Mean minus 3 (Mean minus Median).

It cannot be taken as the group which contains the highest frequency, for that depends upon the units of grouping adopted.

*Range.*—The distance between the lowest and highest values observed.

*Mean Deviation.*—The arithmetic average of all the differences between the observations and their mean, the differences being added without regard to their sign, *i.e.* ignoring whether the observation is above or below the mean.

*Standard Deviation.*—The square root of the arithmetic average of the squares of the differences between the observations and their mean. In practice, a slightly better estimate of the variability of the characteristic under study is, on the average, reached by dividing the sum of the squared deviations by one less than the total number of observations, *i.e.* by $n - 1$ in place of $n$.

*Coefficient of Variation.*—The standard deviation expressed as a percentage of the mean, or (S.D. ÷ Mean) × 100.

## Sampling

*Simple Random Sampling.*—Drawing a sample from a universe (or parent population) by a random method, *e.g.* by the use of random sampling numbers, which gives every individual in the universe an *equal* chance of appearing in the sample.

*Stratified Random Sampling.*—Drawing a sample from a universe which has first been divided into sub-groups or strata. From each sub-group a sample is drawn by a random method which gives every individual *in the sub-group an equal chance* of appearing in the sample. The chances can deliberately be made to vary from one sub-group to another but in that event each such chance must have a *known* value.

*Two (or more) Stage Sampling.*—A process of sampling a universe in a series of consecutive steps, *e.g.* a town may be divided into a number of areas and a number of those areas drawn by a random process; within these drawn areas the schools may be listed and a number of these schools drawn by a random process. The pupils within those schools are then the sample to be examined (or further stage sampling can be applied by the random selection of a sample of the pupils).

*Systematic Sampling.*—Drawing a sample from a universe by a systematic procedure, *e.g.* by taking every *n*th patient entering a ward.

### Tests of Significance

The *standard error* of any statistical value is a measure, on certain simple assumptions, of the standard deviation that that value would show in taking repeated samples from the same universe of observations. In other words, it shows how much variation might be expected to occur merely by chance in the various characteristics of samples drawn equally randomly from one and the same population. In practice, the values are calculated as follows.

*Standard Error of the Mean.*—The standard deviation of the observations in the sample $\div$ the square root of the number of observations.

*Standard Error of a Percentage.*—$\sqrt{(p \times q) \div n}$, where $p$ is the percentage in the sample having the characteristic which is being discussed (*e.g.* the percentage dying), $q$ is the percentage not having the characteristic (*e.g.* the percentage alive), and $n$ is the number of observations. $p + q$ must equal 100.

*Standard Error of the Difference between Two Means.*—Either $\sqrt{(\text{S.D.}_1)^2/n_1 + (\text{S.D.}_2)^2/n_2}$, where $\text{S.D.}_1$ and $\text{S.D.}_2$ are the standard deviations of the observations in the two samples and $n_1$ and $n_2$ are the numbers of observations; or $\sqrt{(\text{S.D.})^2/n_1 + (\text{S.D.})^2/n_2}$, where S.D. is an estimate of the standard deviation of the universe sampled derived from all the observations available in the two samples.

*Standard Error of the Difference between Two Proportions.*—Either $\sqrt{(p_1 \times q_1)/n_1 + (p_2 \times q_2)/n_2}$, where $p_1$ and $q_1$ are the percentages in one sample which have and do not have the characteristic, and $p_2$ and $q_2$ are the corresponding percentages in the second sample; or $\sqrt{(p \times q)/n_1 + (p \times q)/n_2}$, where $p$ and $q$ are the percentages in both samples combined which have and do not have the characteristic and $n_1$ and $n_2$ are the numbers of observations in the two samples.

" *Significance.*"—If two means or two proportions differ by more than twice the value of the standard error of the difference, the difference is said to be " significant," *i.e.* more than is easily likely to have arisen by chance. In fact, such a difference would arise by chance, roughly, once in 20 times; if the difference is $2\frac{1}{2}$ times its standard error, it would arise by chance once in 80 times, and if it is 3 times its standard error, once in 370 times.

*Test of Significance of the Correlation Coefficient.*—A certain correlation coefficient is observed in a sample; to test whether that figure might easily have arisen by chance in taking a sample from a universe in which there is no correlation at all between the two characteristics measured, the standard error is $1/\sqrt{n-1}$, where $n$ is the number of observations in which the two characteristics have been noted. If the coefficient is more than twice this value, it is unlikely to have arisen by chance.

$\chi^2$, *or the Chi-square Test.*—A test as to whether an observed series of frequencies differ between themselves, or from a series of frequencies expected on some hypothesis, to a greater degree than might be expected to occur by chance.

## Correlation

*Correlation Coefficient.*—A measure of the degree of association found between two characteristics in a series of observations (on the assumption that the relationship between the two characteristics is adequately described by a straight line). Its value must lie between $+1$ and $-1$, either plus or minus 1 denoting complete dependence of one characteristic on the other, and 0 denoting no association whatever between them. A plus sign shows that an upward movement of one characteristic is accompanied by an upward movement in the other ; a negative sign that an upward movement of one is accompanied by a downward movement of the other.

*Regression Coefficient.*—The amount of change that will on the average take place in one characteristic when the other characteristic changes by a unit (*e.g.* as age increases by one year the average increase in weight at ages 4–14 years is, say, 4 lb.). If one characteristic is termed $x$ and the other $y$, then the coefficient showing how much $x$ changes, on the average, for a unit change in $y$ is equal to (the correlation coefficient between the observed values of $x$ and $y$)

$$\times \frac{\text{standard deviation of the observed values of } x}{\text{standard deviation of the observed values of } y}, \text{ i.e. } r_{xy}\frac{\sigma_x}{\sigma_y}.$$

*Regression Equation.*—The equation to the straight line describing the association between the two characteristics and enabling the value of one characteristic to be estimated when the value of the other is known. To estimate the value of $x$ from a known value of $y$ the required equation is : ($x$ – mean of observed values of $x$)= Regression Coefficient ($y$ – mean of observed values of $y$), where the regression coefficient is as in the previous definition.

*Scatter Diagram.*—A graph upon which each individual measured is entered as a point or dot, the position of each point being determined by the values observed in the individual for the two characteristics measured (*e.g.* height and weight, each dot representing the associated height and weight).

## Rates of Birth and Death

*Birth-rate.*—The live births occurring (or sometimes registered) in the calendar year ÷ the estimated total population of the area at the middle of the year (usually expressed per 1000 of population).

*Fertility-rate.*—The live births occurring (or sometimes registered) ÷ the female population at child-bearing ages (usually taken as 15–44 years) or the legitimate live births occurring (or registered) ÷ the married female population at child-bearing ages. If the age of mother is given on the birth certificate, fertility-rates at certain ages may be calculated, viz. live births to mothers aged 15–19 ÷ married female population aged 15–19 (usually expressed per 1000).

*Crude Death-rate or Mortality-rate.*—The total deaths occurring (or sometimes registered) in the calendar year ÷ the estimated total population of the area at the middle of the year (usually expressed per 1000 of population).

*Standardised Death-rate or Mortality-rate.*—The death-rate at all ages calculated for comparative purposes in such a way that allowance is made for the age and sex composition of the population involved.

*Standardised Mortality Ratio.*—The ratio of deaths at all ages observed in a given population to the deaths that would have occurred in that population if in each age (and sex) group it had been exposed to some selected standard rates.

*Infant Mortality-rate.*—The deaths under 1 year of age occurring (or sometimes registered) in the calendar year ÷ total live births occurring (or registered) in the calendar year (usually expressed per 1000). The neonatal rate relates to the deaths that take place in the first 28 days of life.

*Still-birth Rate.*—A still birth in England and Wales applies to any child " which has issued forth from its mother after the twenty-eighth week of pregnancy and which did not at any time after being completely expelled from its mother breathe or show other signs of life." The rate is number of still births occurring, or registered, ÷ total births occurring, or registered (usually expressed per 1000).

*Maternal Mortality-rate.*—The deaths ascribed to puerperal causes ÷ the total live births and still births (usually expressed per 1000). When a record of still births is not available the denominator consists of live births only).

*Proportional Mortality-rate.*—The ratio of deaths from a given cause to the total deaths (usually expressed per cent., *e.g.* deaths from tuberculosis at all ages form 7 per cent. of all deaths).

## Morbidity Rates

(Morbidity, illness, and sickness are regarded as synonymous)

*The Incidence Rate.*—The number of illnesses (number of spells of illness or number of persons sick as applicable) *beginning* within a specified period of time related to the average number of persons exposed to risk during that period (or at its mid-point).

*The Period Prevalence Rate.*—The number of illnesses (number of spells of illness or number of persons sick as applicable) *existing at any time* within a specified period of time related to the average number of persons exposed to risk during that period (or at its mid-point).

*The Point Prevalence Rate.*—The number of illnesses (number of spells of illness or number of persons sick as applicable) *existing at a specified point of time* related to the number of persons exposed to risk at that point of time.

*The Average Duration of Sickness.*—The total number of days of illness in a defined period of time (*a*) divided by the average number of persons exposed to risk during that period (or at its mid-point) to give the *average duration of sickness per person* ; (*b*) divided by the number of persons sick during the period of time to give the *average duration of sickness per sick person* ; or (*c*) divided by the number of spells of sickness during the period of time to give the *average duration of sickness per illness*.

## Life-Table Symbols

(In each case *x* can take any value within the human span of life.)

$q_x$ is the probability of dying between any two ages $x$ and $x+1$ ; it corresponds to the ratio of the deaths that take place between the two ages to the population starting that year of life (*e.g.* if there are 150 persons who reach their 30th birthday and 5 die before reaching their 31st, then the probability of dying is 5/150).

$p_x$ is the probability of living ; it corresponds to the ratio of those who survive a year of life to those starting that year of life (the probability of living in the example above is therefore 145/150). $p_x + q_x$ must equal 1.

$l_x$ is the number in the life table living at each age $x$ (*e.g.* English Life Table No. 11 shows that out of 100,000 males at birth 96,186 survive at age 5 ; 96,186 is the value of $l_5$).

$d_x$ is the number of deaths that occur in the life table between any two adjacent ages (*e.g.* the number living at age 3 is 96,365 and at 4 is 96,267 and $d_3$ is therefore 98).

$\overset{o}{e}_x$ is the " expectation of life " at age $x$ and is the *average* length of subsequent life lived by those who have reached age $x$ (*e.g.* the average length of life lived after age 5 by the 96,186 male survivors at age 5 is 64·0 years).

X

# EXERCISES

## Chapter II.   Collection of Statistics:  Sampling

1. The following 240 observations represent the ages in years last birthday of children entering a hospital.

(a) Number them from 1 to 240 and, using random sampling numbers, draw a sample of 30 observations (for checking the answer start at Random Sampling Numbers III, columns 3, 4, and 5 on line 6, p. 346, and continue with columns 6, 7, and 8, etc.).

| (1) | (2) | (3) | (4) | (5) | (6) |
|-----|-----|-----|-----|-----|-----|
| 2   | 8   | 10  | 3   | 10  | 7   |
| 5   | 12  | 13  | 7   | 14  | 5   |
| 5   | 2   | 11  | 6   | 11  | 7   |
| 5   | 1   | 5   | 2   | 2   | 6   |
| 9   | 2   | 3   | 4   | 5   | 13  |
| 4   | 4   | 1   | 1   | 3   | 2   |
| 13  | 1   | 15  | 6   | 1   | 2   |
| 8   | 5   | 2   | 6   | 5   | 5   |
| 5   | 10  | 14  | 9   | 2   | 8   |
| 14  | 7   | 6   | 14  | 3   | 4   |
| 5   | 8   | 2   | 1   | 8   | 3   |
| 1   | 1   | 4   | 2   | 1   | 4   |
| 13  | 15  | 1   | 1   | 2   | 9   |
| 8   | 5   | 3   | 4   | 5   | 3   |
| 14  | 3   | 7   | 11  | 6   | 2   |
| 1   | 3   | 8   | 10  | 9   | 11  |
| 3   | 6   | 1   | 1   | 1   | 8   |
| 15  | 8   | 1   | 5   | 5   | 2   |
| 6   | 1   | 2   | 9   | 14  | 1   |
| 2   | 12  | 5   | 6   | 10  | 4   |
| 2   | 2   | 11  | 1   | 4   | 15  |
| 11  | 10  | 5   | 7   | 9   | 7   |
| 6   | 2   | 2   | 2   | 15  | 1   |
| 4   | 5   | 2   | 1   | 4   | 13  |
| 14  | 15  | 13  | 3   | 1   | 10  |
| 3   | 2   | 9   | 4   | 3   | 6   |
| 1   | 2   | 5   | 7   | 8   | 4   |
| 6   | 12  | 13  | 3   | 11  | 1   |
| 5   | 9   | 3   | 11  | 1   | 14  |
| 10  | 1   | 5   | 2   | 4   | 10  |
| 2   | 14  | 9   | 3   | 7   | 3   |
| 9   | 10  | 1   | 9   | 13  | 12  |
| 2   | 5   | 14  | 5   | 1   | 5   |
| 13  | 12  | 3   | 6   | 7   | 12  |
| 3   | 2   | 3   | 1   | 3   | 3   |
| 7   | 10  | 8   | 12  | 9   | 2   |
| 4   | 5   | 5   | 9   | 2   | 9   |
| 7   | 1   | 2   | 3   | 4   | 4   |
| 12  | 5   | 12  | 1   | 1   | 1   |
| 3   | 14  | 7   | 7   | 10  | 8   |

(b) Draw a sample systematically of every 8th entry (for checking the answer start with the 4th entry).

(c) Stratify the data into 3 age-groups, 1–5, 6–10, and 11–15. Draw a random sample from these groups with sampling fractions of 1 in 12, 1 in 8, and 1 in 4 respectively. (For checking the answer start for ages 1–5 at Random Sampling Numbers VI, columns 1, 2, and 3, line 29, p. 349, and then use columns 1 and 2, line 1, Set VII, p. 350, for ages 6–10 and columns 3 and 4, line 1, for ages 11–15).

Calculate the average of each of these three samples and compare the values with the average of the whole population.

[*Answer on pp. 323–4.*]

## Chapter V.  Presentation of Statistics

2. From the 120 figures below construct a table to show the number of towns with still-birth rates of various levels. Draw a histogram of the results.

THE STILL-BIRTH RATE IN 1936 IN EACH OF 120 LARGE TOWNS
(Still Births per 1000 Total Births)

| (1) | (2) | (3) | (4) | (5) |
|-----|-----|-----|-----|-----|
| 27 | 36 | 34 | 46 | 43 |
| 28 | 29 | 37 | 40 | 43 |
| 40 | 33 | 50 | 37 | 41 |
| 32 | 27 | 43 | 34 | 32 |
| 30 | 41 | 54 | 42 | 47 |
| 35 | 49 | 49 | 54 | 36 |
| 36 | 51 | 36 | 24 | 35 |
| 25 | 33 | 38 | 38 | 36 |
| 29 | 51 | 32 | 36 | 53 |
| 30 | 35 | 44 | 46 | 38 |
| 29 | 44 | 48 | 30 | 34 |
| 46 | 47 | 36 | 37 | 36 |
| 30 | 58 | 42 | 46 | 49 |
| 29 | 38 | 44 | 40 | 63 |
| 35 | 35 | 63 | 47 | 37 |
| 32 | 48 | 32 | 38 | 53 |
| 36 | 36 | 53 | 28 | 35 |
| 37 | 38 | 34 | 41 | 41 |
| 29 | 54 | 37 | 30 | 43 |
| 29 | 37 | 42 | 41 | 47 |
| 42 | 46 | 35 | 38 | 38 |
| 32 | 20 | 50 | 55 | 47 |
| 27 | 43 | 39 | 50 | 36 |
| 35 | 24 | 45 | 40 | 39 |

[*Answer on p. 325.*]

## Chapter VI.   The Average

3.  Calculate the arithmetic mean of the following distribution :—

| No. of Colds experienced in 12 Months | No. of Persons with given Experience |
|---|---|
| 0 | 15 |
| 1 | 46 |
| 2 | 91 |
| 3 | 162 |
| 4 | 110 |
| 5 | 95 |
| 6 | 82 |
| 7 | 26 |
| 8 | 13 |
| 9 | 2 |
| Total | 642 |

[Answer on p. 325.

4.  Calculate the mean median, and mode of the following distribution :—

| Haemoglobin Percentage Level | No. of Schoolgirls with given Level |
|---|---|
| 60– | 2 |
| 65– | .. |
| 70– | 7 |
| 75– | 32 |
| 80– | 90 |
| 85– | 166 |
| 90– | 245 |
| 95– | 200 |
| 100– | 162 |
| 105– | 97 |
| 110–114 | 21 |
| Total | 1022 |

[Answer on p. 326.

5.  The mean numbers of colds reported in 12 months in 10 groups of workers within a factory is given below.  Calculate the mean number for the whole factory.

| Group | Mean No. of Colds of Group | Number of Workers in Group |
|---|---|---|
| 1 | 2·0 | 22 |
| 2 | 7·2 | 41 |
| 3 | 1·8 | 34 |
| 4 | 5·4 | 110 |
| 5 | 6·0 | 46 |
| 6 | 5·0 | 59 |
| 7 | 4·4 | 12 |
| 8 | 2·4 | 12 |
| 9 | 5·6 | 32 |
| 10 | 4·0 | 164 |

Calculate the mean for the whole factory, presuming that each group contained 123 workpeople.                                    [Answer on p. 326.

Chapters VII and VIII.   The Variability of Observations

6. The age of onset is noted for two diseases, A and B.   Calculate the
mean and standard deviation for each of them.

*27 observations of disease A.*   Age of patient at onset of disease, in
years :—

> 39, 50, 26, 45, 47, 71, 51, 33, 40, 40, 51, 66, 63, 55, 36, 57, 41, 61,
> 47, 44, 48, 59, 42, 54, 47, 53, 54.

*36 observations of disease B.*   Age of patient at onset of disease, in
years :—

> 45, 44, 52, 46, 49, 58, 51, 48, 50, 53, 51, 49, 49, 47, 52, 54, 56, 58, 48,
> 45, 54, 47, 50, 50, 49, 41, 47, 52, 53, 55, 45, 54, 48, 52, 54, 49.

[*Answer on p. 327.*

7. Calculate the coefficient of variation for the following observations.
Check the answer roughly and then accurately.

| Haemoglobin Percentage Level | No. of Schoolgirls with given Level |
|---|---|
| 60– | 2 |
| 65– | .. |
| 70– | 7 |
| 75– | 32 |
| 80– | 90 |
| 85– | 166 |
| 90– | 245 |
| 95– | 200 |
| 100– | 162 |
| 105– | 97 |
| 110–114 | 21 |
| Total | 1022 |

[*Answer on p. 328.*

Chapter IX.   Problems of Sampling : Averages

8. Using the figures given in Table XV, p. 110, find the distribution of
means given by samples of 25 persons by taking the figures of Samples
Nos. 1–5 as the first sample of 25 persons, Samples Nos. 6–10 as the second
sample, Samples Nos. 11–15 as the third sample, and so on until Samples
Nos. 96–100 give the twentieth sample.   Compare this distribution for
samples of 25 persons with those given by samples of 5, 10, 20, and 50 in
Table XVI, p. 111.   Calculate the observed standard deviation of these 20
means and compare it with their expected standard deviation and with
the values given in Table XVII, p. 114.            [*Answer on p. 328.*

9. Find the standard error of the mean of the distribution given in
Question 3 above and the limits within which it is likely that the mean
of the population sampled will lie.            [*Answer on p. 329.*

## Chapter X.    Problems of Sampling: Proportions

**10.** Of the children entering a school at the age of 6 years 30 per cent. are reported to have had previously an attack of whooping-cough. Calculate the percentage frequency with which in samples of 5 children 0, 1, 2, 3, 4, and 5 would be found (in the long run) to have had a previous attack. Calculate the mean and standard deviation of this distribution ; check this standard deviation by calculating it from the formula $\sqrt{(pq/n)}$.

[*Answer on p. 329.*

**11.** If a sample of 9 children is taken from the above population, calculate the probability that it will contain at least 7 who have previously had whooping-cough, *i.e.* 78 per cent. or more, instead of the expected 30 per cent.                                                   [*Answer on p. 330.*

**12.** If a sample of 350 children is taken from the above population, calculate the range within which the proportion with a positive history is likely to lie.                                                   [*Answer on p. 330.*

## Chapter XI.    Problems of Sampling : Differences between Proportions

**13.** Imagine that a list of random sampling numbers represents a universe of persons in which the numbers 8 and 9 denote left-handed individuals and the remaining numbers right-handed individuals. A series of pairs of samples of 5 persons is drawn from this universe as shown in Table XV, p. 110, where Samples Nos. 1 and 2 represent the first two groups, Nos. 3 and 4 the second two groups . . . Nos. 99 and 100 the 50th pair of groups. Construct a frequency distribution to show the degree to which the proportion of left-handed persons differs between the pairs of samples. Calculate the mean and standard deviation of this distribution and compare these observed values with those expected on theoretical grounds.                                             [*Answer on p. 331.*

**14.** Of patients admitted consecutively to hospital every third one is treated by method A and the remainder by method B. Of the 150 on method A 15 die, and of the 300 on method B 45 die. Test whether the difference in fatality is more than might easily occur by chance.

[*Answer on p. 332.*

## Chapter XII.    Problems of Sampling: Differences between Averages

**15.** Given the erythrocyte sedimentation rates set out in the table below, test (1) whether the mean rate for Group A before treatment differs significantly from the mean of Group B ; (2) whether any significant effect followed the treatment of Group A.

| Group B | Group A | |
|---|---|---|
| Control group of persons uninfected | Before treatment of infection | After treatment of infection |
| 3 | 10 | 6 |
| 9 | 13 | 9 |
| 8 | 6 | 3 |
| 6 | 11 | 10 |
| 5 | 10 | 10 |
| 5 | 7 | 4 |
| 7 | 8 | 2 |
| 3 | 8 | 5 |
| 10 | 5 | 3 |
| 8 | 9 | 5 |
| 10 | | |
| 4 | | |

[*Answer on p. 332.*

Chapters XIII and XIV.   Problems of Sampling: $\chi^2$

16. Taking the observations given in Table XVI, p. 111, test whether the distribution of the means for samples of 20 differs significantly from the distribution for samples of 50.                    [*Answer on p 333.*]

17. Apply the $\chi^2$ test to Question No. 14 above.
                                                [*Answer on p. 333.*]

18. The following figures (adapted from Daley and Benjamin, *Med. Off.*, 1948) show the notifications in London of poliomyelitis and polio-encephalitis in 1937–46 and in the epidemic of 1947. Compare the age distributions and test by $\chi^2$ whether the epidemic year showed a significant variation from the previous experience.

| Age of the attacked in Years | No. of Notifications | |
|---|---|---|
| | 1937–46 | 1947 |
| 0–14 | 467 | 453 |
| 15 and over | 131 | 249 |
| Total | 598 | 702 |

                                                [*Answer on p. 334.*]

19. The data given in the table below (adapted from a paper by Hotelling, H., and Hotelling, F., 1932) show the frequency with which different durations of pregnancy occur, as reported by four different investigators. Compare these distributions from the four different sources and test whether they differ from one another by more than could readily be ascribed to chance. In other words, test whether they may be legitimately regarded as homogeneous material, *i.e.* samples from a common population.

| Estimated Duration of Pregnancy in Days (Live Births) | Number of Cases of each Duration found by : | | | |
|---|---|---|---|---|
| | Reid | Schlichting | Ahlfeld | Hotelling |
| 254–263 | 29 | 31 | 5 | 23 |
| 264–273 | 82 | 63 | 32 | 89 |
| 274–283 | 172 | 132 | 56 | 180 |
| 284–293 | 146 | 99 | 38 | 149 |
| 294–319 | 71 | 57 | 17 | 60 |
| Total | 500 | 382 | 148 | 501 |

                                                [*Answer on p. 334.*]

Chapters XV and XVI.    The Coefficient of Correlation

20. An inquiry has been made into the sickness experience of a number of boarding-schools. A note is made of the number of times during five years of observation that an infectious disease made its appearance— measles, scarlet fever, mumps, etc. For instance, in one school during the five years measles appeared three times, german measles four times, chicken-pox twice, and scarlet fever, mumps, and whooping-cough once each, giving a total figure of 12 " appearances." The figures below suggest that the number of times an infectious disease will occur is a function of the size of the school. Measure the relationship by means of the correlation coefficient and find the expected number of appearances for schools with 300 and 700 boys. Make a scatter diagram of the observations and draw through it the calculated regression line relating number of times to population size. (The figures are based upon fact but the correlation in the example is somewhat exaggerated.)

| School | Average Population of School (to nearest 100) | No. of Times in 5 Years that an Infectious Disease appeared |
|--------|--------|--------|
| A | 300 | 14 |
| B | 700 | 28 |
| C | 800 | 25 |
| D | 300 | 11 |
| E | 200 | 19 |
| F | 500 | 15 |
| G | 300 | 15 |
| H | 200 | 12 |
| I | 500 | 19 |
| J | 700 | 19 |
| K | 300 | 16 |
| L | 600 | 24 |
| M | 600 | 28 |
| N | 400 | 13 |
| O | 500 | 16 |
| P | 600 | 26 |
| Q | 400 | 19 |
| R | 400 | 21 |
| S | 900 | 41 |
| T | 700 | 38 |

[*Answer on p. 336.*]

21. The following (imaginary) figures refer to 80 factory operatives and show for each man (a) the average number of days lost from work per annum over a number of years, and (b) the average number of hours of overtime worked per week over the same period of observation. Construct a grouped correlation table from these observations (using three units for the class interval for each variable). Having considered by eye whether the table reveals any association, calculate (a) the correlation coefficient, (b) the observed regression line of days lost for a given amount of overtime, (c) the corresponding calculated regression line. Plot these two lines.

| Works No. of Man | No. of Days Lost | Hours of Overtime | Works No. of Man | No. of Days Lost | Hours of Overtime |
|---|---|---|---|---|---|
| 1 | 6·2 | 4·5 | 41 | 12·6 | 24·6 |
| 2 | 15·4 | 21·2 | 42 | 13·5 | 13·2 |
| 3 | 4·2 | 5·7 | 43 | 9·8 | 9·7 |
| 4 | 10·0 | 17·8 | 44 | 9·1 | 14·2 |
| 5 | 14·2 | 16·6 | 45 | 5·3 | 10·1 |
| 6 | 10·6 | 15·4 | 46 | 2·9 | 9·7 |
| 7 | 4·9 | 18·3 | 47 | 7·8 | 11·5 |
| 8 | 0·7 | 12·1 | 48 | 17·9 | 16·3 |
| 9 | 7·5 | 21·6 | 49 | 8·5 | 7·1 |
| 10 | 7·9 | 13·6 | 50 | 5·1 | 17·6 |
| 11 | 14·3 | 19·5 | 51 | 17·2 | 7·7 |
| 12 | 4·1 | 10·9 | 52 | 17·9 | 10·0 |
| 13 | 7·3 | 11·2 | 53 | 15·7 | 12·8 |
| 14 | 6·1 | 15·9 | 54 | 9·6 | 6·5 |
| 15 | 10·1 | 5·8 | 55 | 13·7 | 18·5 |
| 16 | 12·9 | 23·2 | 56 | 1·3 | 10·8 |
| 17 | 11·1 | 12·2 | 57 | 6·3 | 13·0 |
| 18 | 17·2 | 15·7 | 58 | 13·8 | 20·6 |
| 19 | 4·6 | 20·2 | 59 | 6·5 | 15·0 |
| 20 | 6·9 | 14·1 | 60 | 11·1 | 14·4 |
| 21 | 6·7 | 13·4 | 61 | 8·5 | 18·7 |
| 22 | 9·7 | 11·3 | 62 | 15·1 | 9·2 |
| 23 | 10·3 | 11·1 | 63 | 10·6 | 13·6 |
| 24 | 12·6 | 15·9 | 64 | 6·2 | 15·5 |
| 25 | 8·7 | 10·1 | 65 | 7·5 | 20·9 |
| 26 | 12·5 | 10·1 | 66 | 9·3 | 13·2 |
| 27 | 7·5 | 18·5 | 67 | 5·6 | 13·5 |
| 28 | 8·1 | 10·7 | 68 | 6·5 | 15·4 |
| 29 | 9·8 | 20·3 | 69 | 6·2 | 23·9 |
| 30 | 7·6 | 19·5 | 70 | 10·4 | 13·6 |
| 31 | 6·3 | 21·2 | 71 | 2·9 | 15·4 |
| 32 | 7·1 | 11·8 | 72 | 9·1 | 9·2 |
| 33 | 8·6 | 16·0 | 73 | 17·5 | 16·6 |
| 34 | 12·4 | 24·2 | 74 | 6·4 | 20·8 |
| 35 | 16·8 | 8·3 | 75 | 10·2 | 4·7 |
| 36 | 5·0 | 14·6 | 76 | 3·6 | 5·1 |
| 37 | 7·0 | 10·6 | 77 | 12·6 | 4·6 |
| 38 | 6·3 | 16·8 | 78 | 10·3 | 6·4 |
| 39 | 16·3 | 16·8 | 79 | 6·7 | 8·4 |
| 40 | 13·6 | 19·7 | 80 | 13·5 | 16·3 |

*Answer on p. 337.*

Chapter XVII.    Calculation of Standardised Death-rates

22. The crude death-rate (from all causes) of England and Wales was 17·5 per 1000 persons living in 1898 and 11·6 in 1938. From the figures below calculate and compare the standardised death-rates, using the population of 1932 as the standard population. (If the question is answered without a calculating machine, use the population to the nearest 100,000 in each age and sex group.)

| Age in Years | Death-rates per 1000 | | | | Population of England and Wales | |
| | 1898 | | 1938 | | 1932 | |
| | Male | Female | Male | Female | Male | Female |
|---|---|---|---|---|---|---|
| 0– | 63·4 | 53·5 | 17·1 | 13·3 | 1,503,200 | 1,466,400 |
| 5– | 3·8 | 3·9 | 1·9 | 1·8 | 1,605,000 | 1,576,900 |
| 10– | 2·2 | 2·3 | 1·3 | 1·1 | 1,694,300 | 1,654,800 |
| 15– | 3·5 | 3·3 | 2·0 | 1·7 | 1,656,000 | 1,658,900 |
| 20– | 4·8 | 4·1 | 2·8 | 2·3 | 1,709,100 | 1,780,300 |
| 25– | 6·3 | 5·5 | 2·9 | 2·5 | 3,146,300 | 3,390,200 |
| 35– | 10·7 | 8·9 | 4·5 | 3·5 | 2,539,200 | 2,987,400 |
| 45– | 17·6 | 13·9 | 10·2 | 6·9 | 2,301,800 | 2,647,800 |
| 55– | 33·2 | 26·7 | 23·0 | 15·3 | 1,808,800 | 2,018,200 |
| 65– | 66·4 | 57·5 | 54·1 | 39·4 | 984,200 | 1,218,800 |
| 75– | 140·3 | 126·0 | 130·1 | 100·4 | 299,900 | 454,020 |
| 85+ | 282·6 | 259·6 | 263·8 | 236·5 | 32,200 | 67,280 |
| All Ages | 18·6 | 16·5 | 12·5 | 10·8 | 19,280,000 | 20,921,000 |

[Answer on p. 339.

23. In 1932 the crude death-rates in Greater London were 58 per million from diphtheria and 1491 per million from cancer. From the figures below, using as standard rates the death-rates in England and Wales in 1938, calculate the standardised rates in Greater London in 1932 for these two causes of death.

| Age in Years | Population of Greater London (00's) | | Population of England and Wales (00's) | | Deaths in England and Wales in 1938 | | | |
| | 1932 | | 1938 | | Diphtheria | | Cancer | |
| | Male | Female | Male | Female | Male | Female | Male | Female |
|---|---|---|---|---|---|---|---|---|
| 0– | 291,7 | 284,5 | 1,433,7 | 1,383,9 | 529 | 482 | 59 | 49 |
| 5– | 632,1 | 620,0 | 3,043,2 | 2,982,2 | 827 | 906 | 67 | 63 |
| 15– | 707,3 | 777,6 | 3,293,2 | 3,278,6 | 39 | 53 | 185 | 148 |
| 25– | 670,3 | 763,7 | 3,331,3 | 3,485,4 | 19 | 26 | 461 | 544 |
| 35 | 524,3 | 644,8 | 2,843,7 | 3,190,0 | 9 | 13 | 1,333 | 2,258 |
| 45– | 467,1 | 559,6 | 2,350,2 | 2,784,3 | 4 | 4 | 3,819 | 5,634 |
| 55– | 352,2 | 412,7 | 1,953,6 | 2,286,8 | 3 | 12 | 9,142 | 9,318 |
| 65– | 180,2 | 244,9 | 1,151,1 | 1,409,9 | 2 | 2 | 11,748 | 10,444 |
| 75+ | 59,8 | 109,5 | 392,0 | 621,9 | .. | 1 | 5,878 | 7,455 |
| All Ages | 3,885,0 | 4,417,3 | 19,792,0 | 21,423,0 | 1432 | 1499 | 32,692 | 35,913 |

[Answer on p. 339.

24. In the three departments of a large factory the number of days lost by sickness per man per annum were : Department A, 9·03 ; Department B, 8·68 ; Department C, 9·42. From the following (imaginary) figures compare the losses at ages and calculate a standardised rate for each department, using the total population of the factory as the standard.

| Age in Years | Department A | | Department B | | Department C | |
|---|---|---|---|---|---|---|
| | No. of Men | Days Lost | No. of Men | Days Lost | No. of Men | Days Lost |
| 20– | 100 | 650 | 350 | 2450 | 50 | 300 |
| 30– | 220 | 1540 | 400 | 3400 | 70 | 455 |
| 40– | 420 | 3570 | 100 | 1000 | 120 | 840 |
| 50– | 300 | 3000 | 50 | 600 | 300 | 2850 |
| 60+ | 140 | 1890 | 50 | 800 | 250 | 3000 |
| All Ages | 1180 | 10650 | 950 | 8250 | 790 | 7445 |

[*Answer on p. 340.*

## Chapter XVIII.   Life Tables

25. Below is given an extract from English Life Table No. 10 (based upon the mortality of 1930–32). Calculate the following values from it :—

(a) For each sex the probability at birth of becoming a centenarian.
(b) For each sex the probability that a person aged 25 will not survive to age 50.
(c) For each sex the probability that a person aged 25 will live to be 80
(d) For each sex the expectation of life at age 90.

| Age in Years | Number surviving at each Age | |
|---|---|---|
| | Male | Female |
| 0 | 100,000 | 100,000 |
| .. | .. | .. |
| .. | .. | .. |
| .. | .. | .. |
| .. | .. | .. |
| 10 | 89,023 | 91,082 |
| .. | .. | .. |
| .. | .. | .. |
| .. | .. | .. |
| .. | .. | .. |
| 25 | 85,824 | 88,133 |
| .. | .. | .. |
| .. | .. | .. |
| .. | .. | .. |
| .. | .. | .. |
| 50 | 74,794 | 78,958 |
| .. | .. | .. |
| .. | .. | .. |
| .. | .. | .. |
| .. | .. | .. |
| 80 | 16,199 | 24,869 |
| 81 | 13,850 | 21,920 |
| 82 | 11,677 | 19,086 |
| 83 | 9,700 | 16,402 |
| 84 | 7,932 | 13,897 |
| 85 | 6,377 | 11,594 |
| 86 | 5,035 | 9,514 |
| 87 | 3,900 | 7,671 |
| 88 | 2,961 | 6,072 |
| 89 | 2,205 | 4,725 |
| 90 | 1,609 | 3,611 |
| 91 | 1,149 | 2,706 |
| 92 | 801 | 1,986 |
| 93 | 545 | 1,425 |
| 94 | 361 | 998 |
| 95 | 232 | 681 |
| 96 | 145 | 452 |
| 97 | 87 | 291 |
| 98 | 51 | 182 |
| 99 | 29 | 110 |
| 100 | 15 | 64 |
| 101 | 8 | 37 |
| 102 | 4 | 19 |
| 103 | 2 | 10 |
| 104 | 1 | 5 |
| 105 | .. | 2 |
| 106 | .. | 1 |
| 107 | .. | .. |

[Answers on p. 340.

# ANSWERS TO EXERCISES

1. (*a*) Using Random Sampling Numbers III, columns 3, 4, and 5, line 6, etc., the required 30 numbers of 240 or less are given in column (1) below and the ages corresponding to them are given in column (2).

(*b*) With every 8th entry, starting at the 4th, the required 30 numbers are given in column (3) and the ages corresponding to them in column (4).

| (a) | | (b) | |
|---|---|---|---|
| (1) | (2) | (3) | (4) |
| 080 | 14 | 4 | 5 |
| 223 | 1 | 12 | 1 |
| 062 | 10 | 20 | 2 |
| 039 | 12 | 28 | 6 |
| 060 | 12 | 36 | 7 |
| 225 | 10 | 44 | 1 |
| 119 | 12 | 52 | 1 |
| 231 | 3 | 60 | 12 |
| 130 | 14 | 68 | 12 |
| 012 | 1 | 76 | 10 |
| 215 | 2 | 84 | 5 |
| 099 | 2 | 92 | 4 |
| 163 | 11 | 100 | 5 |
| 129 | 9 | 108 | 13 |
| 195 | 3 | 116 | 8 |
| 035 | 3 | 124 | 2 |
| 091 | 2 | 132 | 2 |
| 011 | 5 | 140 | 6 |
| 240 | 8 | 148 | 3 |
| 194 | 7 | 156 | 12 |
| 186 | 3 | 164 | 2 |
| 027 | 1 | 172 | 1 |
| 050 | 7 | 180 | 10 |
| 174 | 5 | 188 | 11 |
| 170 | 3 | 196 | 9 |
| 165 | 5 | 204 | 6 |
| 173 | 2 | 212 | 4 |
| 178 | 5 | 220 | 4 |
| 070 | 1 | 228 | 1 |
| 191 | 7 | 236 | 2 |

(c) The stratified observations are shown in columns 1 to 8 with the required values chosen by the random sampling numbers put in parentheses.

| Ages 1–5 132 observations | | | | Ages 6–10 65 observations | | Ages 11–15 43 observations | |
|---|---|---|---|---|---|---|---|
| (1) | (2) | (3) | (4) | (5) | (6) | (7) | (8) |
| 2 | 5 | 4 | 2 | 9 | (9) | 13 | (14) |
| 5 | 1 | 3 | 1 | 8 | (7) | 14 | 12 |
| 5 | 5 | 2 | 4 | 8 | 10 | (13) | (12) |
| 5 | 5 | 3 | 1 | 6 | 8 | 14 | |
| 4 | 3 | 5 | 4 | 6 | 6 | 15 | |
| 5 | 1 | 1 | 1 | (6) | 9 | 11 | |
| (5) | 2 | 3 | 3 | 10 | 10 | (14) | |
| 1 | 2 | 1 | 5 | 9 | 9 | (13) | |
| 1 | 4 | (2) | (3) | (7) | 8 | 12 | |
| 3 | 1 | 5 | 2 | 7 | 7 | 12 | |
| 2 | 3 | 3 | 4 | 8 | (7) | 15 | |
| (2) | 1 | 1 | 1 | 10 | 9 | 12 | |
| 4 | 1 | 5 | | 7 | 10 | (15) | |
| 3 | 2 | 2 | | 8 | 7 | 12 | |
| 1 | 5 | 3 | | 6 | 7 | (14) | |
| (5) | 5 | 1 | | 8 | 6 | 12 | |
| 2 | 2 | 2 | | 10 | 8 | 14 | |
| 2 | 2 | (5) | | 9 | 9 | 13 | |
| (3) | 5 | 1 | | 10 | 8 | 11 | |
| 4 | 3 | 5 | | 10 | 7 | (15) | |
| 3 | 5 | 4 | | 10 | 10 | 14 | |
| (2) | 1 | 4 | | 6 | 6 | 11 | |
| 1 | 3 | 1 | | (7) | 10 | 13 | |
| 2 | 3 | 3 | | 8 | 9 | 13 | |
| 4 | 5 | 1 | | 9 | 8 | (14) | |
| 1 | 2 | 4 | | 9 | | 12 | |
| 5 | 3 | 1 | | 8 | | 14 | |
| 1 | 2 | 3 | | 7 | | 11 | |
| 5 | 4 | 2 | | 7 | | 11 | |
| 3 | 1 | (4) | | (6) | | 12 | |
| 3 | 1 | 1 | | 6 | | (14) | |
| 1 | 2 | (5) | | 6 | | 11 | |
| 2 | 1 | (2) | | (9) | | 14 | |
| 2 | 4 | 2 | | 10 | | (15) | |
| 5 | 1 | 5 | | 9 | | 11 | |
| 2 | 5 | 4 | | 6 | | 13 | |
| 2 | 1 | 3 | | 7 | | 13 | |
| 1 | 2 | 4 | | 7 | | 11 | |
| 5 | 1 | 3 | | 9 | | 15 | |
| 2 | 3 | 2 | | 6 | | 13 | |

Adding up the observations and dividing by their number gives the averages as follows :—

(a)  $180/30 = 6 \cdot 0$ years

(b)  $167/30 = 5 \cdot 6$ years

(c)  $(38 \times \frac{132}{11}) + (58 \times \frac{65}{8}) + (153 \times \frac{43}{11})$
    $= (456 \cdot 00 + 471 \cdot 25 + 598 \cdot 09)/240$
    $= 1525 \cdot 34/240$
    $= 6 \cdot 4$ years

The population sampled :  $1445/240 = 6 \cdot 0$ year.

2. The highest and lowest rates occurring are 20 and 63. The difference is 43, and a class interval of 4 units will give 11 groups. The preliminary tabulation and final table may therefore be as follows :—

| PRELIMINARY TABULATION | | | FINAL TABLE | |
| --- | --- | --- | --- | --- |
| Rate | | | The Distribution of the Still-birth Rate in 120 Large Towns in the Year 1936 | |
| | | | Still-birth Rate (Still Births per 1000 Total Births) | Number of Towns recording given Still-birth Rate |
| 20– | ǀ | 1 | 20– | 1 |
| 24– | ₩ ǀ | 6 | 24– | 6 |
| 28– | ₩ ₩ ǀǀǀ | 13 | 28– | 13 |
| 32– | ₩ ₩ ₩ ₩ | 20 | 32– | 20 |
| 36– | ₩ ₩ ₩ ₩ ₩ ǀǀǀ | 28 | 36– | 28 |
| 40– | ₩ ₩ ₩ ǀǀǀ | 18 | 40– | 18 |
| 44– | ₩ ₩ ǀǀǀǀ | 14 | 44– | 14 |
| 48– | ₩ ₩ | 10 | 48– | 10 |
| 52– | ₩ ǀǀ | 7 | 52– | 7 |
| 56– | ǀ | 1 | 56– | 1 |
| 60–63 | ǀǀ | 2 | 60–63 | 2 |
| Total | | 120 | Total | 120 |

3.

| No. of Colds experienced in 12 Months | No. of Persons with given Experience | No. of Colds experienced by each Group |
| --- | --- | --- |
| (1) | (2) | (1)×(2) |
| 0 | 15 | 0 |
| 1 | 46 | 46 |
| 2 | 91 | 182 |
| 3 | 162 | 486 |
| 4 | 110 | 440 |
| 5 | 95 | 475 |
| 6 | 82 | 492 |
| 7 | 26 | 182 |
| 8 | 13 | 104 |
| 9 | 2 | 18 |
| Total | 642 | 2425 |

As the numbers of colds vary only from 0 to 9 the multiplications are simple and there is no gain in using any working units. The total number of colds experienced by the 642 persons is 2425, and the arithmetic mean is therefore 2425/642 = 3·78 colds per person.

4.

| Haemoglobin Percentage Level | No. of School-girls with given Level | Working Units | Sum of Haemoglobin Values in Working Units |
|---|---|---|---|
| (1) | (2) | (3) | (2)×(3) |
| 60– | 2 | – 6 | – 12 |
| 65– | .. | – 5 | 0 |
| 70– | 7 | – 4 | – 28 |
| 75– | 32 | – 3 | – 96 |
| 80– | 90 | – 2 | – 180 |
| 85– | 166 | – 1 | – 166 |
| 90– | 245 | 0 | 0   – 482 |
| 95– | 200 | +1 | +200 |
| 100– | 162 | +2 | +324 |
| 105– | 97 | +3 | +291 |
| 110–114 | 21 | +4 | +84 |
| | | | +899 |
| Total | 1022 | | |

The sum in working units $=(+899-482)=+417$, and the mean is $+417/1022=+0\cdot408$. The real mean is therefore $92\cdot5+5(0\cdot408)=94\cdot54$. (The centre of the group 90–95 has been taken as 92·5. If it were known that readings were made to, say, the nearest whole number, the group would in reality run from 89·5 to 94·5 and its centre be 92·0.)

The median is estimated as lying at the exact mid-point, *i.e.* $1022/2=511$. $2+0+7+32+90+166=297$, and the 511th value is 214 values beyond this. The median, therefore, equals $90+(214/245$ of $5)=90+(0\cdot8735\times5)=94\cdot37$.

The mode $=$ Mean $-3$(Mean $-$ Median)
$$=94\cdot54-3(94\cdot54-94\cdot37)$$
$$=94\cdot54-0\cdot51$$
$$=94\cdot03.$$

5.

| Group | Mean No. of Colds | Number of Workers in Group | Total Number of Colds experienced by each Group |
|---|---|---|---|
| | (1) | (2) | (1)×(2) |
| 1 | 2·0 | 22 | 44·0 |
| 2 | 7·2 | 41 | 295·2 |
| 3 | 1·8 | 34 | 61·2 |
| 4 | 5·4 | 110 | 594·0 |
| 5 | 6·0 | 46 | 276·0 |
| 6 | 5·0 | 59 | 295·0 |
| 7 | 4·4 | 12 | 52·8 |
| 8 | 2·4 | 12 | 28·8 |
| 9 | 5·6 | 32 | 179·2 |
| 10 | 4·0 | 164 | 656·0 |
| Total | .. | 532 | 2482·2 |

The mean number per worker for the whole factory is $2482\cdot2/532=4\cdot67$.

If each group contained the *same* number of workpeople, 123, or any other number, the " weights " are uniform and the 10 means may be added and divided by 10, *i.e.* $2\cdot0+7\cdot2+\ldots+4\cdot0=43\cdot8$, and the mean number per person is 4·38. In other words, we have $(2\cdot0\times123)+(7\cdot2\times123)+(1\cdot8\times123)+$etc. divided by $10(123)$. The top and bottom of the fraction can be divided by 123 throughout, giving $2\cdot0+7\cdot2+1\cdot8$ etc./10.

6

| DISEASE A | | DISEASE B | | |
|---|---|---|---|---|
| Ages at Onset | Squares of Ages | Ages at Onset | (Observation −50) | Squares of (Observation −50) |
| 39 | 1521 | 45 | −5 | 25 |
| 50 | 2500 | 44 | −6 | 36 |
| 26 | 676 | 52 | +2 | 4 |
| 45 | 2025 | 46 | −4 | 16 |
| 47 | 2209 | 49 | −1 | 1 |
| 71 | 5041 | 58 | +8 | 64 |
| 51 | 2601 | 51 | +1 | 1 |
| 33 | 1089 | 48 | −2 | 4 |
| 40 | 1600 | 50 | 0 | 0 |
| 40 | 1600 | 53 | +3 | 9 |
| 51 | 2601 | 51 | +1 | 1 |
| 66 | 4356 | 49 | −1 | 1 |
| 63 | 3969 | 49 | −1 | 1 |
| 55 | 3025 | 47 | −3 | 9 |
| 36 | 1296 | 52 | +2 | 4 |
| 57 | 3249 | 54 | +4 | 16 |
| 41 | 1681 | 56 | +6 | 36 |
| 61 | 3721 | 58 | +8 | 64 |
| 47 | 2209 | 48 | −2 | 4 |
| 44 | 1936 | 45 | −5 | 25 |
| 48 | 2304 | 54 | +4 | 16 |
| 59 | 3481 | 47 | −3 | 9 |
| 42 | 1764 | 50 | 0 | 0 |
| 54 | 2916 | 50 | 0 | 0 |
| 47 | 2209 | 49 | −1 | 1 |
| 53 | 2809 | 41 | −9 | 81 |
| 54 | 2916 | 47 | −3 | 9 |
| | | 52 | +2 | 4 |
| | | 53 | +3 | 9 |
| | | 55 | +5 | 25 |
| | | 45 | −5 | 25 |
| | | 54 | +4 | 16 |
| | | 48 | −2 | 4 |
| | | 52 | +2 | 4 |
| | | 54 | +4 | 16 |
| | | 49 | −1 | 1 |
| Total 1320 | 67304 | Total | +5 | 541 |

Mean 48·89
Sum of squared deviations
round the mean
$= 67304 - (1320)^2/27$
$\qquad = 2770·67$

Variance $= 2770·67/26$
$\qquad = 106·56$
Standard deviation
$\qquad = 10·32$
and Mean $= 48·89$

Mean deviation from $50 = +0·1389$
Sum of squared deviations round
the mean
$\qquad = 541 - (5)^2/36 \qquad = 540·31$

Variance $= 540·31/35 \qquad = 15·44$

Standard deviation $\qquad = 3·93$

and Mean $= 50 + 0·1389 \qquad = 50·14$

It will be noted that the mean age at onset is nearly the same with Disease A and with Disease B, but A is nearly 3 times as variable as

Y

measured by its standard deviation.  If the student worked this example by using 0 as an arbitrary origin, he or she should note that all the values in B lie so close to 50 that the working is much simplified by using 50 as the arbitrary point ;  with Group A, too, it would shorten the arithmetic. It would be well, for practice, to re-work the example on that basis.

7.

| Haemoglobin Percentage Level | No. of Schoolgirls | Working Units | Sum of Values in Working Units | Sum of Squares in Working Units |
|---|---|---|---|---|
| (1) | (2) | (3) | (2)×(3) (4) | (4)×(3) (5) |
| 60– | 2 | – 6 | – 12 | 72 |
| 65– | .. | – 5 | 0 | 0 |
| 70– | 7 | – 4 | – 28 | 112 |
| 75– | 32 | – 3 | – 96 | 288 |
| 80– | 90 | – 2 | – 180 | 360 |
| 85– | 166 | – 1 | – 166 | 166 |
| 90– | 245 | 0 | 0 −482 | 0 |
| 95– | 200 | +1 | +200 | 200 |
| 100– | 162 | +2 | +324 | 648 |
| 105– | 97 | +3 | +291 | 873 |
| 110–114 | 21 | +4 | + 84 | 336 |
| | | | +899 | |
| Total | 1022 | .. | +417 | 3055 |

Mean in working units $= +417 \div 1022 = +0.408$.

Sum of squared deviations round the mean in

working units $= 3055 - (417)^2/1022$

$= 2884.85$

Variance in working units $= 2884.85/1021 = 2.8255$

Standard deviation in working units $= 1.6809$

Mean in real units $= 92.5 + 5(0.408)$

$= 94.54$

Standard deviation in real units (the original

unit of grouping is 5) $= 5(1.6809)$

$= 8.40$

Coefficient of variation $= (8.40/94.54) \times 100$

$= 8.89$

The distribution is fairly symmetrical, and as a rough check of the standard deviation we may take Mean $+ 3$ times the S.D. and Mean $- 3$ times the S.D. and this should cover nearly all the observations.  This gives $94.5 + 25 = 119.5$ and $94.5 - 25 = 69.5$, a range which adequately fits the observations.  For an accurate check re-work with the 0 placed against another group.

8.

The sum of the 25 observations in Samples Nos. 1–5 is 112 and their mean, therefore, $112 \div 25 = 4.48$.  It is, however, with the data given, unnecessary to sum the 25 individual observations.  The required mean can be more simply reached by summing the means given for Samples 1 to 5 and dividing by 5, *i.e.* $2\cdot0+7\cdot2+1\cdot8+5\cdot4+6\cdot0=22\cdot4$ and $22\cdot4\div5=4\cdot48$. In other words, the sum of the observations in a group is the mean multiplied by the number of observations upon which it is based, and so the required total for the 25 persons is $(2\cdot0\times5)+(7\cdot2\times5)+(1\cdot8\times5)+(5\cdot4\times5)+(6\cdot0\times5)$. This has to be divided by 25, but since the numerator and denominator can both be divided by 5 initially this reduces to the sum of the means divided by 5. In dividing $22\cdot4$ (and similar totals) by 5 it is simpler, too, to divide by 10 and multiply the answer by 2, *i.e.* put the decimal mentally one place to the left and double $2\cdot24$. The statistician invariably looks for such ways of saving or easing the arithmetic.

| Sample Nos. | Mean of 25 Observations | Square of Mean | Value of Mean in Sample | Frequency with which Mean Values occurred |
|---|---|---|---|---|
| 1–5 | 4·48 | 20·0704 | 0·75– | .. |
| 6–10 | 4·28 | 18·3184 | 1·25– | .. |
| 11–15 | 4·04 | 16·3216 | 1·75– | .. |
| 16–20 | 5·36 | 28·7296 | 2·25– | .. |
| 21–25 | 4·20 | 17·6400 | 2·75– | .. |
| 26–30 | 4·80 | 23·0400 | 3·25– | 2 |
| 31–35 | 5·16 | 26·6256 | 3·75– | 5 |
| 36–40 | 4·88 | 23·8144 | 4·25– | 6 |
| 41–45 | 4·76 | 22·6576 | 4·75– | 6 |
| 46–50 | 3·96 | 15·6816 | 5·25– | 1 |
| 51–55 | 5·04 | 25·4016 | 5·75– | .. |
| 56–60 | 4·36 | 19·0096 | 6·25– | .. |
| 61–65 | 4·84 | 23·4256 | 6·75– | .. |
| 66–70 | 4·52 | 20·4304 | 7·25–7·75 | .. |
| 71–75 | 4·32 | 18·6624 | | |
| 76–80 | 3·32 | 11·0224 | Total | 20 |
| 81–85 | 4·56 | 20·7936 | | |
| 86–90 | 3·92 | 15·3664 | | |
| 91–95 | 3·60 | 12·9600 | | |
| 96–100 | 4·16 | 17·3056 | | |
| Sum    20 | 88·56 | 397·2768 | | |

(Frequencies 5, 6, 6 braced with 85%)

Mean $=4\cdot428$
Variance $=5\cdot1331/19$
$=0\cdot2702$
S.D. $=0\cdot52$
Expected S.D. $=2\cdot87\div\sqrt{25}$ $=0\cdot57$

The number of means is small, 20 only, but their distribution is in keeping with those given for 20 and 50 observations, and the observed S.D., 0·52, is of the right order since 0·57 is the expected value. With so small a number as 20, observation and expectation would be unlikely to show precise agreement.

**9.**

The mean number of colds was found to be $3\cdot78$ per person, and continuing with the calculation set out in the answer on p. 325 the standard deviation will be found to be $1\cdot79$. The S.E. of the mean is therefore $1\cdot79\div\sqrt{642}=1\cdot79\div25\cdot34=0\cdot07$. The limits within which the true mean is likely to lie are $3\cdot78\pm2(0\cdot07)$ or between $3\cdot64$ and $3\cdot92$.

**10.**

The probability that a child will have had a previous attack of whooping-cough is 3/10 and, therefore, that there has been no previous attack is 7/10.  The probabilities of the various possible events in a group of 5 children are :—

$$
\begin{array}{llll}
\text{5 with previous attacks} & (\tfrac{3}{10})^5 & = & 243/100{,}000 \\
\text{4} \quad ,, \quad ,, & 5(\tfrac{3}{10})^4(\tfrac{7}{10}) & = & 2{,}835/ \quad ,, \\
\text{3} \quad ,, \quad ,, & 10(\tfrac{3}{10})^3(\tfrac{7}{10})^2 & = & 13{,}230/ \quad ,, \\
\text{2} \quad ,, \quad ,, & 10(\tfrac{3}{10})^2(\tfrac{7}{10})^3 & = & 30{,}870/ \quad ,, \\
\text{1} \quad ,, \quad ,, & 5(\tfrac{3}{10})\,(\tfrac{7}{10})^4 & = & 36{,}015/ \quad ,, \\
\text{0} \quad ,, \quad ,, & (\tfrac{7}{10})^5 & = & 16{,}807/ \quad ,, \\
& & \text{Total} = & 100{,}000/ \quad ,,
\end{array}
$$

The percentage frequency with which different previous attack rates should be observed in groups of 5 and the calculation of the mean and standard deviation are then :—

| Previous Attacks | Previous Attack Rate in Sample. Per cent. | Percentage Number of Groups of 5 with given Attack Rate | Attack Rate multiplied by Number of Observations | (Attack Rate)$^2$ Multiplied by Number of Observations |
|---|---|---|---|---|
| (1) | (2) | (3) | (4) $(2)\times(3)$ | (5) $(4)\times(2)$ |
| 5 | 100 | 0·243 | 24·30 | 2,430 |
| 4 | 80 | 2·835 | 226·80 | 18,144 |
| 3 | 60 | 13·230 | 793·80 | 47,628 |
| 2 | 40 | 30·870 | 1234·80 | 49,392 |
| 1 | 20 | 36·015 | 720·30 | 14,406 |
| 0 | 0 | 16·807 | 0 | 0 |
| | Total | 100·000 | 3000·00 | 132,000 |

$\therefore$  Mean of distribution $= 3000/100 = 30$ per cent.
and S.D. of  ,,  $= \sqrt{(132{,}000 - 90{,}000)/100}$
  $= \sqrt{420} = 20\cdot5$
From formula, S.D. $= \sqrt{(pq/n)} = \sqrt{[(30 \times 70)/5]} = \sqrt{420} = 20\cdot5$.


**11.**
To have *at least* 7 children, in the sample of 9, who have previously had whooping-cough the sample must contain either 9 or 8 or 7 children with a positive history.  Since the probability of having had a previous attack is 3/10 the required probabilities are :—

$$
\begin{array}{llll}
\text{9 previously attacked} = & (\tfrac{3}{10})^9 & = & 19{,}683/1{,}000{,}000{,}000 \\
\text{8} \quad ,, \quad ,, & = 9(\tfrac{3}{10})^8(\tfrac{7}{10}) & = & 413{,}343/ \quad ,, \\
\text{7} \quad ,, \quad ,, & = 36(\tfrac{3}{10})^7(\tfrac{7}{10})^2 & = & 3{,}857{,}868/ \quad ,,
\end{array}
$$

$\therefore$  Probability of one or other of
  these events occurring $= 4{,}290{,}894/$  ,,
  $=$ approx. $0\cdot0043$


**12.**
S.D. of distribution of events $= \sqrt{(pq/n)}$, where $p =$ percentage  previously
  attacked and $q =$ percentage not
  previously attacked
  $= \sqrt{[(30 \times 70)/350]}$
  $= \sqrt{6}$
  $= 2\cdot45$

Range within which proportion is likely to lie is therefore the expected $30\% \pm 2(2\cdot45)$ or between $25\cdot1$ and $34\cdot9$.

13.

| Sample Nos. | Nos. of 8's and 9's | | Difference in Percentages, A—B |
|---|---|---|---|
| A     B | A | B | |
| 1 and 2 | 0 | 2 | − 40 |
| 3 and 4 | 0 | 2 | − 40 |
| 5 and 6 | 0 | 1 | − 20 |
| 7 and 8 | 1 | 0 | + 20 |
| 9 and 10 | 1 | 0 | + 20 |
| 11 and 12 | 3 | 0 | + 60 |
| 13 and 14 | 1 | 0 | + 20 |
| 15 and 16 | 1 | 2 | − 20 |
| 17 and 18 | 1 | 3 | − 40 |
| 19 and 20 | 0 | 1 | − 20 |
| 21 and 22 | 0 | 0 | 0 |
| 23 and 24 | 1 | 0 | + 20 |
| 25 and 26 | 0 | 0 | 0 |
| 27 and 28 | 1 | 1 | 0 |
| 29 and 30 | 1 | 1 | 0 |
| 31 and 32 | 1 | 0 | + 20 |
| 33 and 34 | 0 | 3 | − 60 |
| 35 and 36 | 1 | 0 | + 20 |
| 37 and 38 | 0 | 1 | − 20 |
| 39 and 40 | 2 | 1 | + 20 |
| 41 and 42 | 3 | 1 | + 40 |
| 43 and 44 | 0 | 1 | − 20 |
| 45 and 46 | 0 | 0 | 0 |
| 47 and 48 | 0 | 3 | − 60 |
| 49 and 50 | 0 | 0 | 0 |
| 51 and 52 | 2 | 2 | 0 |
| 53 and 54 | 1 | 1 | 0 |
| 55 and 56 | 3 | 0 | + 60 |
| 57 and 58 | 0 | 2 | − 40 |
| 59 and 60 | 1 | 1 | 0 |
| 61 and 62 | 1 | 1 | 0 |
| 63 and 64 | 1 | 1 | 0 |
| 65 and 66 | 1 | 1 | 0 |
| 67 and 68 | 1 | 1 | 0 |
| 69 and 70 | 2 | 0 | + 40 |
| 71 and 72 | 0 | 1 | − 20 |
| 73 and 74 | 2 | 2 | 0 |
| 75 and 76 | 1 | 0 | + 20 |
| 77 and 78 | 1 | 1 | 0 |
| 79 and 80 | 0 | 2 | − 40 |
| 81 and 82 | 0 | 1 | − 20 |
| 83 and 84 | 1 | 1 | 0 |
| 85 and 86 | 2 | 1 | + 20 |
| 87 and 88 | 1 | 1 | 0 |
| 89 and 90 | 0 | 0 | 0 |
| 91 and 92 | 0 | 1 | − 20 |
| 93 and 94 | 0 | 1 | − 20 |
| 95 and 96 | 0 | 0 | 0 |
| 97 and 98 | 1 | 1 | 0 |
| 99 and 100 | 3 | 0 | + 60 |

| Difference in Percentages A—B | No. of Observations | .. | .. |
|---|---|---|---|
| (1) | (2) | (1)×(2) (3) | (1)×(3) (4) |
| − 60 | 2 | − 120 | 7200 |
| − 40 | 5 | − 200 | 8000 |
| − 20 | 9 | − 180 | 3600 |
| 0 | 20 | − 500 | |
| +20 | 9 | +180 | 3600 |
| +40 | 2 | + 80 | 3200 |
| +60 | 3 | +180 | 10800 |
| Total | 50 | +440 | 36400 |

$$\text{Mean} = -60/50 = -1\cdot2$$
$$\text{S.D.} = \sqrt{(36400 - 72)/49} = 27\cdot23$$
$$\text{Expected Mean} = 0$$
$$,,\qquad \text{S.D.} = \sqrt{[(20 \times 80)/5 + (20 \times 80)/5]}$$
$$= 25\cdot30$$

Though only 50 observations are available, it will be seen that the results of the experiment agree reasonably well with theory.

### 14.

150 patients on method A.    15 die.    Fatality-rate 10 per cent.
300    ,,    ,,    B.    45 ,,    ,,    ,, 15    ,,
450 total patients.    60 ,,    ,,    ,, 13·3    ,,
Difference between fatality-rates = 5 per cent.

$$\text{Standard error of difference} = \sqrt{[(13\cdot3 \times 86\cdot7)/150 + (13\cdot3 \times 86\cdot7)/300]}$$
$$= \sqrt{(7\cdot69 + 3\cdot84)}$$
$$= \sqrt{11\cdot53}$$
$$= 3\cdot4$$

Difference/S.E. = 5/3·4 = 1·47.
The difference may quite easily have arisen by chance.

### 15.

| Group B | | Group A | | Group A Difference after treatment | |
|---|---|---|---|---|---|
| Observed rate | Square of observed rate | Observed rate | Square of observed rate | Value | (Value)² |
| 3 | 9 | 10 | 100 | − 4 | 16 |
| 9 | 81 | 13 | 169 | − 4 | 16 |
| 8 | 64 | 6 | 36 | − 3 | 9 |
| 6 | 36 | 11 | 121 | − 1 | 1 |
| 5 | 25 | 10 | 100 | 0 | 0 |
| 5 | 25 | 7 | 49 | − 3 | 9 |
| 7 | 49 | 8 | 64 | − 6 | 36 |
| 3 | 9 | 8 | 64 | − 3 | 9 |
| 10 | 100 | 5 | 25 | − 2 | 4 |
| 8 | 64 | 9 | 81 | − 4 | 16 |
| 10 | 100 | | | | |
| 4 | 16 | | | | |
| Sum 78 | 578 | 87 | 809 | − 30 | 116 |

(1) Sum of Group B = 78      Mean of Group B = 78/12 = 6·50
    Sum of Group A = 87      Mean of Group A = 87/10 = 8·70
    $Sum\ (B-B)^2 = 578 - (78)^2/12 = 578 - 507 = 71·0$
    $Sum\ (A-A)^2 = 809 - (87)^2/10 = 809 - 756·9 = 52·1$
    $s^2 = (71·0 + 52·1)/(12 + 10 - 2) = 123·1/20 = 6·155$

$$t = (8·70 - 6·50) \Big/ \sqrt{\frac{6·155}{12} + \frac{6·155}{10}} = 2·2/1·06 = 2·08$$

    P = almost 0·05
(2) Mean change after treatment = $-30/10 = -3·0$
    $Sum\ (x - \bar{x})^2 = 116 - (30)^2/10 = 116 - 90 = 26$
    $s = \sqrt{26/9} = 1·70$
    $s/\sqrt{n} = 1·70/3·16 = 0·538$
    $t = 3·0/0·538 = 5·58$
    P is less than 0·01.

**16.**
The tails of the distributions may be compressed to give expectations in those cells of more than 5.  Thus we have :—

| Mean Value | Samples of 20 Observed | Expected | Samples of 50 Observed | Total |
|---|---|---|---|---|
| 2·75– | 11 | *8·5* | 6 | 17 |
| 3·75– | 24 | *23·0* | 22 | 46 |
| 4·25– | 31 | *38·0* | 45 | 76 |
| 4·75– | 22 | *23·0* | 24 | 46 |
| 5·25–6·25 | 12 | *7·5* | 3 | 15 |
| Total | 100 | 100 | 100 | 200 |

$$\chi^2 = (2·5)^2/8·5 + (2·5)^2/8·5 + (1)^2/23·0 + (1)^2/23·0$$
$$+ (7)^2/38·0 + (7)^2/38·0 + (1)^2/23·0 + (1)^2/23·0$$
$$+ (4·5)^2/7·5 + (4·5)^2/7·5$$
$$= 0·74 + 0·74 + 0·04 + 0·04$$
$$+ 1·29 + 1·29 + 0·04 + 0·04$$
$$+ 2·70 + 2·70$$
$$= 9·62 \qquad n = 4 \text{ and } P \text{ is smaller than } 0·05.$$

The difference between the two distributions is therefore not likely to have arisen merely by chance.

**17.**

|  | Live | Die | Total |
|---|---|---|---|
| Method A | 15 | 135 | 150 |
|    ,,   B | 45 | 255 | 300 |
| Total | 60 | 390 | 450 |

$$\chi^2 = [(45 \times 135) - (15 \times 255)]^2 \times (450)/60 \times 390 \times 150 \times 300$$
$$= 2,278,125,000/1,053,000,000$$
$$= 2·16 \qquad n = 1,\ P \text{ greater than } 0·10.$$

18.

In 1937–46 adolescents and adults formed 21·9 per cent. of the total cases ; in 1947 they were 35·5 per cent., showing therefore a decided increase in the proportion of older persons amongst the attacked.

If age and year of occurrence were independent, the expected number at 0–14 in 1937–46 equals $1300(920/1300 \times 598/1300) = 423·2$.  $(O - E) = (467 - 423·2) = 43·8$, and this value will appear in each cell.

$\chi^2$ therefore equals $(43·8)^2/423·2 + (43·8)^2/174·8 + (43·8)^2/496·8 + (43·8)^2/205·2$

$= 1918·44 \, (1/423·2 + 1/174·8 + 1/496·8 + 1/205·2)$

$= 1918·44 \, (0·002363 + 0·005720 + 0·002013 + 0·004873)$

$= (1918·44 \times 0·014969)$

$= 28·72.$

Alternatively

$\chi^2 = (ad - bc)^2 (a+b+c+d)/(a+b)(c+d)(a+c)(b+d)$

$= \{(467 \times 249) - (453 \times 131)\}^2 (1300)/(598)(702)(920)(380)$

$= 4,214,812,680,000/146,760,681,600$

$= 28·72 \qquad n = 1,\ P$ much less than $0·01$.

The change in age-distribution was therefore highly significant.  (It may, of course, have been due in part to an increase in the number of older persons and a decrease in the number of children at risk, or—perhaps as well—to an increasing recognition of attacks in adults, particularly in epidemic periods.  The test of significance provides *no evidence whatever* of causation.)

19.

To compare the distributions they must be converted to percentages, which gives the following figures :—

| Estimated Duration of Pregnancy in Days | Percentage Frequency of each Duration found by :— | | | |
| --- | --- | --- | --- | --- |
| | Reid | Schlichting | Ahlfeld | Hotelling |
| 254–263 | 5·8 | 8·1 | 3·4 | 4·6 |
| 264–273 | 16·4 | 16·5 | 21·6 | 17·8 |
| 274–283 | 34·4 | 34·6 | 37·8 | 35·9 |
| 284–293 | 29·2 | 25·9 | 25·7 | 29·7 |
| 294–319 | 14·2 | 14·9 | 11·5 | 12·0 |
| Total | 100·0 | 100·0 | 100·0 | 100·0 |

These figures clearly reveal no substantial differences between the distributions—study of such distributions and their differences should *always* be a first step.  $\chi^2$ must be calculated on the absolute numbers and the calculation is as follows :—

| Estimated Duration of Pregnancy in Days | | R | S | A | H | Total |
|---|---|---|---|---|---|---|
| 254–263 | O | 29 | 31 | 5 | 23 | 88 |
| | E | *28·74* | *21·96* | *8·51* | *28·79* | *88·00* |
| 264–273 | O | 82 | 63 | 32 | 89 | 266 |
| | E | *86·88* | *66·37* | *25·72* | *87·04* | *266·01* |
| 274–283 | O | 172 | 132 | 56 | 180 | 540 |
| | E | *176·36* | *134·73* | *52·22* | *176·69* | *540·00* |
| 284–293 | O | 146 | 99 | 38 | 149 | 432 |
| | E | *141·09* | *107·78* | *41·77* | *141·35* | *431·99* |
| 294–319 | O | 71 | 57 | 17 | 60 | 205 |
| | E | *66·95* | *51·15* | *19·82* | *67·08* | *205·00* |
| Total | O | 500 | 382 | 148 | 501 | 1531 |
| | E | *500·02* | *381·99* | *148·04* | *500·95* | *1531·00* |
| Proportion of Sub-total to Grand Total | | 0·3266 | 0·2495 | 0·0967 | 0·3272 | 1·0000 |

The total of each column can first be expressed as a proportion of the grand total, *e.g.* $500/1531 = 0\cdot3266$. These proportions are then multiplied in turn by the totals of each row to give the expected numbers in each cell, *e.g.* $0\cdot3266 \times 88 = 28\cdot74$, $0\cdot3266 \times 266 = 86\cdot88$, $0\cdot2495 \times 88 = 21\cdot96$, and so on. In other words, according to these marginal totals the chance of an observation being made by R *and* being of duration 254–263 is, on the assumption of independence, $500/1531 \times 88/1531$, and there will, in the total 1531 observations, be $1531/(500/1531 \times 88/1531)$ of this type $= 500/1531 \times 88 = 0\cdot3266 \times 88 = 28\cdot74$. The addition of these E figures for each column and row gives a check upon the arithmetic up to this point.

The next step is to calculate $O - E$ for each cell, then $(O - E)^2$, and lastly $(O - E)^2/E$. Thus we have :—

| Group | | R | S | A | H | Total |
|---|---|---|---|---|---|---|
| 254–263 | O − E | +0·26 | +9·04 | − 3·51 | − 5·79 | 0·00 |
| | (O − E)² | 0·07 | 81·72 | 12·32 | 33·52 | |
| | (O − E)²/E | *0·00* | *3·72* | *1·45* | *1·16* | |
| 264–273 | O − E | − 4·88 | − 3·37 | +6·28 | +1·96 | − 0·01 |
| | (O − E)² | 23·81 | 11·36 | 39·44 | 3·84 | |
| | (O − E)²/E | *0·27* | *0·17* | *1·53* | *0·04* | |
| 274–283 | O − E | − 4·36 | − 2·73 | +3·78 | +3·31 | 0·00 |
| | (O − E)² | 19·01 | 7·45 | 14·29 | 10·96 | |
| | (O − E)²/E | *0·11* | *0·06* | *0·27* | *0·06* | |
| 284–293 | O − E | +4·91 | − 8·78 | − 3·77 | +7·65 | +0·01 |
| | (O − E)² | 24·11 | 77·09 | 14·21 | 58·52 | |
| | (O − E)²/E | *0·17* | *0·72* | *0·34* | *0·41* | |
| 294–319 | O − E | +4·05 | +5·85 | − 2·82 | − 7·08 | 0·00 |
| | (O − E)² | 16·40 | 34·22 | 7·95 | 50·13 | |
| | (O − E)²/E | *0·24* | *0·67* | *0·40* | *0·75* | |

Lastly, $\chi^2$ equals the sum of the 20 values of $(O - E)^2/E = 12\cdot54$, $n = 12$, and $P$ is between $0\cdot5$ and $0\cdot3$. The differences between the four distributions might, therefore, have very easily arisen by chance.

20.

| Average Population of School (to nearest 100) | No. of Times in 5 Years that an Infectious Disease appeared | Squares | | Product |
|---|---|---|---|---|
| | | Population | Times | |
| 300 | 14 | 90,000 | 196 | 4,200 |
| 700 | 28 | 490,000 | 784 | 19,600 |
| 800 | 25 | 640,000 | 625 | 20,000 |
| 300 | 11 | 90,000 | 121 | 3,300 |
| 200 | 19 | 40,000 | 361 | 3,800 |
| 500 | 15 | 250,000 | 225 | 7,500 |
| 300 | 15 | 90,000 | 225 | 4,500 |
| 200 | 12 | 40,000 | 144 | 2,400 |
| 500 | 19 | 250,000 | 361 | 9,500 |
| 700 | 19 | 490,000 | 361 | 13,300 |
| 300 | 16 | 90,000 | 256 | 4,800 |
| 600 | 24 | 360,000 | 576 | 14,400 |
| 600 | 28 | 360,000 | 784 | 16,800 |
| 400 | 13 | 160,000 | 169 | 5,200 |
| 500 | 16 | 250,000 | 256 | 8,000 |
| 600 | 26 | 360,000 | 676 | 15,600 |
| 400 | 19 | 160,000 | 361 | 7,600 |
| 400 | 21 | 160,000 | 441 | 8,400 |
| 900 | 41 | 810,000 | 1,681 | 36,900 |
| 700 | 38 | 490,000 | 1,444 | 26,600 |
| Total 9900 | 419 | 5,670,000 | 10,047 | 232,400 |

Sum of squared deviations round the mean :—
$$\text{Population} = 5,670,000 - (9900)^2/20$$
$$= 769,500$$
$$\text{Times of appearance} = 10,047 - (419)^2/20$$
$$= 1268 \cdot 95$$
Sum of Products round the means
$$= 232,400 - (9900)(419)/20$$
$$= +24,995.$$
Coefficient of correlation
$$= +24,995/\sqrt{769,500 \times 1268 \cdot 95}$$
$$= +0 \cdot 80.$$

The regression equation required is : —

No. of times – Mean No. $= r\dfrac{\sigma \text{Times}}{\sigma \text{Pop.}}$ (Population – Mean Pop.),

$\therefore$ No. of times $- 20 \cdot 95 = +0 \cdot 80 \dfrac{8 \cdot 17}{201 \cdot 25}$ (Population $- 495 \cdot 00$),

$\therefore$ No. of times $= +0 \cdot 0325$ Population $+ 4 \cdot 8625$

Expected No. of times when population is $300 = 14 \cdot 61$

„　　　　„　　　　„　　　　„　　　　$700 = 27 \cdot 61$.

The following points should be noted : (a) in the squares of the population and the product of times and population there is no need to write down the noughts the number of which is constant ; (b) the scatter diagram shows (so far as one can judge by eye) that the relationship is linear ; (c) the scatter round the regression line is wide for schools of a given size, so that, although there is a close association between size and the chance of a disease appearing, the number of times could not be very accurately predicted for an *individual* school, though the mean figure for a *group* of schools of the same size might be estimated with fair accuracy.

21.                              HOURS OF OVERTIME

| No. of Days Lost | 4– | 7– | 10– | 13– | 16– | 19– | 22–25 | Total | |
|---|---|---|---|---|---|---|---|---|---|
| 0– | .. | 1 | 2 | 1 | .. | .. | .. | 4 | *–2* |
| 3– | 2 | .. | 2 | 2 | 2 | 1 | .. | 9 | *–1* |
| 6– | 1 | 2 | 6 | 8 | 4 | 5 | 1 | 27 | *0* |
| 9– | 4 | 2 | 3 | 6 | 1 | 1 | .. | 17 | *+1* |
| 12– | 1 | .. | 1 | 2 | 3 | 3 | 3 | 13 | *+2* |
| 15–18 | .. | 3 | 2 | 1 | 3 | 1 | .. | 10 | *+3* |
| Total | 8 | 8 | 16 | 20 | 13 | 11 | 4 | 80 | |

$$-3 \quad -2 \quad -1 \quad 0 \quad +1 \quad +2 \quad +3$$

| $x$ | $f$ | $fx$ | $fx^2$ | $y$ | $f$ | $fy$ | $fy^2$ |
|---|---|---|---|---|---|---|---|
| No. of Days Lost W.U. | No. of Persons | $(1)\times(2)$ | $(1)\times(3)$ | Hours of Overtime W.U. | No. of Persons | $(1)\times(2)$ | $(1)\times(3)$ |
| (1) | (2) | (3) | (4) | (1) | (2) | (3) | (4) |
| –2 | 4 | –8 | 16 | –3 | 8 | –24 | 72 |
| –1 | 9 | –9 | 9 | –2 | 8 | –16 | 32 |
| 0 | 27 | $\overline{-17}$ | .. | –1 | 16 | –16 | 16 |
| +1 | 17 | $+\overline{17}$ | 17 | 0 | 20 | $\overline{-56}$ | .. |
| +2 | 13 | +26 | 52 | +1 | 13 | $+\overline{13}$ | 13 |
| +3 | 10 | +30 | 90 | +2 | 11 | +22 | 44 |
|  |  |  |  | +3 | 4 | +12 | 36 |
| Total | 80 | +73 | 184 | Total | 80 | +47 | 213 |
|  | .. | +56 | .. |  | .. | –9 | .. |

Mean days lost in W.U. $= +\dfrac{56}{80} = +0.7$  Mean overtime in W.U. $= \dfrac{-9}{80} = -0.1125$

Mean days lost in real units $= 7.5 + 3(0.7)$  Mean overtime in real units $= 14.5 - 3(0.1125)$
$= 9.6$  $= 14.16$

S.D. of days lost in W.U. $= \sqrt{\dfrac{184 - (56)^2/80}{79}}$  S.D. of overtime in W.U. $= \sqrt{\dfrac{213 - (-9)^2/80}{79}}$
$= \sqrt{144.80/79}$  $= \sqrt{211.99/79}$
$= 1.354$  $= 1.6381$

S.D. of days lost in real units $= 4.06$  S.D. of overtime in real units $= 4.91$

| Hours of Overtime | Sum of Days Lost for each Overtime Group | Product of Days Lost and Overtime | No. of Persons in each Overtime Group | Mean Days Lost by Persons in each Over-time Group | |
|---|---|---|---|---|---|
| W.U. | W.U. | | | W.U. | Real Units |
| | | $(1)\times(2)$ | | $(2)\div(4)$ | |
| (1) | (2) | (3) | (4) | (5) | (6) |
| $-3$ | $+4$ | $-12$ | 8 | $+0.50$ | 9.00 |
| $-2$ | $+9$ | $-18$ | 8 | $+1.13$ | 10.89 |
| $-1$ | $+5$ | $-5$ | 16 | $+0.31$ | 8.43 |
| 0 | $+9$ | $-35$ | 20 | $+0.45$ | 8.85 |
| $+1$ | $+14$ | $+14$ | 13 | $+1.08$ | 10.74 |
| $+2$ | $+9$ | $+18$ | 11 | $+0.82$ | 9.96 |
| $+3$ | $+6$ | $+18$ | 4 | $+1.50$ | 12.00 |
| Total | $+56$ | $+50$ | 80 | .. | .. |
| | .. | $+15$ | .. | .. | .. |

$$\text{Correlation coefficient} = \frac{+15 - (56)(-9)/80}{\sqrt{144 \cdot 80 \times 211 \cdot 99}}$$
$$= \frac{+21 \cdot 3}{175 \cdot 20}$$
$$= +0 \cdot 12$$

$$\text{Standard error} = \frac{1}{\sqrt{(n-1)}} = \frac{1}{\sqrt{79}} = 0 \cdot 11$$

Regression equation :—

$$\text{Days lost} - 9 \cdot 6 = +0 \cdot 12 \, \frac{4 \cdot 06}{4 \cdot 91} \, (\text{Overtime} - 14 \cdot 16),$$

$$\therefore \text{ days lost} = 0 \cdot 10 \text{ overtime hours} + 8 \cdot 19$$

When overtime is 5 hours, days lost $= 8 \cdot 69$

,,    ,,    ,, 15 ,,    ,,    ,, $= 9 \cdot 69$

*Notes on Working.*—In reaching the products needed for the numerator of the coefficient of correlation one can proceed as in Chapter XVI by finding the value for each cell separately and entering it in the table. An alternative method, used above, is to find, in the working units, the *sum* of the days lost in each overtime column and then multiply this sum by the appropriate overtime value in working units.    Thus in the over-time column 4–7 hours one can enter the values in the cells, namely, $2(-1)(-3), 1 (0)(-3), 4(+1)(-3), 1(+2)(-3)$, the sum of which is $-12$; or, mentally, add $2(-1) + 1(0) + 4(+1) + 1(+2) = +4$ and then multiply by the $-3$ which is common to all.    The advantage of the latter method is that it automatically gives the sum of days lost for each overtime column and thus, readily, the observed mean values at each overtime point, *i.e.* the observed regression.    It should be noted that the total sum of these separate column sums (here $+56$) must equal the value previously reached from the marginal totals for days lost, which provides an automatic check on this part of the working.

Inspection of the table suggests very little correlation between the two variables, for in each overtime column nearly all the different values for days lost are represented, and for different numbers of days lost most values of overtime are to be found.    The amount of correlation actually found might easily have arisen by chance in sampling a universe in which there was no correlation.    The observed and calculated regression lines have therefore practically no slope.    For the calculated line only two values, of course, need be found to enable one to draw it.

22.

| Age in Years | Expected Deaths in Standard Population | | | |
| --- | --- | --- | --- | --- |
| | At Rates of 1898 | | At Rates of 1938 | |
| | Male | Female | Male | Female |
| 0– | 95,303 | 78,452 | 25,705 | 19,503 |
| 5– | 6,099 | 6,150 | 3,050 | 2,838 |
| 10– | 3,727 | 3,806 | 2,203 | 1,820 |
| 15– | 5,796 | 5,474 | 3,312 | 2,820 |
| 20– | 8,204 | 7,299 | 4,785 | 4,095 |
| 25– | 19,822 | 18,646 | 9,124 | 8,476 |
| 35– | 27,169 | 26,588 | 11,426 | 10,456 |
| 45– | 40,512 | 36,804 | 23,478 | 18,270 |
| 55– | 60,052 | 53,886 | 41,602 | 30,878 |
| 65– | 65,351 | 70,081 | 53,245 | 48,021 |
| 75– | 42,076 | 57,207 | 39,017 | 45,584 |
| 85+ | 9,100 | 17,466 | 8,494 | 15,912 |
| All ages | 383,211 | 381,859 | 225,441 | 208,673 |

Standardised death-rate in $1898 = \dfrac{383,211 + 381,859}{19,280,000 + 20,921,000}$
$= 19 \cdot 0$ per 1000.

„         „    $1938 = \dfrac{225,441 + 208,673}{19,280,000 + 20,921,000}$
$= 10 \cdot 8$ per 1000.

Ratio of 1938 to $1898 = 10 \cdot 8/19 \cdot 0 = 57\%$.
(The ratio of 1938 to 1898 as standardised by R.G. on 1901 population
    was $8 \cdot 5/17 \cdot 4$, or $49\%$.)

23.

| Age in Years | Death-rates per Million in England and Wales 1938 | | | | Expected Deaths in Greater London 1932 | | | |
| --- | --- | --- | --- | --- | --- | --- | --- | --- |
| | Diphtheria | | Cancer | | Diphtheria | | Cancer | |
| | Male | Female | Male | Female | Male | Female | Male | Female |
| 0– | 369 | 348 | 41 | 35 | 107·6 | 99·0 | 12·0 | 10·0 |
| 5– | 272 | 304 | 22 | 21 | 171·9 | 188·5 | 13·9 | 13·0 |
| 15– | 12 | 16 | 56 | 45 | 8·5 | 12·4 | 39·6 | 35·0 |
| 25– | 6 | 7 | 138 | 156 | 4·0 | 5·3 | 92·5 | 119·1 |
| 35– | 3 | 4 | 469 | 708 | 1·6 | 2·6 | 245·9 | 456·5 |
| 45– |  |  | 1,625 | 2,023 |  |  | 759·0 | 1132·1 |
| 55– | } 2 | } 3 | 4,680 | 4,075 | } 2·1 | } 4·0 | 1648·3 | 1681·8 |
| 65– |  |  | 10,206 | 7,408 |  |  | 1839·1 | 1814·2 |
| 75+ |  |  | 14,995 | 11,987 |  |  | 896·7 | 1312·6 |
| All ages | 71 | | 1665 | | 295·7 | 311·8 | 5547·0 | 6574·3 |

Index death-rates in London are :—
    Diphtheria $(295 \cdot 7 + 311 \cdot 8)/(3,885,000 + 4,417,300) = 73$ per million.
    Cancer $(5547 \cdot 0 + 6574 \cdot 3)/(3,885,000 + 4,417,300) = 1460$ per million.
Standardising factors are :—Diphtheria $71/73 = 0 \cdot 9726$.
                            Cancer $1665/1460 = 1 \cdot 1404$.
Standardised rates for Greater London are :—
            Diphtheria $58 \times 0 \cdot 9726 = 56$.
            Cancer $1,491 \times 1 \cdot 1404 = 1700$.

24.

| Age in Years | Days Lost per Man per Annum at Ages | | | Population of Factory | Expected Days in Standard Population at Departmental Rates at Ages | | |
|---|---|---|---|---|---|---|---|
| | A | B | C | | A | B | C |
| 20– | 6·5 | 7·0 | 6·0 | 500 | 3,250 | 3,500 | 3,000 |
| 30– | 7·0 | 8·5 | 6·5 | 690 | 4,830 | 5,865 | 4,485 |
| 40– | 8·5 | 10·0 | 7·0 | 640 | 5,440 | 6,400 | 4,480 |
| 50– | 10·0 | 12·0 | 9·5 | 650 | 6,500 | 7,800 | 6,175 |
| 60+ | 13·5 | 16·0 | 12·0 | 440 | 5,940 | 7,040 | 5,280 |
| All ages | 9·03 | 8·68 | 9·42 | 2920 | 25,960 | 30,605 | 23,420 |

Standardised rates for days lost per man per annum :—

$$A \quad 25,960/2920 = 8·89$$
$$B \quad 30,605/2920 = 10·48$$
$$C \quad 23,420/2920 = 8·02$$

It will be seen that according to the crude rates the order of the Departments is C highest loss, A intermediate, B lowest. The rates at ages reveal, however, that C has consistently the lowest rate of sickness absence and B the highest. The crude rates are seriously affected by the fact that the sickness rate rises with age and the departments differ materially in the age-distributions of their workmen. The standardised rates give a more satisfactory measure of their average losses for all ages combined.

25.

(a) M. 15/100,000 or 1 in 6667.
    F. 64/100,000 or 1 in 1563.
(b) M. Deaths between ages 25 and 50 are $85,824 - 74,794 = 11,030$.
        Probability of dying $= 11,030/85,824 = 0·1285$.
    F. Deaths between ages 25 and 50 are $88,133 - 78,958 = 9175$.
        Probability of dying $= 9175/88,133 = 0·1041$.
(c) M. Probability of surviving $= 16,199/85,824 = 0·1887$.
    F.     „          „          „      $= 24,869/88,133 = 0·2822$.
(d) M. Expectation at 90
        $= [(1149 + 801 + 545 + 361 + 232 + 145 + 87 + 51 + 29 + 15 + 8 + 4 + 2 + 1)/1609] + \frac{1}{2}$
        $= [3,430/1609] + \frac{1}{2} = 2·63$.
    F. Expectation at 90
        $= [(2706 + 1986 + 1425 + 998 + 681 + 452 + 291 + 182 + 110 + 64 + 37 + 19 + 10 + 5 + 2 + 1)/3611] + \frac{1}{2}$
        $= [8,969/3611] + \frac{1}{2} = 2·98$.

# RANDOM SAMPLING NUMBERS

## Illustrations of Use

(1) In a controlled clinical trial the aim is to give about half the patients treatment X and the other half treatment Y. To allocate the treatments at random let an *even* number denote treatment X and an *odd* number denote treatment Y. Start at random at any point within the numbers, *e.g.* at Set IV, column 11, row 8. Continuing down column 11 from that point the numbers, and consequent treatments, are :—

| Random No. | | Treatment | Patient No. |
|---|---|---|---|
| 5 | odd | Y | 1 |
| 2 | even | X | 2 |
| 2 | ,, | X | 3 |
| 7 | odd | Y | 4 |
| 9 | ,, | Y | 5 |
| 4 | even | X | 6 |
| 1 | odd | Y | 7 |
| 1 | ,, | Y | 8 |
| 7 | ,, | Y | 9 |
| 2 | even | X | 10 |
| 8 | ,, | X | 11 |
| 3 | odd | Y | 12 |
| etc. | etc. | etc. | etc. |

(2) A simple expansion of the above method allows for three, or more, treatments. Thus numbers 1, 2 and 3 can be taken to denote treatment X, numbers 4, 5 and 6 treatment Y, and numbers 7, 8 and 9 treatment Z. Number 0 will be ignored. Starting randomly at, *e.g.* Set VI, column 6, row 36, and continuing downwards to the end of column 6 and then down column 7 we have :—

| Random No. | Treatment | Patient No. |
|---|---|---|
| 6 | Y | 1 |
| 7 | Z | 2 |
| 5 | Y | 3 |
| 3 | X | 4 |
| 4 | Y | 5 |
| 8 | Z | 6 |
| 8 | Z | 7 |
| 6 | Y | 8 |
| 3 | X | 9 |
| 6 | Y | 10 |
| 8 | Z | 11 |
| 0 | .. | .. |
| 5 | Y | 12 |
| etc. | etc. | etc. |

341

(3) In the short run a disadvantage of the above methods may lie in too many instances of one treatment and too few of the other treatment occurring. Thus by chance the first 7 patients might all fall to treatment X and none to treatment Y. In example (2) there are, in fact, in the first 12 patients, 6 on treatment Y, 4 on treatment Z, and only 2 on treatment X. To prevent this it may be wise to equalise the numbers of patients who will be on each treatment at short intervals. Thus let us decide that in each 12 patients 4 shall be on treatment X, 4 on treatment Y and 4 on treatment Z. List these required treatments in numerical order thus :—

| Numerical Order | Treatment | Random Order in which Treatments are to be given |
|---|---|---|
| 01 | X | 12 |
| 02 | X | 10 |
| 03 | X | 1 |
| 04 | X | 2 |
| 05 | Y | 9 |
| 06 | Y | 8 |
| 07 | Y | 7 |
| 08 | Y | 11 |
| 09 | Z | 4 |
| 10 | Z | 6 |
| 11 | Z | 5 |
| 12 | Z | 3 |

Start randomly at any point of the pages, *e.g.* Set I, columns 5 and 6, row 22. Proceed down columns 5 and 6, and then columns 7 and 8, 9 and 10, etc., as needed, noting, *in order as they occur*, the numbers from 01 to 12 (ignoring all other pairs). Thus columns 5 and 6 run, from row 22, as follows :—

$$85$$
$$03$$
$$94$$
$$55$$
$$04$$
$$69$$
$$12$$
$$80$$
$$86$$
$$09$$
$$51$$
$$11$$

Of the twelve listed numbers 03 is the first to appear and therefore treatment X, standing against 03, is given to the first patient ; 04 is the second to appear and treatment X is therefore given to the second patient ; 12 is the third to appear and treatment Z, standing against 12, is therefore given to the third patient. Continuing thus the order of treatments becomes X, X, Z, Z, Z, Z, Y, Y, Y, X, Y, X. It will be seen that a run of 4 Z's has appeared by chance. If even a run of this length were un- desirable the three treatments could have been equalized, by the same technique, at 9, 6 or 3 patients.

(4) If it is desired to give two alternate treatments to pairs of patients

but at the same time to randomise the order of their presentation, the following technique can be adopted. Let an odd number denote treatment X and an even number denote treatment Y. Starting randomly at Set XIII, column 1, row 6, the first number is 3 and since this is an odd number the first patient has treatment X. As the treatments are to be given in pairs, the second patient automatically receives treatment Y. The next number in the column is likewise 3 and therefore patient 3 receives treatment X and patient 4 receives treatment Y. The next number is even, number 8, and therefore patients 5 and 6 receive Y and X respectively. The random order is, therefore, X, Y, X, Y, Y, X, etc.

(5) It is desired to take a 10 per cent. random sample of the records of 6780 hospital patients numbered in serial order from 1 to 6780. Start randomly at, *e.g.* Set II, row 1, columns 1, 2, 3 and 4. Read the numbers in 4's and mark down those between 0001 and 6780, ignoring all higher numbers. Thus the records to be included in the sample are those of patients numbered 2869, 4040, 1602, 4434, 3723, etc. If the same number appears a second time it is ignored and the list continued until 678 separate numbers have been drawn. When the total population numbers less than 1000 the figures can be read in threes, *e.g.* Set II, row 1, columns 1, 2 and 3, give 286, 404, 160, etc.

Z

Random Sampling Numbers—I

|  | 1 2 | 3 4 | 5 6 | 7 8 | 9 10 | 11 12 | 13 14 | 15 16 |
|---|---|---|---|---|---|---|---|---|
| 1 | 0 6 | 2 8 | 3 5 | 7 6 | 4 9 | 0 7 | 6 6 | 8 0 |
| 2 | 3 4 | 2 5 | 2 0 | 3 0 | 5 1 | 5 1 | 3 5 | 7 1 |
| 3 | 3 4 | 7 4 | 1 5 | 8 8 | 9 9 | 4 0 | 3 4 | 3 6 |
| 4 | 4 7 | 5 0 | 4 8 | 3 3 | 0 5 | 7 4 | 8 4 | 5 9 |
| 5 | 9 3 | 5 6 | 8 1 | 1 7 | 2 0 | 7 8 | 3 5 | 8 6 |
| 6 | 8 6 | 1 5 | 7 5 | 3 7 | 6 6 | 4 9 | 5 0 | 7 1 |
| 7 | 2 2 | 2 3 | 2 7 | 1 2 | 4 4 | 3 6 | 2 6 | 5 0 |
| 8 | 2 3 | 3 4 | 7 5 | 8 2 | 0 2 | 8 7 | 4 4 | 1 8 |
| 9 | 2 0 | 4 2 | 6 0 | 5 7 | 9 4 | 8 5 | 4 6 | 0 3 |
| 10 | 6 5 | 3 3 | 1 1 | 0 3 | 6 9 | 0 2 | 7 3 | 1 7 |
| 11 | 3 9 | 2 9 | 8 9 | 5 4 | 4 6 | 4 6 | 8 6 | 3 3 |
| 12 | 7 2 | 2 1 | 8 4 | 5 9 | 5 6 | 5 9 | 2 5 | 3 2 |
| 13 | 7 4 | 0 7 | 3 7 | 4 2 | 6 8 | 6 5 | 3 1 | 8 9 |
| 14 | 9 7 | 2 2 | 8 0 | 3 9 | 9 8 | 1 5 | 7 4 | 7 9 |
| 15 | 1 9 | 9 8 | 9 3 | 9 4 | 4 2 | 2 1 | 4 6 | 5 7 |
| 16 | 7 2 | 9 4 | 6 1 | 6 7 | 9 8 | 7 5 | 3 7 | 4 6 |
| 17 | 9 1 | 5 2 | 3 0 | 2 6 | 5 8 | 1 2 | 2 3 | 7 9 |
| 18 | 6 9 | 3 4 | 5 2 | 8 0 | 6 2 | 4 7 | 9 2 | 9 6 |
| 19 | 6 2 | 1 6 | 5 6 | 2 9 | 5 3 | 2 7 | 4 1 | 0 8 |
| 20 | 0 7 | 4 1 | 1 6 | 0 6 | 2 1 | 8 2 | 7 8 | 3 7 |
| 21 | 3 6 | 7 6 | 7 2 | 6 0 | 2 7 | 7 2 | 5 6 | 8 3 |
| 22 | 4 9 | 3 0 | 8 5 | 6 9 | 5 9 | 4 9 | 7 5 | 4 3 |
| 23 | 1 4 | 1 2 | 0 3 | 3 6 | 7 0 | 1 4 | 4 1 | 5 1 |
| 24 | 7 5 | 5 6 | 9 4 | 1 6 | 0 8 | 9 2 | 6 0 | 7 0 |
| 25 | 7 4 | 0 6 | 5 5 | 8 4 | 6 7 | 3 6 | 5 2 | 6 5 |
| 26 | 2 1 | 4 1 | 0 4 | 6 1 | 2 0 | 8 5 | 2 2 | 7 1 |
| 27 | 7 0 | 0 2 | 6 9 | 1 0 | 3 7 | 4 5 | 9 5 | 9 4 |
| 28 | 4 6 | 4 7 | 1 2 | 4 6 | 9 6 | 9 1 | 1 1 | 7 9 |
| 29 | 6 1 | 2 9 | 8 0 | 3 9 | 5 0 | 7 4 | 8 6 | 2 3 |
| 30 | 2 9 | 1 0 | 8 6 | 7 4 | 5 2 | 9 5 | 6 2 | 1 5 |
| 31 | 3 7 | 9 8 | 0 9 | 7 1 | 9 1 | 3 8 | 7 7 | 3 8 |
| 32 | 9 6 | 5 0 | 5 1 | 0 6 | 9 7 | 1 5 | 4 7 | 5 9 |
| 33 | 2 2 | 9 3 | 1 1 | 0 5 | 1 5 | 8 4 | 4 9 | 7 6 |
| 34 | 5 8 | 9 9 | 9 7 | 1 0 | 7 9 | 6 9 | 4 3 | 4 6 |
| 35 | 1 9 | 8 0 | 6 6 | 5 2 | 4 1 | 0 7 | 1 0 | 1 6 |
| 36 | 6 6 | 9 3 | 9 0 | 9 3 | 3 5 | 6 6 | 9 0 | 3 0 |
| 37 | 3 1 | 7 4 | 7 0 | 0 5 | 9 6 | 9 4 | 5 3 | 0 2 |
| 38 | 9 8 | 0 3 | 4 9 | 1 2 | 4 0 | 7 7 | 6 9 | 6 1 |
| 39 | 9 9 | 7 3 | 1 0 | 3 3 | 8 8 | 2 2 | 4 3 | 4 6 |
| 40 | 6 3 | 8 2 | 0 7 | 2 6 | 1 6 | 4 3 | 1 1 | 1 8 |

Random Sampling Numbers—II

|     | 1 2 | 3 4 | 5 6 | 7 8 | 9 10 | 11 12 | 13 14 | 15 16 |
|-----|-----|-----|-----|-----|------|-------|-------|-------|
| 1   | 2 8 | 6 9 | 3 0 | 9 6 | 6 3 | 9 2 | 9 6 | 6 5 |
| 2   | 4 0 | 4 0 | 5 8 | 7 3 | 9 4 | 3 7 | 7 6 | 6 4 |
| 3   | 1 6 | 0 2 | 7 7 | 3 1 | 0 4 | 9 9 | 4 2 | 7 9 |
| 4   | 8 4 | 1 3 | 1 8 | 5 0 | 5 6 | 3 7 | 4 7 | 2 9 |
| 5   | 8 5 | 7 5 | 3 7 | 7 0 | 3 2 | 4 9 | 4 0 | 1 5 |
| 6   | 4 4 | 3 4 | 8 5 | 0 2 | 6 6 | 2 5 | 8 6 | 8 0 |
| 7   | 3 7 | 2 3 | 0 4 | 6 0 | 3 0 | 7 3 | 4 0 | 1 8 |
| 8   | 7 0 | 0 9 | 8 0 | 7 4 | 9 2 | 6 6 | 6 9 | 1 9 |
| 9   | 9 7 | 6 5 | 6 0 | 9 7 | 4 4 | 7 0 | 8 0 | 5 8 |
| 10  | 3 2 | 5 9 | 9 3 | 9 7 | 8 3 | 6 1 | 8 1 | 0 4 |
| 11  | 9 8 | 3 6 | 0 3 | 8 9 | 7 4 | 5 0 | 4 9 | 4 2 |
| 12  | 1 8 | 2 9 | 0 1 | 3 2 | 1 4 | 6 8 | 2 6 | 9 8 |
| 13  | 2 1 | 2 6 | 4 9 | 8 3 | 0 4 | 6 1 | 9 8 | 0 6 |
| 14  | 9 5 | 1 4 | 7 5 | 6 4 | 1 4 | 0 3 | 2 7 | 4 3 |
| 15  | 0 5 | 1 0 | 5 5 | 2 9 | 4 8 | 8 7 | 7 8 | 2 1 |
| 16  | 2 8 | 8 4 | 5 9 | 7 8 | 7 4 | 2 3 | 3 7 | 4 9 |
| 17  | 6 5 | 6 3 | 2 6 | 0 5 | 0 0 | 4 9 | 6 6 | 7 0 |
| 18  | 8 8 | 8 0 | 1 6 | 9 6 | 1 8 | 6 8 | 6 3 | 3 3 |
| 19  | 3 1 | 9 3 | 5 3 | 3 6 | 5 0 | 9 6 | 5 0 | 1 8 |
| 20  | 4 1 | 4 6 | 6 7 | 1 1 | 4 4 | 5 1 | 0 0 | 5 9 |
| 21  | 4 7 | 4 0 | 7 5 | 0 6 | 8 5 | 6 6 | 4 4 | 4 2 |
| 22  | 1 8 | 7 5 | 4 8 | 2 6 | 7 1 | 3 0 | 6 2 | 3 7 |
| 23  | 8 0 | 3 6 | 6 5 | 2 5 | 9 9 | 3 9 | 0 8 | 8 9 |
| 24  | 4 4 | 7 0 | 2 1 | 8 1 | 9 7 | 8 5 | 7 5 | 3 5 |
| 25  | 2 9 | 1 9 | 8 6 | 2 0 | 4 5 | 0 3 | 5 4 | 4 1 |
| 26  | 0 3 | 4 2 | 5 9 | 4 8 | 6 2 | 1 5 | 7 2 | 7 2 |
| 27  | 9 1 | 5 9 | 4 6 | 8 6 | 4 5 | 2 0 | 4 8 | 7 6 |
| 28  | 0 1 | 9 6 | 8 5 | 3 7 | 3 1 | 5 9 | 4 7 | 0 8 |
| 29  | 6 1 | 6 2 | 0 1 | 3 6 | 9 6 | 6 0 | 1 1 | 8 7 |
| 30  | 5 9 | 3 6 | 0 5 | 4 9 | 4 8 | 9 2 | 9 1 | 8 5 |
| 31  | 0 9 | 0 2 | 7 8 | 9 9 | 0 4 | 6 7 | 1 2 | 0 7 |
| 32  | 7 5 | 0 3 | 5 8 | 7 2 | 7 6 | 8 3 | 8 7 | 4 5 |
| 33  | 6 4 | 0 4 | 7 3 | 6 1 | 3 7 | 2 7 | 1 2 | 7 4 |
| 34  | 3 8 | 5 1 | 4 5 | 2 4 | 5 0 | 8 2 | 2 9 | 1 5 |
| 35  | 4 4 | 8 1 | 9 7 | 6 9 | 4 0 | 5 7 | 4 6 | 2 9 |
| 36  | 3 1 | 2 3 | 9 6 | 2 2 | 1 4 | 6 8 | 8 5 | 1 2 |
| 37  | 1 4 | 1 9 | 4 7 | 1 8 | 6 4 | 7 3 | 1 3 | 2 6 |
| 38  | 3 3 | 3 9 | 5 5 | 6 0 | 5 3 | 2 0 | 6 7 | 6 3 |
| 39  | 1 8 | 4 8 | 5 6 | 3 8 | 4 3 | 7 8 | 2 2 | 7 7 |
| 40  | 8 8 | 3 5 | 8 6 | 3 9 | 0 6 | 0 3 | 4 7 | 4 5 |

z 2

Random Sampling Numbers—III

|  | 1 2 | 3 4 | 5 6 | 7 8 | 9 10 | 11 12 | 13 14 | 15 16 |
|---|---|---|---|---|---|---|---|---|
| 1 | 3 2 | 7 4 | 4 4 | 6 4 | 5 6 | 1 2 | 4 2 | 2 3 |
| 2 | 7 2 | 0 1 | 7 4 | 6 7 | 5 8 | 6 5 | 8 9 | 8 3 |
| 3 | 0 0 | 0 6 | 2 2 | 7 6 | 4 4 | 0 7 | 4 7 | 3 5 |
| 4 | 1 3 | 2 4 | 9 1 | 1 9 | 0 1 | 1 1 | 7 0 | 1 3 |
| 5 | 7 9 | 3 8 | 9 2 | 3 1 | 6 2 | 5 4 | 9 3 | 7 5 |
| 6 | 9 4 | 3 9 | 6 6 | 0 6 | 3 3 | 2 1 | 6 5 | 8 7 |
| 7 | 6 0 | 9 8 | 6 9 | 1 8 | 3 5 | 1 6 | 5 0 | 6 2 |
| 8 | 2 1 | 4 2 | 5 7 | 0 0 | 5 9 | 2 7 | 7 7 | 5 2 |
| 9 | 9 9 | 8 4 | 4 1 | 3 0 | 5 6 | 7 5 | 0 4 | 9 9 |
| 10 | 3 2 | 3 0 | 7 3 | 4 3 | 8 2 | 2 4 | 6 9 | 0 0 |
| 11 | 2 5 | 0 8 | 0 3 | 7 0 | 2 7 | 3 5 | 0 4 | 9 1 |
| 12 | 9 9 | 5 3 | 3 6 | 6 0 | 3 9 | 9 1 | 7 3 | 1 8 |
| 13 | 1 9 | 2 2 | 3 3 | 7 0 | 6 1 | 2 7 | 8 2 | 9 2 |
| 14 | 3 6 | 3 1 | 8 6 | 0 0 | 6 6 | 6 6 | 7 7 | 1 9 |
| 15 | 1 9 | 9 9 | 0 0 | 1 2 | 2 4 | 0 3 | 3 1 | 2 4 |
| 16 | 6 6 | 7 6 | 4 2 | 1 5 | 1 9 | 4 5 | 5 7 | 5 4 |
| 17 | 8 0 | 0 6 | 2 7 | 5 4 | 9 9 | 8 5 | 9 8 | 4 7 |
| 18 | 3 1 | 6 0 | 7 0 | 9 9 | 3 9 | 4 6 | 9 0 | 4 6 |
| 19 | 5 5 | 9 5 | 2 1 | 6 3 | 6 2 | 1 6 | 8 2 | 3 4 |
| 20 | 9 0 | 2 2 | 3 7 | 0 9 | 8 8 | 0 1 | 7 8 | 8 4 |
| 21 | 4 3 | 9 5 | 3 1 | 2 9 | 8 4 | 8 0 | 7 0 | 6 5 |
| 22 | 8 8 | 4 3 | 3 0 | 9 9 | 4 6 | 3 9 | 7 9 | 5 9 |
| 23 | 4 1 | 6 3 | 0 6 | 7 1 | 7 2 | 1 8 | 5 3 | 7 1 |
| 24 | 3 7 | 5 2 | 1 9 | 9 3 | 7 6 | 0 1 | 9 1 | 9 0 |
| 25 | 1 2 | 3 5 | 1 8 | 3 1 | 2 6 | 4 0 | 3 9 | 0 2 |
| 26 | 6 0 | 0 3 | 9 7 | 2 8 | 4 4 | 5 2 | 5 9 | 3 4 |
| 27 | 7 5 | 5 0 | 5 6 | 7 8 | 8 0 | 5 6 | 2 1 | 3 1 |
| 28 | 5 5 | 0 6 | 0 1 | 9 5 | 7 8 | 5 8 | 1 1 | 6 5 |
| 29 | 1 4 | 8 5 | 0 2 | 7 6 | 9 3 | 0 3 | 8 9 | 8 6 |
| 30 | 5 3 | 8 9 | 9 0 | 3 5 | 6 8 | 7 0 | 1 0 | 1 9 |
| 31 | 6 5 | 8 8 | 1 8 | 6 8 | 8 6 | 6 6 | 3 7 | 7 5 |
| 32 | 5 5 | 8 2 | 5 0 | 3 5 | 1 8 | 6 3 | 7 5 | 7 2 |
| 33 | 0 7 | 6 1 | 0 6 | 0 0 | 3 8 | 8 8 | 0 7 | 2 9 |
| 34 | 8 1 | 4 1 | 5 0 | 9 1 | 0 2 | 7 5 | 0 6 | 5 8 |
| 35 | 7 6 | 3 7 | 8 9 | 6 5 | 0 5 | 0 0 | 8 2 | 1 9 |
| 36 | 6 9 | 2 9 | 6 9 | 4 5 | 2 5 | 5 9 | 0 0 | 2 9 |
| 37 | 0 3 | 8 1 | 5 5 | 9 1 | 1 7 | 4 3 | 8 8 | 4 9 |
| 38 | 6 7 | 5 2 | 9 5 | 5 3 | 7 9 | 5 3 | 1 2 | 8 2 |
| 39 | 9 0 | 2 9 | 8 6 | 2 7 | 5 1 | 3 8 | 6 1 | 1 0 |
| 40 | 8 1 | 2 2 | 5 5 | 6 1 | 7 1 | 4 5 | 6 2 | 4 5 |

## Random Sampling Numbers—IV

|    | 1 2 | 3 4 | 5 6 | 7 8 | 9 10 | 11 12 | 13 14 | 15 16 |
|----|-----|-----|-----|-----|------|-------|-------|-------|
| 1  | 4 1 | 4 5 | 9 4 | 1 5 | 9 4 | 6 4 | 0 2 | 8 0 |
| 2  | 1 1 | 8 6 | 0 6 | 7 4 | 2 2 | 2 9 | 5 9 | 0 1 |
| 3  | 1 1 | 0 0 | 7 9 | 3 3 | 5 4 | 9 1 | 3 1 | 9 4 |
| 4  | 2 3 | 8 7 | 9 0 | 5 4 | 4 3 | 5 3 | 1 3 | 1 1 |
| 5  | 5 5 | 6 5 | 6 1 | 2 1 | 4 3 | 9 7 | 8 1 | 6 5 |
| 6  | 9 5 | 4 8 | 8 4 | 9 6 | 4 2 | 4 6 | 5 1 | 2 8 |
| 7  | 7 3 | 0 8 | 4 7 | 4 1 | 4 7 | 2 6 | 1 6 | 9 4 |
| 8  | 7 2 | 3 3 | 4 9 | 4 6 | 1 0 | 5 2 | 5 7 | 2 6 |
| 9  | 5 5 | 1 7 | 5 1 | 2 1 | 7 6 | 2 6 | 7 8 | 2 0 |
| 10 | 7 1 | 4 8 | 5 1 | 7 2 | 4 9 | 2 7 | 8 2 | 9 5 |
| 11 | 7 4 | 0 6 | 8 0 | 8 6 | 0 8 | 7 5 | 9 7 | 4 1 |
| 12 | 6 0 | 8 5 | 3 9 | 5 1 | 1 2 | 9 5 | 2 4 | 8 7 |
| 13 | 3 7 | 3 5 | 1 0 | 5 7 | 6 7 | 4 6 | 8 0 | 4 6 |
| 14 | 2 4 | 2 7 | 9 1 | 9 4 | 3 9 | 1 6 | 4 7 | 4 9 |
| 15 | 4 8 | 5 5 | 7 2 | 2 0 | 0 9 | 1 3 | 4 7 | 2 5 |
| 16 | 8 1 | 2 6 | 1 0 | 0 6 | 0 4 | 7 6 | 6 4 | 4 4 |
| 17 | 7 7 | 2 2 | 8 1 | 2 1 | 4 8 | 2 8 | 7 6 | 4 3 |
| 18 | 8 8 | 4 4 | 6 4 | 8 8 | 8 7 | 8 8 | 8 9 | 2 6 |
| 19 | 8 5 | 7 9 | 5 2 | 9 0 | 7 5 | 3 3 | 8 0 | 5 5 |
| 20 | 4 0 | 1 9 | 8 1 | 0 2 | 3 7 | 1 3 | 6 0 | 3 1 |
| 21 | 5 2 | 4 5 | 2 9 | 1 0 | 4 5 | 6 0 | 5 0 | 2 7 |
| 22 | 6 8 | 8 0 | 5 7 | 5 8 | 0 7 | 8 2 | 0 2 | 9 9 |
| 23 | 7 1 | 2 6 | 1 4 | 0 9 | 8 8 | 9 7 | 9 3 | 8 8 |
| 24 | 9 4 | 7 5 | 6 1 | 9 1 | 0 8 | 8 3 | 7 9 | 7 0 |
| 25 | 0 8 | 4 1 | 8 6 | 2 2 | 2 7 | 0 2 | 5 5 | 3 5 |
| 26 | 5 3 | 1 4 | 9 2 | 6 4 | 4 7 | 8 3 | 7 2 | 5 9 |
| 27 | 0 7 | 7 3 | 4 7 | 1 2 | 5 0 | 3 9 | 3 9 | 3 3 |
| 28 | 4 2 | 8 4 | 2 3 | 1 6 | 5 5 | 1 9 | 9 8 | 6 6 |
| 29 | 5 7 | 1 3 | 4 3 | 8 0 | 2 7 | 7 8 | 8 1 | 4 9 |
| 30 | 3 8 | 8 5 | 4 1 | 7 8 | 5 7 | 8 2 | 0 6 | 3 9 |
| 31 | 0 0 | 1 6 | 5 8 | 3 2 | 4 8 | 6 8 | 2 0 | 7 5 |
| 32 | 7 4 | 6 0 | 9 4 | 5 1 | 3 0 | 2 0 | 9 6 | 5 0 |
| 33 | 6 9 | 6 1 | 3 4 | 7 2 | 0 7 | 9 6 | 3 2 | 0 4 |
| 34 | 0 3 | 4 8 | 7 6 | 7 0 | 5 6 | 0 2 | 6 7 | 8 0 |
| 35 | 2 4 | 5 7 | 7 2 | 6 3 | 8 2 | 5 6 | 1 7 | 7 1 |
| 36 | 7 2 | 9 4 | 1 6 | 8 2 | 4 5 | 9 0 | 1 8 | 2 9 |
| 37 | 2 7 | 7 6 | 0 8 | 2 1 | 4 5 | 0 2 | 1 6 | 4 6 |
| 38 | 4 6 | 0 7 | 5 9 | 4 3 | 9 6 | 9 8 | 6 4 | 3 5 |
| 39 | 7 1 | 6 0 | 8 1 | 0 3 | 5 6 | 1 2 | 3 5 | 7 2 |
| 40 | 3 3 | 9 3 | 5 0 | 1 7 | 1 3 | 3 8 | 2 8 | 0 4 |

Random Sampling Numbers—V

| | 1 2 | 3 4 | 5 6 | 7 8 | 9 10 | 11 12 | 13 14 | 15 16 |
|---|---|---|---|---|---|---|---|---|
| 1 | 7 8 | 7 4 | 4 6 | 0 9 | 3 6 | 7 3 | 9 9 | 8 4 |
| 2 | 7 8 | 0 4 | 0 8 | 0 4 | 7 9 | 8 5 | 0 5 | 9 6 |
| 3 | 5 6 | 9 9 | 1 4 | 9 9 | 4 3 | 8 6 | 5 6 | 8 4 |
| 4 | 8 0 | 7 7 | 6 0 | 2 0 | 7 1 | 4 5 | 8 6 | 0 7 |
| 5 | 5 4 | 2 0 | 4 4 | 2 8 | 9 0 | 2 8 | 8 9 | 3 3 |
| 6 | 7 1 | 7 5 | 9 2 | 5 2 | 3 7 | 0 3 | 5 9 | 5 6 |
| 7 | 6 7 | 1 2 | 9 4 | 1 0 | 1 1 | 9 3 | 4 2 | 4 4 |
| 8 | 1 2 | 1 8 | 2 8 | 9 3 | 7 9 | 9 7 | 1 1 | 6 0 |
| 9 | 7 0 | 5 6 | 1 1 | 4 2 | 1 3 | 2 0 | 5 3 | 8 9 |
| 10 | 3 6 | 4 3 | 6 5 | 3 8 | 1 1 | 3 5 | 9 3 | 9 1 |
| 11 | 4 6 | 2 0 | 3 6 | 3 5 | 4 8 | 7 5 | 2 4 | 7 9 |
| 12 | 4 3 | 2 6 | 4 9 | 2 2 | 3 0 | 6 6 | 2 4 | 9 6 |
| 13 | 1 5 | 7 3 | 1 6 | 1 3 | 3 8 | 7 0 | 2 8 | 7 7 |
| 14 | 9 1 | 1 3 | 3 2 | 7 6 | 9 2 | 1 7 | 5 2 | 0 9 |
| 15 | 5 6 | 1 5 | 9 4 | 6 8 | 8 6 | 9 6 | 1 2 | 5 5 |
| 16 | 1 2 | 7 3 | 7 3 | 3 9 | 6 5 | 4 0 | 7 0 | 1 1 |
| 17 | 1 8 | 7 1 | 2 7 | 4 8 | 5 5 | 7 5 | 3 3 | 4 0 |
| 18 | 0 7 | 5 5 | 8 2 | 3 8 | 2 2 | 1 2 | 9 7 | 0 6 |
| 19 | 6 1 | 8 1 | 6 3 | 2 7 | 2 6 | 2 0 | 1 8 | 4 0 |
| 20 | 4 1 | 5 1 | 3 4 | 5 9 | 2 8 | 5 9 | 5 3 | 0 9 |
| 21 | 2 9 | 2 9 | 1 3 | 0 7 | 8 8 | 6 5 | 2 8 | 7 9 |
| 22 | 9 0 | 9 8 | 9 9 | 9 2 | 8 6 | 4 3 | 6 1 | 8 2 |
| 23 | 9 3 | 1 8 | 2 3 | 6 2 | 2 4 | 0 0 | 8 1 | 2 4 |
| 24 | 5 9 | 3 0 | 4 8 | 1 0 | 3 9 | 7 5 | 7 0 | 8 7 |
| 25 | 4 1 | 6 3 | 3 7 | 8 1 | 5 7 | 9 3 | 4 4 | 7 1 |
| 26 | 9 2 | 4 8 | 8 4 | 7 9 | 4 7 | 3 9 | 3 3 | 6 6 |
| 27 | 4 0 | 7 1 | 3 1 | 1 3 | 6 0 | 3 4 | 2 6 | 1 0 |
| 28 | 1 3 | 6 5 | 2 7 | 8 6 | 2 5 | 3 0 | 7 1 | 8 1 |
| 29 | 3 9 | 5 7 | 1 1 | 1 7 | 5 9 | 1 2 | 6 9 | 9 0 |
| 30 | 1 2 | 4 2 | 5 7 | 3 0 | 1 5 | 7 0 | 7 4 | 6 6 |
| 31 | 1 8 | 0 5 | 7 6 | 8 6 | 4 0 | 9 1 | 0 9 | 7 6 |
| 32 | 5 8 | 3 1 | 2 1 | 0 8 | 5 4 | 0 3 | 6 4 | 6 9 |
| 33 | 9 4 | 6 0 | 5 1 | 9 9 | 4 4 | 6 6 | 4 1 | 7 7 |
| 34 | 4 3 | 0 7 | 7 9 | 9 2 | 7 5 | 6 9 | 5 1 | 8 0 |
| 35 | 9 1 | 0 5 | 8 4 | 9 0 | 8 9 | 0 2 | 3 4 | 2 7 |
| 36 | 0 8 | 1 6 | 7 9 | 9 4 | 3 3 | 4 3 | 1 8 | 0 8 |
| 37 | 2 0 | 8 0 | 0 4 | 6 7 | 6 5 | 7 8 | 1 4 | 1 9 |
| 38 | 1 0 | 1 2 | 2 4 | 6 2 | 5 7 | 4 7 | 1 1 | 5 7 |
| 39 | 4 2 | 5 7 | 2 3 | 1 3 | 5 0 | 9 8 | 6 7 | 1 7 |
| 40 | 6 0 | 9 9 | 3 9 | 7 4 | 9 3 | 1 6 | 5 5 | 4 9 |

## Random Sampling Numbers—VI

|     | 1 2 | 3 4 | 5 6 | 7 8 | 9 10 | 11 12 | 13 14 | 15 16 |
| --- | --- | --- | --- | --- | --- | --- | --- | --- |
| 1  | 9 3 | 3 1 | 5 3 | 8 6 | 8 5 | 8 2 | 5 6 | 2 8 |
| 2  | 5 6 | 6 7 | 4 4 | 8 4 | 1 2 | 1 1 | 9 7 | 4 8 |
| 3  | 4 5 | 3 0 | 8 9 | 6 9 | 6 7 | 0 2 | 1 1 | 2 1 |
| 4  | 3 3 | 3 8 | 5 8 | 3 3 | 6 0 | 2 2 | 3 8 | 9 1 |
| 5  | 7 3 | 6 4 | 9 6 | 6 7 | 2 9 | 1 1 | 1 8 | 1 6 |
| 6  | 5 9 | 3 4 | 4 4 | 8 3 | 2 3 | 9 6 | 7 8 | 8 4 |
| 7  | 7 2 | 5 2 | 3 7 | 0 8 | 9 9 | 9 6 | 3 3 | 9 2 |
| 8  | 0 4 | 7 7 | 2 8 | 5 3 | 3 7 | 7 3 | 4 9 | 6 2 |
| 9  | 4 9 | 5 6 | 3 3 | 6 2 | 6 4 | 6 9 | 8 2 | 7 1 |
| 10 | 3 1 | 3 3 | 0 5 | 4 0 | 5 9 | 3 3 | 3 5 | 8 4 |
| 11 | 4 1 | 0 8 | 2 5 | 8 8 | 7 8 | 2 8 | 4 6 | 4 2 |
| 12 | 3 3 | 6 3 | 4 0 | 1 5 | 1 5 | 6 1 | 2 0 | 0 5 |
| 13 | 1 6 | 2 6 | 2 4 | 6 6 | 0 7 | 6 7 | 3 8 | 0 7 |
| 14 | 2 4 | 8 5 | 4 8 | 6 3 | 5 6 | 2 6 | 1 4 | 5 7 |
| 15 | 9 0 | 3 8 | 8 8 | 3 1 | 2 1 | 5 6 | 9 9 | 4 0 |
| 16 | 8 2 | 8 5 | 2 3 | 2 6 | 2 5 | 6 7 | 2 4 | 2 6 |
| 17 | 5 7 | 8 8 | 1 2 | 2 3 | 6 1 | 1 3 | 5 2 | 4 6 |
| 18 | 2 1 | 2 4 | 6 2 | 7 4 | 5 7 | 9 7 | 1 8 | 5 6 |
| 19 | 5 7 | 3 4 | 9 1 | 4 4 | 5 6 | 6 0 | 2 4 | 1 0 |
| 20 | 9 7 | 3 1 | 7 1 | 3 6 | 2 5 | 1 9 | 4 2 | 5 8 |
| 21 | 2 2 | 3 8 | 1 7 | 6 8 | 0 3 | 5 0 | 0 1 | 6 3 |
| 22 | 7 7 | 8 4 | 0 1 | 4 4 | 5 8 | 1 2 | 1 7 | 6 1 |
| 23 | 5 2 | 7 9 | 7 3 | 5 3 | 4 0 | 0 7 | 0 6 | 8 6 |
| 24 | 4 8 | 7 7 | 1 8 | 1 2 | 9 3 | 0 6 | 7 7 | 8 0 |
| 25 | 3 8 | 8 6 | 9 1 | 9 7 | 4 5 | 4 7 | 3 4 | 4 2 |
| 26 | 2 7 | 3 5 | 8 8 | 8 0 | 9 6 | 9 7 | 2 4 | 7 7 |
| 27 | 5 9 | 0 5 | 9 4 | 9 5 | 7 3 | 4 2 | 2 5 | 1 6 |
| 28 | 4 4 | 7 6 | 9 2 | 9 5 | 8 3 | 0 4 | 0 7 | 3 1 |
| 29 | 1 3 | 3 8 | 1 3 | 3 8 | 3 2 | 4 8 | 4 2 | 0 2 |
| 30 | 9 0 | 2 8 | 1 3 | 3 0 | 1 5 | 5 9 | 4 0 | 6 0 |
| 31 | 8 0 | 5 7 | 0 0 | 1 4 | 9 5 | 9 5 | 5 1 | 8 5 |
| 32 | 2 6 | 5 3 | 8 8 | 6 4 | 3 2 | 6 6 | 9 9 | 3 4 |
| 33 | 2 8 | 8 3 | 2 4 | 2 8 | 0 6 | 1 4 | 6 6 | 2 7 |
| 34 | 3 4 | 8 0 | 1 9 | 9 7 | 2 0 | 9 8 | 8 1 | 7 4 |
| 35 | 5 8 | 1 4 | 2 4 | 5 7 | 0 2 | 3 7 | 9 3 | 7 1 |
| 36 | 1 4 | 8 1 | 6 6 | 9 2 | 5 9 | 0 8 | 4 6 | 5 3 |
| 37 | 1 1 | 0 6 | 6 7 | 0 1 | 2 2 | 3 2 | 2 5 | 3 3 |
| 38 | 7 5 | 3 1 | 4 5 | 1 7 | 1 4 | 8 4 | 8 5 | 8 1 |
| 39 | 7 8 | 1 7 | 9 3 | 9 5 | 8 9 | 0 3 | 9 8 | 0 9 |
| 40 | 9 0 | 9 3 | 6 4 | 3 4 | 1 9 | 4 0 | 9 9 | 9 9 |

Random Sampling Numbers—VII

|  | 1 2 | 3 4 | 5 6 | 7 8 | 9 10 | 11 12 | 13 14 | 15 16 |
|---|---|---|---|---|---|---|---|---|
| 1 | 8 3 | 8 4 | 0 0 | 1 2 | 4 2 | 8 3 | 9 4 | 9 4 |
| 2 | 8 9 | 2 0 | 9 5 | 7 8 | 0 8 | 9 5 | 3 4 | 0 3 |
| 3 | 3 3 | 0 0 | 1 2 | 3 0 | 2 4 | 2 0 | 8 7 | 8 8 |
| 4 | 9 5 | 4 1 | 7 1 | 1 6 | 3 2 | 1 2 | 6 6 | 9 2 |
| 5 | 0 0 | 0 8 | 1 0 | 9 8 | 8 1 | 2 9 | 6 6 | 2 3 |
| 6 | 0 9 | 1 3 | 0 3 | 3 5 | 0 4 | 7 6 | 7 5 | 7 8 |
| 7 | 0 6 | 4 9 | 0 9 | 5 0 | 7 6 | 5 4 | 1 7 | 0 6 |
| 8 | 4 1 | 3 4 | 6 5 | 9 8 | 3 2 | 8 4 | 6 9 | 4 0 |
| 9 | 2 3 | 0 3 | 8 2 | 5 6 | 6 3 | 6 2 | 8 6 | 7 8 |
| 10 | 3 0 | 5 5 | 1 8 | 5 4 | 7 9 | 1 8 | 7 0 | 0 7 |
| 11 | 3 3 | 8 4 | 4 6 | 3 1 | 0 1 | 3 1 | 3 0 | 2 1 |
| 12 | 4 2 | 0 7 | 3 5 | 7 6 | 3 0 | 1 8 | 9 6 | 8 2 |
| 13 | 7 2 | 9 7 | 5 4 | 4 5 | 1 7 | 4 1 | 4 7 | 0 8 |
| 14 | 5 1 | 4 3 | 6 6 | 6 0 | 3 3 | 0 7 | 6 7 | 3 2 |
| 15 | 7 0 | 6 7 | 4 5 | 8 1 | 6 7 | 1 7 | 7 1 | 6 7 |
| 16 | 0 2 | 3 1 | 8 4 | 7 2 | 2 2 | 2 0 | 4 9 | 8 7 |
| 17 | 8 3 | 2 5 | 7 6 | 9 2 | 0 5 | 0 6 | 0 1 | 9 0 |
| 18 | 8 1 | 1 5 | 7 2 | 5 0 | 6 1 | 2 2 | 9 2 | 3 5 |
| 19 | 3 5 | 7 4 | 1 8 | 5 0 | 8 3 | 1 8 | 8 9 | 1 5 |
| 20 | 7 4 | 5 7 | 3 1 | 8 7 | 1 5 | 1 8 | 6 1 | 3 3 |
| 21 | 2 9 | 2 7 | 2 3 | 1 6 | 5 0 | 7 2 | 5 4 | 4 0 |
| 22 | 8 3 | 4 0 | 0 5 | 3 2 | 7 2 | 8 8 | 1 5 | 8 9 |
| 23 | 3 3 | 6 2 | 0 5 | 5 8 | 9 0 | 9 1 | 3 2 | 0 1 |
| 24 | 3 3 | 4 3 | 2 2 | 5 1 | 1 6 | 3 7 | 9 2 | 6 1 |
| 25 | 9 8 | 0 4 | 1 9 | 3 9 | 6 8 | 8 8 | 9 3 | 6 7 |
| 26 | 3 1 | 0 7 | 0 5 | 3 2 | 9 6 | 5 3 | 7 2 | 5 1 |
| 27 | 4 3 | 9 2 | 3 0 | 8 6 | 3 2 | 2 9 | 1 7 | 2 5 |
| 28 | 7 8 | 9 9 | 4 6 | 7 0 | 8 5 | 3 6 | 2 3 | 3 3 |
| 29 | 6 6 | 9 4 | 8 1 | 3 5 | 7 1 | 0 8 | 1 4 | 1 2 |
| 30 | 6 6 | 4 1 | 6 7 | 9 7 | 7 5 | 1 8 | 9 9 | 0 0 |
| 31 | 6 6 | 8 4 | 8 6 | 0 2 | 6 9 | 2 7 | 5 5 | 0 2 |
| 32 | 8 9 | 9 4 | 6 4 | 5 2 | 5 2 | 3 3 | 7 7 | 3 1 |
| 33 | 7 2 | 3 1 | 8 7 | 4 8 | 9 7 | 4 1 | 0 5 | 9 1 |
| 34 | 6 4 | 4 8 | 7 2 | 8 4 | 8 0 | 5 9 | 2 4 | 3 7 |
| 35 | 6 0 | 3 9 | 0 2 | 9 3 | 5 8 | 5 0 | 3 8 | 7 9 |
| 36 | 4 8 | 9 5 | 8 4 | 0 2 | 0 6 | 3 4 | 0 3 | 8 4 |
| 37 | 4 0 | 9 4 | 0 8 | 2 1 | 2 8 | 5 7 | 3 1 | 8 2 |
| 38 | 5 6 | 9 9 | 9 5 | 0 1 | 2 0 | 7 6 | 5 7 | 4 2 |
| 39 | 9 9 | 1 0 | 3 5 | 4 6 | 6 1 | 9 5 | 3 2 | 3 3 |
| 40 | 2 9 | 5 2 | 3 1 | 1 2 | 1 0 | 1 4 | 3 2 | 4 4 |

## Random Sampling Numbers—VIII

|    | 1 2 | 3 4 | 5 6 | 7 8 | 9 10 | 11 12 | 13 14 | 15 16 |
|----|-----|-----|-----|-----|------|-------|-------|-------|
| 1  | 1 0 | 0 2 | 5 7 | 3 5 | 0 5 | 2 3 | 2 0 | 1 7 |
| 2  | 1 7 | 5 0 | 7 4 | 9 9 | 6 0 | 2 5 | 2 9 | 6 5 |
| 3  | 9 9 | 7 0 | 3 4 | 0 5 | 7 2 | 4 6 | 0 1 | 7 2 |
| 4  | 2 4 | 3 6 | 7 0 | 4 7 | 9 0 | 9 2 | 1 9 | 4 8 |
| 5  | 6 5 | 1 2 | 9 0 | 9 1 | 9 2 | 3 3 | 5 6 | 4 0 |
| 6  | 1 0 | 1 4 | 3 7 | 3 2 | 5 3 | 9 0 | 9 3 | 3 5 |
| 7  | 3 1 | 5 3 | 3 1 | 0 8 | 6 6 | 6 8 | 4 4 | 4 9 |
| 8  | 6 7 | 3 1 | 1 4 | 2 7 | 5 1 | 9 0 | 2 8 | 0 4 |
| 9  | 2 2 | 6 3 | 6 2 | 7 4 | 2 2 | 1 7 | 2 9 | 7 8 |
| 10 | 6 7 | 1 7 | 8 4 | 3 5 | 9 2 | 3 4 | 7 7 | 2 9 |
| 11 | 5 0 | 9 7 | 4 2 | 5 9 | 6 4 | 8 3 | 9 7 | 2 1 |
| 12 | 5 1 | 5 1 | 9 7 | 8 0 | 6 6 | 5 2 | 5 0 | 3 1 |
| 13 | 6 2 | 4 7 | 2 4 | 4 0 | 7 5 | 4 6 | 3 2 | 9 5 |
| 14 | 4 7 | 3 6 | 9 0 | 1 2 | 1 4 | 5 3 | 2 9 | 9 7 |
| 15 | 7 1 | 7 8 | 6 3 | 7 5 | 7 2 | 7 6 | 6 7 | 4 7 |
| 16 | 0 2 | 0 9 | 5 3 | 9 5 | 9 9 | 5 2 | 8 4 | 4 6 |
| 17 | 2 7 | 6 1 | 3 7 | 0 2 | 0 5 | 2 7 | 8 0 | 5 1 |
| 18 | 8 2 | 6 4 | 3 0 | 5 0 | 8 4 | 0 6 | 2 9 | 5 5 |
| 19 | 8 6 | 2 2 | 4 8 | 1 0 | 9 2 | 8 2 | 1 5 | 3 5 |
| 20 | 4 9 | 0 6 | 3 8 | 2 6 | 4 2 | 4 5 | 4 5 | 7 4 |
| 21 | 8 7 | 1 7 | 3 6 | 3 1 | 9 8 | 2 9 | 1 4 | 0 3 |
| 22 | 2 4 | 8 4 | 1 0 | 3 9 | 6 2 | 5 5 | 3 7 | 0 1 |
| 23 | 2 2 | 4 6 | 4 3 | 1 4 | 3 9 | 7 2 | 1 2 | 1 5 |
| 24 | 6 4 | 5 5 | 5 5 | 0 5 | 7 9 | 8 1 | 2 3 | 2 1 |
| 25 | 1 1 | 2 3 | 8 6 | 1 6 | 5 5 | 9 6 | 0 2 | 1 5 |
| 26 | 0 5 | 6 9 | 9 1 | 9 3 | 7 5 | 9 4 | 2 6 | 3 1 |
| 27 | 3 6 | 8 0 | 7 5 | 8 3 | 9 7 | 1 3 | 8 4 | 9 2 |
| 28 | 4 2 | 2 8 | 9 0 | 1 8 | 1 0 | 9 9 | 9 7 | 4 1 |
| 29 | 8 5 | 2 8 | 1 7 | 6 3 | 9 6 | 3 0 | 2 2 | 7 0 |
| 30 | 9 2 | 6 4 | 9 0 | 1 5 | 2 7 | 2 7 | 1 4 | 2 1 |
| 31 | 9 9 | 1 5 | 3 0 | 6 8 | 1 7 | 8 3 | 9 4 | 3 5 |
| 32 | 1 5 | 4 7 | 8 1 | 4 2 | 1 3 | 8 7 | 9 3 | 6 8 |
| 33 | 3 0 | 7 8 | 4 7 | 2 4 | 7 8 | 7 0 | 5 1 | 7 8 |
| 34 | 2 3 | 5 6 | 8 8 | 0 1 | 9 1 | 8 0 | 2 5 | 9 7 |
| 35 | 2 3 | 7 2 | 5 6 | 9 0 | 3 7 | 6 1 | 0 6 | 0 3 |
| 36 | 2 3 | 0 1 | 0 8 | 7 7 | 9 9 | 1 1 | 6 6 | 0 6 |
| 37 | 7 2 | 2 5 | 6 8 | 1 6 | 4 5 | 4 1 | 8 5 | 6 9 |
| 38 | 0 2 | 3 5 | 3 6 | 4 0 | 7 8 | 4 1 | 1 3 | 0 7 |
| 39 | 8 7 | 2 0 | 4 1 | 8 9 | 8 0 | 0 5 | 2 1 | 5 9 |
| 40 | 9 9 | 4 5 | 2 5 | 3 8 | 1 3 | 4 0 | 0 2 | 5 9 |

Random Sampling Numbers—IX

|    | 1 2 | 3 4 | 5 6 | 7 8 | 9 10 | 11 12 | 13 14 | 15 16 |
|----|-----|-----|-----|-----|------|-------|-------|-------|
| 1  | 6 0 | 4 6 | 8 3 | 0 8 | 8 7  | 3 7   | 6 9   | 0 9   |
| 2  | 5 1 | 3 1 | 5 2 | 7 8 | 9 2  | 0 5   | 5 1   | 0 6   |
| 3  | 8 7 | 9 7 | 1 7 | 7 4 | 8 2  | 5 3   | 7 9   | 2 2   |
| 4  | 2 4 | 5 2 | 6 5 | 3 4 | 8 6  | 2 1   | 0 3   | 0 9   |
| 5  | 6 5 | 2 4 | 7 8 | 9 3 | 4 9  | 4 7   | 3 3   | 9 1   |
| 6  | 9 0 | 0 1 | 1 5 | 0 9 | 2 8  | 4 2   | 4 3   | 4 7   |
| 7  | 8 7 | 2 9 | 1 7 | 8 8 | 4 7  | 9 8   | 5 2   | 5 6   |
| 8  | 6 2 | 0 2 | 6 3 | 7 5 | 8 3  | 7 6   | 3 4   | 1 7   |
| 9  | 6 4 | 0 5 | 1 2 | 9 2 | 3 3  | 9 9   | 6 0   | 9 5   |
| 10 | 3 3 | 8 3 | 0 2 | 6 3 | 6 7  | 7 4   | 0 7   | 3 2   |
| 11 | 0 7 | 9 0 | 0 2 | 2 6 | 0 7  | 0 2   | 9 6   | 5 2   |
| 12 | 4 2 | 8 8 | 7 7 | 2 5 | 2 3  | 2 6   | 0 8   | 9 8   |
| 13 | 7 8 | 4 8 | 2 6 | 5 8 | 4 8  | 1 9   | 2 6   | 7 5   |
| 14 | 3 1 | 9 5 | 5 6 | 1 7 | 9 6  | 3 8   | 0 6   | 2 4   |
| 15 | 9 9 | 8 9 | 3 7 | 6 2 | 5 6  | 1 2   | 7 7   | 5 6   |
| 16 | 7 8 | 2 2 | 8 9 | 0 5 | 4 4  | 8 5   | 6 3   | 4 8   |
| 17 | 3 5 | 7 6 | 4 2 | 2 3 | 3 6  | 8 9   | 3 5   | 1 8   |
| 18 | 5 1 | 1 1 | 9 7 | 1 3 | 5 8  | 5 9   | 3 8   | 4 3   |
| 19 | 9 6 | 3 8 | 1 3 | 1 7 | 2 6  | 2 8   | 9 7   | 1 9   |
| 20 | 9 2 | 6 0 | 8 4 | 1 7 | 1 4  | 6 1   | 0 2   | 6 5   |
| 21 | 5 2 | 3 0 | 8 9 | 7 6 | 1 4  | 3 5   | 7 5   | 6 8   |
| 22 | 3 3 | 8 0 | 7 6 | 0 3 | 9 1  | 6 1   | 3 6   | 1 4   |
| 23 | 6 8 | 3 0 | 5 8 | 2 1 | 0 3  | 3 8   | 9 9   | 5 1   |
| 24 | 2 9 | 5 9 | 8 0 | 1 4 | 6 6  | 0 7   | 9 7   | 3 6   |
| 25 | 7 5 | 2 8 | 7 5 | 8 4 | 6 5  | 5 5   | 8 0   | 2 4   |
| 26 | 5 5 | 4 2 | 1 1 | 0 5 | 5 3  | 7 9   | 6 2   | 9 0   |
| 27 | 5 3 | 4 2 | 6 6 | 8 9 | 8 8  | 0 6   | 2 9   | 0 8   |
| 28 | 3 3 | 5 5 | 3 8 | 3 4 | 3 2  | 3 7   | 0 1   | 6 9   |
| 29 | 5 3 | 9 4 | 2 1 | 8 6 | 0 3  | 4 2   | 9 8   | 2 0   |
| 30 | 0 8 | 0 5 | 2 1 | 7 7 | 4 3  | 1 5   | 5 1   | 3 5   |
| 31 | 2 9 | 0 8 | 5 6 | 0 8 | 5 1  | 3 2   | 3 8   | 5 7   |
| 32 | 4 2 | 7 5 | 8 9 | 0 9 | 1 1  | 8 9   | 9 0   | 0 1   |
| 33 | 7 5 | 2 8 | 9 7 | 6 9 | 9 3  | 4 2   | 3 0   | 2 3   |
| 34 | 4 3 | 3 5 | 2 9 | 5 8 | 9 1  | 1 8   | 2 9   | 3 2   |
| 35 | 2 3 | 5 8 | 7 7 | 1 9 | 3 4  | 5 9   | 3 3   | 0 4   |
| 36 | 4 3 | 4 6 | 9 0 | 1 8 | 4 4  | 6 1   | 3 2   | 6 8   |
| 37 | 0 8 | 4 9 | 1 7 | 0 1 | 1 4  | 9 5   | 9 4   | 9 7   |
| 38 | 6 4 | 6 7 | 1 5 | 9 7 | 2 3  | 1 4   | 8 1   | 1 1   |
| 39 | 0 1 | 9 8 | 8 2 | 6 6 | 8 0  | 6 1   | 9 1   | 6 8   |
| 40 | 5 1 | 3 6 | 2 6 | 9 9 | 0 8  | 2 6   | 0 6   | 5 2   |

## Random Sampling Numbers—X

| | 1 2 | 3 4 | 5 6 | 7 8 | 9 10 | 11 12 | 13 14 | 15 16 |
|---|---|---|---|---|---|---|---|---|
| 1 | 8 1 | 5 4 | 0 6 | 9 6 | 0 7 | 9 8 | 7 7 | 4 0 |
| 2 | 0 2 | 3 2 | 4 2 | 5 0 | 8 6 | 4 5 | 9 8 | 5 0 |
| 3 | 9 5 | 5 7 | 9 4 | 5 4 | 2 5 | 2 3 | 5 7 | 3 9 |
| 4 | 0 1 | 3 7 | 7 7 | 0 7 | 3 0 | 1 7 | 5 5 | 9 5 |
| 5 | 3 8 | 2 2 | 5 5 | 6 4 | 5 5 | 8 2 | 7 8 | 0 5 |
| 6 | 7 9 | 3 9 | 0 9 | 2 9 | 5 9 | 0 1 | 9 0 | 0 7 |
| 7 | 6 6 | 7 4 | 0 1 | 3 7 | 7 6 | 0 9 | 4 7 | 8 4 |
| 8 | 7 9 | 6 2 | 4 9 | 8 3 | 6 5 | 2 5 | 1 7 | 2 4 |
| 9 | 8 4 | 2 2 | 2 9 | 6 6 | 6 0 | 9 2 | 8 3 | 3 0 |
| 10 | 0 4 | 7 1 | 4 6 | 8 9 | 0 2 | 3 0 | 6 8 | 9 1 |
| 11 | 6 1 | 4 1 | 3 1 | 5 8 | 9 9 | 7 0 | 9 3 | 1 0 |
| 12 | 7 9 | 5 6 | 5 7 | 7 6 | 9 3 | 8 8 | 1 7 | 4 7 |
| 13 | 1 1 | 1 2 | 7 8 | 9 6 | 5 4 | 1 2 | 3 8 | 1 4 |
| 14 | 8 8 | 9 6 | 0 7 | 2 0 | 6 5 | 1 8 | 1 2 | 1 4 |
| 15 | 2 8 | 2 2 | 4 2 | 9 7 | 5 4 | 3 9 | 5 2 | 8 9 |
| 16 | 8 9 | 3 1 | 3 0 | 4 3 | 5 7 | 8 6 | 6 7 | 0 9 |
| 17 | 9 5 | 8 4 | 2 2 | 8 9 | 5 2 | 4 8 | 8 4 | 7 5 |
| 18 | 3 4 | 0 1 | 2 6 | 1 4 | 5 2 | 7 8 | 0 3 | 9 0 |
| 19 | 8 5 | 9 6 | 8 9 | 9 9 | 3 3 | 5 9 | 7 9 | 3 8 |
| 20 | 1 0 | 6 2 | 0 2 | 4 6 | 8 7 | 2 0 | 2 8 | 7 3 |
| 21 | 6 0 | 7 9 | 1 7 | 8 4 | 0 3 | 3 6 | 5 0 | 1 1 |
| 22 | 4 3 | 4 3 | 7 3 | 4 6 | 0 9 | 2 2 | 6 6 | 1 7 |
| 23 | 1 9 | 8 7 | 4 1 | 6 4 | 8 9 | 2 3 | 0 1 | 4 3 |
| 24 | 9 2 | 5 5 | 7 3 | 3 2 | 5 0 | 5 7 | 0 7 | 4 0 |
| 25 | 9 2 | 6 9 | 8 9 | 6 0 | 7 1 | 5 6 | 3 9 | 7 5 |
| 26 | 2 4 | 6 2 | 4 0 | 9 0 | 7 0 | 4 4 | 7 7 | 6 5 |
| 27 | 2 6 | 9 2 | 1 7 | 6 9 | 9 4 | 8 8 | 5 7 | 0 0 |
| 28 | 6 2 | 8 9 | 6 8 | 9 2 | 6 8 | 8 4 | 1 6 | 4 0 |
| 29 | 5 3 | 3 0 | 6 9 | 8 4 | 0 5 | 0 9 | 9 9 | 3 1 |
| 30 | 6 0 | 3 1 | 8 1 | 3 3 | 0 0 | 8 8 | 9 6 | 7 2 |
| 31 | 6 9 | 5 0 | 0 1 | 2 9 | 2 1 | 5 2 | 4 2 | 3 1 |
| 32 | 3 4 | 8 2 | 0 3 | 6 8 | 0 8 | 2 2 | 2 9 | 0 2 |
| 33 | 0 7 | 0 5 | 4 3 | 9 1 | 7 8 | 2 8 | 3 6 | 4 7 |
| 34 | 3 9 | 3 3 | 3 5 | 5 8 | 4 2 | 1 8 | 8 4 | 6 1 |
| 35 | 1 7 | 7 2 | 6 3 | 6 8 | 9 1 | 8 5 | 9 2 | 7 9 |
| 36 | 9 3 | 0 9 | 3 3 | 0 3 | 5 4 | 1 1 | 9 5 | 4 9 |
| 37 | 8 7 | 5 9 | 7 4 | 6 3 | 0 6 | 7 5 | 6 3 | 7 0 |
| 38 | 8 3 | 7 5 | 2 9 | 3 7 | 0 0 | 0 0 | 6 3 | 4 2 |
| 39 | 1 9 | 8 1 | 5 9 | 1 1 | 4 0 | 5 5 | 2 8 | 1 3 |
| 40 | 7 4 | 0 8 | 0 4 | 7 3 | 5 7 | 0 8 | 3 6 | 6 1 |

## Random Sampling Numbers—XI

|    | 1 2 | 3 4 | 5 6 | 7 8 | 9 10 | 11 12 | 13 14 | 15 16 |
|----|-----|-----|-----|-----|------|-------|-------|-------|
| 1  | 2 8 | 9 9 | 3 0 | 5 8 | 1 4 | 1 9 | 5 7 | 3 5 |
| 2  | 4 0 | 8 3 | 1 8 | 7 9 | 8 7 | 1 5 | 7 2 | 9 1 |
| 3  | 7 5 | 4 5 | 2 0 | 2 1 | 3 5 | 3 3 | 2 7 | 0 0 |
| 4  | 1 8 | 3 6 | 6 6 | 3 5 | 0 0 | 9 2 | 5 1 | 0 1 |
| 5  | 4 2 | 2 8 | 6 8 | 5 7 | 4 6 | 4 3 | 9 1 | 8 4 |
| 6  | 2 1 | 0 2 | 3 8 | 0 5 | 1 0 | 8 1 | 4 9 | 4 0 |
| 7  | 6 6 | 5 3 | 4 5 | 9 7 | 8 9 | 2 1 | 1 1 | 2 9 |
| 8  | 1 3 | 2 5 | 5 5 | 5 6 | 1 3 | 3 6 | 8 6 | 7 5 |
| 9  | 3 7 | 3 0 | 9 0 | 3 7 | 0 6 | 6 2 | 0 8 | 9 9 |
| 10 | 7 7 | 2 3 | 2 1 | 7 6 | 2 8 | 1 9 | 5 0 | 0 4 |
| 11 | 7 4 | 2 2 | 1 6 | 8 0 | 9 7 | 6 8 | 4 9 | 7 2 |
| 12 | 5 5 | 6 8 | 0 2 | 7 5 | 5 1 | 5 5 | 7 6 | 5 0 |
| 13 | 3 0 | 5 4 | 2 0 | 8 4 | 1 4 | 7 2 | 3 5 | 5 2 |
| 14 | 2 6 | 9 4 | 3 1 | 0 0 | 0 0 | 8 4 | 3 2 | 0 7 |
| 15 | 7 4 | 0 3 | 9 4 | 2 9 | 7 6 | 4 7 | 9 9 | 2 5 |
| 16 | 2 9 | 3 9 | 1 2 | 8 2 | 8 8 | 0 4 | 2 8 | 2 4 |
| 17 | 9 4 | 3 9 | 0 5 | 3 4 | 4 3 | 1 2 | 7 5 | 1 3 |
| 18 | 4 2 | 7 8 | 1 6 | 5 5 | 4 8 | 8 6 | 8 8 | 7 7 |
| 19 | 3 1 | 0 8 | 7 5 | 2 7 | 6 6 | 5 7 | 9 4 | 3 6 |
| 20 | 6 2 | 6 3 | 3 9 | 8 5 | 4 1 | 8 6 | 2 7 | 3 4 |
| 21 | 6 1 | 1 9 | 3 9 | 3 0 | 0 4 | 0 0 | 7 9 | 9 9 |
| 22 | 0 3 | 8 5 | 2 7 | 3 4 | 0 9 | 4 8 | 1 1 | 1 8 |
| 23 | 6 8 | 1 8 | 1 4 | 8 5 | 9 5 | 1 8 | 6 5 | 6 7 |
| 24 | 7 6 | 7 4 | 2 1 | 3 1 | 8 2 | 2 4 | 1 1 | 7 4 |
| 25 | 7 7 | 0 6 | 5 5 | 8 3 | 3 6 | 2 7 | 4 2 | 8 6 |
| 26 | 0 1 | 5 4 | 6 2 | 2 8 | 2 3 | 3 2 | 9 3 | 7 1 |
| 27 | 8 3 | 7 8 | 5 8 | 8 7 | 4 4 | 9 3 | 6 3 | 4 7 |
| 28 | 5 2 | 4 8 | 7 1 | 4 5 | 2 8 | 3 3 | 4 1 | 4 3 |
| 29 | 2 4 | 5 7 | 0 6 | 3 4 | 9 5 | 7 1 | 5 6 | 7 2 |
| 30 | 2 0 | 0 1 | 1 0 | 7 3 | 9 5 | 4 0 | 7 2 | 4 3 |
| 31 | 8 8 | 3 6 | 3 0 | 6 2 | 4 5 | 6 3 | 7 5 | 5 6 |
| 32 | 2 4 | 8 3 | 6 0 | 7 1 | 6 7 | 8 3 | 8 3 | 9 5 |
| 33 | 9 8 | 4 7 | 2 9 | 2 2 | 0 9 | 0 1 | 2 8 | 9 3 |
| 34 | 4 1 | 5 4 | 9 3 | 3 3 | 8 3 | 1 8 | 9 0 | 4 9 |
| 35 | 7 9 | 7 6 | 0 9 | 3 4 | 6 5 | 5 9 | 1 3 | 1 7 |
| 36 | 2 9 | 7 1 | 0 1 | 1 6 | 3 7 | 1 6 | 2 7 | 6 2 |
| 37 | 2 9 | 7 4 | 4 6 | 4 6 | 2 6 | 7 7 | 8 3 | 9 2 |
| 38 | 2 6 | 4 2 | 5 0 | 6 0 | 9 1 | 5 4 | 8 7 | 8 3 |
| 39 | 0 5 | 2 3 | 8 8 | 7 6 | 9 3 | 0 3 | 2 6 | 8 7 |
| 40 | 3 8 | 2 1 | 6 3 | 5 0 | 8 9 | 2 1 | 4 0 | 8 2 |

## Random Sampling Numbers—XII

| | 1 2 | 3 4 | 5 6 | 7 8 | 9 10 | 11 12 | 13 14 | 15 16 |
|---|---|---|---|---|---|---|---|---|
| 1 | 7 9 | 8 0 | 0 1 | 6 5 | 1 2 | 7 6 | 8 2 | 6 7 |
| 2 | 9 8 | 4 1 | 7 2 | 5 0 | 4 8 | 6 5 | 9 2 | 3 7 |
| 3 | 3 7 | 5 0 | 5 3 | 5 8 | 4 6 | 8 3 | 1 8 | 9 2 |
| 4 | 0 1 | 0 6 | 1 7 | 8 0 | 0 8 | 6 9 | 1 3 | 5 7 |
| 5 | 8 5 | 0 9 | 3 7 | 3 8 | 0 9 | 3 2 | 3 3 | 7 9 |
| 6 | 0 9 | 7 0 | 7 1 | 7 8 | 7 7 | 4 1 | 4 5 | 1 6 |
| 7 | 0 7 | 5 5 | 2 4 | 2 5 | 2 9 | 5 2 | 0 7 | 3 4 |
| 8 | 9 0 | 3 9 | 1 0 | 8 7 | 8 6 | 4 9 | 0 7 | 3 7 |
| 9 | 2 2 | 7 2 | 5 8 | 5 4 | 2 6 | 0 2 | 2 8 | 7 3 |
| 10 | 9 0 | 9 5 | 2 3 | 3 6 | 4 2 | 2 8 | 7 3 | 6 6 |
| 11 | 6 7 | 8 9 | 3 4 | 5 6 | 9 1 | 1 1 | 7 1 | 8 6 |
| 12 | 2 9 | 0 2 | 9 3 | 6 4 | 9 4 | 5 5 | 7 7 | 4 3 |
| 13 | 5 1 | 1 6 | 9 4 | 9 3 | 0 0 | 0 8 | 9 7 | 6 1 |
| 14 | 4 5 | 7 6 | 5 5 | 2 2 | 3 0 | 2 4 | 3 9 | 9 9 |
| 15 | 6 9 | 3 4 | 4 5 | 0 0 | 4 4 | 3 9 | 8 8 | 2 5 |
| 16 | 1 7 | 3 8 | 5 1 | 6 8 | 0 4 | 0 6 | 3 4 | 7 4 |
| 17 | 2 0 | 2 6 | 7 6 | 3 3 | 6 6 | 0 2 | 5 5 | 1 3 |
| 18 | 5 5 | 4 0 | 5 4 | 9 5 | 9 2 | 7 0 | 9 6 | 8 1 |
| 19 | 6 9 | 5 4 | 7 6 | 9 8 | 8 7 | 0 1 | 6 0 | 1 8 |
| 20 | 6 9 | 4 3 | 6 0 | 2 9 | 2 4 | 3 7 | 6 8 | 7 9 |
| 21 | 9 5 | 8 2 | 5 5 | 0 2 | 6 9 | 1 7 | 6 4 | 4 6 |
| 22 | 0 3 | 3 0 | 4 6 | 3 4 | 2 1 | 2 2 | 0 1 | 8 8 |
| 23 | 2 3 | 0 4 | 0 7 | 0 2 | 9 8 | 9 5 | 7 7 | 9 7 |
| 24 | 1 6 | 0 8 | 6 0 | 4 7 | 7 4 | 9 0 | 3 2 | 6 5 |
| 25 | 0 0 | 8 6 | 4 2 | 9 0 | 1 6 | 3 2 | 7 3 | 2 3 |
| 26 | 8 4 | 2 3 | 1 0 | 2 8 | 8 6 | 4 2 | 1 5 | 1 0 |
| 27 | 3 6 | 5 3 | 6 7 | 5 7 | 0 3 | 1 7 | 4 9 | 9 6 |
| 28 | 9 4 | 3 2 | 3 1 | 6 1 | 2 2 | 8 7 | 8 7 | 3 9 |
| 29 | 2 8 | 4 8 | 1 4 | 6 9 | 2 0 | 9 7 | 7 2 | 4 0 |
| 30 | 9 9 | 4 4 | 5 8 | 6 1 | 3 5 | 0 4 | 1 8 | 8 7 |
| 31 | 2 8 | 4 7 | 0 5 | 8 9 | 6 0 | 8 6 | 7 8 | 9 5 |
| 32 | 0 0 | 7 5 | 0 7 | 5 9 | 0 4 | 3 3 | 9 7 | 9 2 |
| 33 | 5 6 | 3 5 | 4 6 | 8 4 | 3 7 | 3 3 | 5 5 | 1 3 |
| 34 | 3 5 | 6 7 | 0 0 | 0 5 | 7 2 | 9 8 | 3 0 | 7 3 |
| 35 | 9 9 | 1 5 | 4 4 | 9 7 | 4 6 | 2 2 | 3 4 | 5 0 |
| 36 | 4 0 | 4 3 | 9 3 | 7 1 | 0 9 | 9 7 | 7 4 | 5 4 |
| 37 | 6 3 | 6 7 | 2 5 | 7 9 | 0 3 | 5 4 | 9 2 | 9 3 |
| 38 | 5 7 | 3 4 | 5 5 | 5 8 | 1 6 | 0 0 | 7 1 | 0 9 |
| 39 | 6 6 | 9 1 | 1 3 | 1 3 | 6 6 | 1 5 | 5 9 | 8 7 |
| 40 | 1 6 | 1 8 | 6 8 | 4 0 | 1 9 | 2 6 | 4 5 | 8 0 |

2 A

Random Sampling Numbers—XIII

|     | 1 2 | 3 4 | 5 6 | 7 8 | 9 10 | 11 12 | 13 14 | 15 16 |
| --- | --- | --- | --- | --- | --- | --- | --- | --- |
| 1   | 5 4 | 7 0 | 8 9 | 4 7 | 0 4 | 2 7 | 9 3 | 3 8 |
| 2   | 0 6 | 5 9 | 3 9 | 6 5 | 7 9 | 7 8 | 5 9 | 0 7 |
| 3   | 6 3 | 2 2 | 9 5 | 1 2 | 0 1 | 0 9 | 4 0 | 4 6 |
| 4   | 8 4 | 0 3 | 7 6 | 0 3 | 5 8 | 4 7 | 4 4 | 1 4 |
| 5   | 9 4 | 3 3 | 4 5 | 9 8 | 8 3 | 2 4 | 8 8 | 9 1 |
| 6   | 3 1 | 1 2 | 4 4 | 3 7 | 0 8 | 1 2 | 5 7 | 5 8 |
| 7   | 3 1 | 2 4 | 3 1 | 4 7 | 6 4 | 2 7 | 7 6 | 3 4 |
| 8   | 8 1 | 8 5 | 9 2 | 3 5 | 6 3 | 0 0 | 6 8 | 2 2 |
| 9   | 6 3 | 6 9 | 4 0 | 5 9 | 7 6 | 1 8 | 9 2 | 4 3 |
| 10  | 2 7 | 0 5 | 7 3 | 6 1 | 4 3 | 5 3 | 3 0 | 3 9 |
| 11  | 6 7 | 4 8 | 0 2 | 4 7 | 4 6 | 4 5 | 0 0 | 5 3 |
| 12  | 5 7 | 9 2 | 6 7 | 0 2 | 6 8 | 8 8 | 9 3 | 1 8 |
| 13  | 3 5 | 8 6 | 8 7 | 6 8 | 6 3 | 3 7 | 7 9 | 9 7 |
| 14  | 3 7 | 2 1 | 5 3 | 5 9 | 4 7 | 8 5 | 6 9 | 7 4 |
| 15  | 0 4 | 1 0 | 6 1 | 8 5 | 2 3 | 5 6 | 0 0 | 7 7 |
| 16  | 7 9 | 1 1 | 2 0 | 9 5 | 8 3 | 2 0 | 1 8 | 9 1 |
| 17  | 2 2 | 3 8 | 6 0 | 9 6 | 7 6 | 4 7 | 1 0 | 0 2 |
| 18  | 8 8 | 6 9 | 7 9 | 3 5 | 4 2 | 9 6 | 6 3 | 0 5 |
| 19  | 1 1 | 0 0 | 6 7 | 1 9 | 1 7 | 8 5 | 1 5 | 7 5 |
| 20  | 2 2 | 5 0 | 9 9 | 8 7 | 7 3 | 6 5 | 1 1 | 5 8 |
| 21  | 5 4 | 8 2 | 2 7 | 9 6 | 8 1 | 8 5 | 9 9 | 2 4 |
| 22  | 6 8 | 5 3 | 6 2 | 2 9 | 4 2 | 0 7 | 2 4 | 4 3 |
| 23  | 7 9 | 1 9 | 4 9 | 7 2 | 5 2 | 4 6 | 6 5 | 7 3 |
| 24  | 2 5 | 5 2 | 2 6 | 6 8 | 8 4 | 1 6 | 7 7 | 3 4 |
| 25  | 2 4 | 6 8 | 8 0 | 7 0 | 3 5 | 6 0 | 7 1 | 6 0 |
| 26  | 9 5 | 1 3 | 3 6 | 3 7 | 5 1 | 0 3 | 3 9 | 9 2 |
| 27  | 8 4 | 2 4 | 9 7 | 6 4 | 1 5 | 7 7 | 1 0 | 4 5 |
| 28  | 1 3 | 2 8 | 5 8 | 2 0 | 2 0 | 5 7 | 1 1 | 4 5 |
| 29  | 0 1 | 0 7 | 3 8 | 3 3 | 3 2 | 4 7 | 2 8 | 4 9 |
| 30  | 1 7 | 1 2 | 3 1 | 8 2 | 2 3 | 0 6 | 7 5 | 8 7 |
| 31  | 9 4 | 9 5 | 4 6 | 9 7 | 2 3 | 8 9 | 2 6 | 9 0 |
| 32  | 1 4 | 5 0 | 8 2 | 8 8 | 7 3 | 7 2 | 4 6 | 5 5 |
| 33  | 4 3 | 8 8 | 6 0 | 7 7 | 6 7 | 8 4 | 6 0 | 6 6 |
| 34  | 4 7 | 3 5 | 5 4 | 3 2 | 4 2 | 7 6 | 7 1 | 3 3 |
| 35  | 1 9 | 1 2 | 2 7 | 6 6 | 7 6 | 8 8 | 4 6 | 5 1 |
| 36  | 9 3 | 8 8 | 9 3 | 5 7 | 0 4 | 5 5 | 8 6 | 8 2 |
| 37  | 8 5 | 5 7 | 8 4 | 5 6 | 5 6 | 9 2 | 9 3 | 5 8 |
| 38  | 4 0 | 5 3 | 7 8 | 1 2 | 7 2 | 6 4 | 5 7 | 0 9 |
| 39  | 1 0 | 6 4 | 0 4 | 1 7 | 7 9 | 1 3 | 4 1 | 8 2 |
| 40  | 3 2 | 6 4 | 4 2 | 0 9 | 2 6 | 5 9 | 6 4 | 0 0 |

## Random Sampling Numbers—XIV

|    | 1 2 | 3 4 | 5 6 | 7 8 | 9 10 | 11 12 | 13 14 | 15 16 |
|----|-----|-----|-----|-----|------|-------|-------|-------|
| 1  | 2 9 | 5 9 | 1 3 | 2 4 | 4 4 | 1 1 | 6 8 | 4 1 |
| 2  | 4 7 | 3 9 | 9 6 | 9 4 | 0 2 | 6 0 | 2 9 | 4 5 |
| 3  | 4 1 | 2 6 | 9 5 | 6 3 | 4 3 | 1 8 | 4 6 | 2 8 |
| 4  | 4 5 | 1 2 | 2 0 | 7 7 | 8 5 | 2 2 | 0 1 | 0 1 |
| 5  | 4 5 | 4 4 | 7 0 | 9 9 | 0 1 | 0 8 | 4 5 | 2 1 |
| 6  | 1 7 | 4 5 | 9 4 | 1 7 | 0 7 | 1 9 | 9 1 | 9 2 |
| 7  | 4 9 | 9 8 | 6 0 | 7 2 | 2 9 | 9 2 | 5 8 | 4 0 |
| 8  | 9 3 | 0 5 | 3 9 | 2 6 | 2 3 | 9 9 | 1 4 | 6 3 |
| 9  | 2 8 | 2 2 | 2 1 | 7 3 | 1 0 | 5 9 | 2 3 | 3 9 |
| 10 | 9 5 | 2 8 | 3 6 | 6 7 | 0 1 | 0 7 | 4 6 | 6 3 |
| 11 | 9 1 | 4 9 | 1 2 | 4 6 | 3 6 | 1 4 | 9 6 | 3 7 |
| 12 | 0 2 | 1 0 | 1 4 | 2 9 | 4 9 | 9 1 | 9 1 | 5 9 |
| 13 | 8 0 | 3 9 | 4 3 | 5 4 | 4 2 | 4 9 | 2 7 | 5 5 |
| 14 | 9 1 | 9 5 | 4 7 | 3 4 | 6 4 | 4 7 | 0 8 | 0 7 |
| 15 | 8 9 | 8 6 | 6 2 | 0 0 | 6 5 | 7 6 | 9 5 | 2 4 |
| 16 | 7 3 | 1 5 | 3 7 | 2 1 | 4 0 | 3 1 | 2 8 | 5 5 |
| 17 | 4 4 | 2 9 | 6 0 | 7 1 | 3 7 | 3 9 | 7 6 | 8 6 |
| 18 | 9 6 | 2 1 | 8 8 | 2 4 | 7 7 | 6 0 | 4 3 | 0 3 |
| 19 | 8 0 | 4 2 | 7 9 | 3 0 | 7 7 | 8 7 | 3 3 | 6 3 |
| 20 | 2 3 | 3 8 | 4 0 | 0 1 | 4 6 | 7 4 | 1 3 | 2 9 |
| 21 | 6 9 | 6 1 | 5 1 | 3 6 | 9 2 | 6 3 | 4 6 | 4 1 |
| 22 | 3 0 | 9 8 | 2 5 | 7 6 | 2 9 | 8 2 | 7 3 | 9 6 |
| 23 | 1 5 | 0 8 | 9 5 | 6 1 | 1 5 | 6 5 | 5 2 | 8 2 |
| 24 | 6 2 | 4 3 | 8 6 | 5 4 | 2 4 | 1 7 | 0 1 | 4 2 |
| 25 | 3 3 | 6 2 | 7 1 | 5 8 | 3 2 | 8 6 | 1 6 | 7 5 |
| 26 | 8 6 | 6 4 | 9 5 | 0 4 | 5 3 | 3 8 | 6 4 | 1 4 |
| 27 | 0 9 | 7 2 | 0 3 | 5 4 | 6 4 | 2 9 | 5 0 | 7 0 |
| 28 | 9 8 | 7 9 | 1 8 | 5 5 | 5 8 | 7 8 | 0 1 | 8 5 |
| 29 | 9 3 | 0 2 | 3 6 | 2 3 | 0 5 | 3 9 | 1 6 | 6 7 |
| 30 | 9 2 | 5 1 | 1 6 | 7 4 | 3 2 | 7 7 | 0 7 | 4 6 |
| 31 | 3 3 | 0 0 | 5 7 | 8 9 | 5 6 | 4 3 | 7 5 | 6 0 |
| 32 | 7 5 | 8 6 | 7 1 | 4 3 | 6 2 | 9 8 | 5 1 | 3 2 |
| 33 | 2 6 | 5 5 | 8 2 | 2 6 | 5 8 | 7 9 | 9 2 | 9 2 |
| 34 | 7 2 | 2 4 | 7 9 | 5 9 | 3 7 | 6 1 | 8 0 | 5 4 |
| 35 | 9 9 | 9 6 | 6 8 | 2 9 | 4 0 | 4 2 | 9 7 | 6 6 |
| 36 | 7 5 | 7 0 | 4 1 | 7 4 | 5 7 | 4 3 | 3 6 | 4 5 |
| 37 | 4 7 | 5 6 | 5 4 | 2 8 | 5 3 | 4 3 | 2 7 | 5 8 |
| 38 | 3 8 | 2 0 | 6 6 | 7 2 | 3 7 | 4 2 | 7 7 | 1 7 |
| 39 | 5 3 | 0 0 | 4 5 | 7 5 | 4 1 | 6 4 | 4 8 | 5 9 |
| 40 | 5 4 | 4 9 | 9 2 | 2 8 | 9 6 | 8 0 | 1 3 | 9 1 |

Random Sampling Numbers—XV

|  | 1 2 | 3 4 | 5 6 | 7 8 | 9 10 | 11 12 | 13 14 | 15 16 |
|---|---|---|---|---|---|---|---|---|
| 1 | 5 6 | 5 4 | 1 7 | 0 8 | 1 4 | 2 0 | 3 3 | 3 3 |
| 2 | 3 3 | 1 6 | 6 4 | 8 3 | 7 0 | 5 7 | 1 0 | 7 4 |
| 3 | 6 1 | 4 2 | 8 4 | 5 1 | 3 6 | 1 2 | 7 3 | 3 8 |
| 4 | 3 6 | 1 3 | 5 8 | 1 5 | 5 2 | 1 4 | 5 0 | 9 6 |
| 5 | 9 7 | 8 1 | 3 9 | 5 1 | 1 4 | 6 6 | 3 9 | 0 9 |
| 6 | 7 2 | 4 8 | 5 9 | 1 2 | 4 7 | 0 5 | 6 0 | 5 8 |
| 7 | 8 6 | 1 5 | 9 6 | 0 0 | 5 3 | 3 8 | 2 1 | 6 7 |
| 8 | 9 5 | 0 2 | 3 1 | 9 3 | 6 2 | 6 7 | 8 5 | 9 7 |
| 9 | 1 0 | 5 5 | 0 0 | 9 4 | 0 5 | 3 8 | 9 4 | 4 7 |
| 10 | 4 2 | 7 3 | 1 3 | 9 9 | 9 7 | 6 0 | 6 6 | 2 9 |
| 11 | 4 4 | 5 2 | 0 2 | 1 0 | 1 9 | 3 5 | 8 8 | 4 8 |
| 12 | 9 9 | 4 2 | 7 6 | 8 7 | 5 6 | 8 0 | 4 9 | 8 0 |
| 13 | 7 3 | 0 6 | 5 7 | 3 7 | 3 8 | 3 1 | 6 5 | 3 6 |
| 14 | 0 1 | 9 3 | 7 2 | 7 5 | 4 6 | 1 6 | 7 8 | 6 8 |
| 15 | 6 0 | 8 4 | 3 2 | 0 7 | 5 4 | 8 4 | 1 6 | 7 9 |
| 16 | 0 3 | 3 9 | 0 2 | 2 2 | 9 7 | 6 8 | 3 3 | 5 0 |
| 17 | 8 9 | 4 6 | 2 1 | 8 4 | 0 5 | 5 5 | 3 2 | 4 9 |
| 18 | 2 7 | 3 6 | 8 9 | 5 7 | 3 1 | 4 3 | 6 3 | 4 3 |
| 19 | 3 7 | 8 3 | 0 2 | 9 1 | 8 5 | 7 6 | 8 0 | 7 8 |
| 20 | 4 8 | 0 5 | 0 2 | 5 3 | 0 4 | 0 8 | 9 5 | 1 2 |
| 21 | 2 9 | 8 9 | 9 9 | 5 3 | 5 1 | 0 1 | 1 3 | 0 7 |
| 22 | 8 1 | 0 5 | 5 2 | 9 6 | 0 4 | 1 6 | 8 3 | 7 8 |
| 23 | 8 8 | 1 5 | 8 7 | 4 5 | 2 6 | 2 6 | 2 3 | 4 1 |
| 24 | 2 1 | 2 3 | 0 1 | 1 5 | 5 2 | 6 7 | 9 7 | 3 8 |
| 25 | 7 1 | 6 3 | 6 2 | 1 5 | 2 4 | 5 2 | 2 7 | 5 7 |
| 26 | 2 8 | 0 7 | 3 2 | 8 6 | 0 5 | 3 8 | 2 0 | 8 4 |
| 27 | 8 8 | 6 7 | 8 5 | 8 8 | 0 0 | 0 6 | 9 4 | 2 5 |
| 28 | 0 7 | 2 1 | 9 9 | 3 3 | 6 0 | 6 1 | 0 5 | 4 9 |
| 29 | 0 6 | 2 1 | 0 2 | 3 1 | 7 9 | 8 8 | 0 1 | 5 4 |
| 30 | 8 1 | 8 6 | 8 9 | 0 8 | 1 0 | 6 7 | 6 7 | 0 7 |
| 31 | 7 4 | 9 6 | 3 7 | 3 1 | 8 5 | 3 2 | 8 6 | 1 1 |
| 32 | 2 8 | 3 5 | 8 2 | 7 2 | 2 3 | 0 9 | 8 2 | 4 7 |
| 33 | 7 1 | 1 9 | 1 0 | 7 7 | 9 9 | 1 3 | 1 4 | 7 8 |
| 34 | 5 9 | 0 6 | 9 8 | 9 7 | 0 0 | 2 3 | 9 9 | 1 3 |
| 35 | 1 7 | 8 3 | 3 8 | 1 4 | 2 0 | 6 0 | 5 9 | 3 3 |
| 36 | 6 1 | 4 5 | 3 1 | 4 4 | 5 8 | 6 7 | 0 4 | 6 7 |
| 37 | 9 2 | 9 5 | 1 2 | 5 1 | 5 9 | 7 5 | 2 0 | 9 9 |
| 38 | 6 6 | 6 3 | 8 3 | 9 8 | 2 1 | 0 7 | 4 5 | 5 3 |
| 39 | 2 2 | 6 8 | 4 4 | 1 3 | 5 2 | 0 5 | 0 5 | 8 1 |
| 40 | 9 0 | 8 2 | 7 4 | 0 7 | 7 7 | 0 2 | 7 9 | 2 5 |

## Random Sampling Numbers—XVI

|  | 1 2 | 3 4 | 5 6 | 7 8 | 9 10 | 11 12 | 13 14 | 15 16 |
|---|---|---|---|---|---|---|---|---|
| 1 | 2 0 | 8 9 | 8 5 | 4 0 | 6 5 | 2 4 | 9 6 | 1 2 |
| 2 | 8 9 | 7 5 | 4 2 | 1 3 | 2 0 | 0 6 | 5 8 | 5 1 |
| 3 | 1 9 | 9 3 | 4 8 | 0 3 | 2 2 | 9 6 | 1 1 | 4 8 |
| 4 | 8 4 | 1 1 | 6 6 | 0 2 | 8 9 | 0 7 | 8 6 | 5 6 |
| 5 | 9 5 | 1 0 | 2 4 | 1 0 | 3 8 | 2 4 | 5 2 | 0 9 |
| 6 | 0 4 | 8 9 | 6 1 | 6 7 | 1 2 | 5 2 | 2 7 | 9 4 |
| 7 | 2 6 | 6 9 | 7 6 | 3 0 | 8 6 | 5 8 | 3 6 | 3 1 |
| 8 | 9 3 | 3 4 | 5 6 | 1 7 | 5 5 | 0 4 | 0 6 | 7 5 |
| 9 | 4 6 | 0 1 | 1 4 | 9 9 | 7 6 | 5 2 | 5 5 | 9 1 |
| 10 | 7 5 | 0 1 | 9 4 | 0 2 | 0 2 | 4 2 | 4 1 | 1 2 |
| 11 | 6 1 | 3 4 | 5 7 | 3 7 | 3 0 | 8 2 | 6 2 | 7 3 |
| 12 | 3 0 | 6 7 | 8 4 | 9 0 | 6 3 | 5 6 | 7 1 | 6 0 |
| 13 | 6 4 | 7 7 | 6 1 | 0 2 | 4 7 | 4 9 | 2 2 | 9 8 |
| 14 | 1 4 | 0 6 | 4 6 | 2 6 | 1 4 | 1 6 | 7 3 | 2 3 |
| 15 | 6 1 | 0 2 | 4 8 | 7 1 | 4 0 | 1 1 | 9 6 | 2 5 |
| 16 | 3 9 | 2 3 | 3 7 | 5 6 | 7 1 | 4 1 | 3 8 | 4 4 |
| 17 | 3 8 | 2 1 | 5 9 | 7 3 | 8 0 | 7 5 | 0 8 | 9 1 |
| 18 | 6 9 | 3 6 | 9 7 | 0 1 | 5 3 | 0 3 | 4 8 | 7 8 |
| 19 | 8 3 | 9 5 | 8 8 | 9 1 | 2 9 | 2 1 | 0 9 | 0 0 |
| 20 | 2 0 | 6 1 | 6 9 | 7 3 | 5 6 | 1 6 | 7 3 | 8 7 |
| 21 | 7 9 | 5 0 | 7 6 | 7 1 | 8 5 | 2 3 | 2 9 | 5 8 |
| 22 | 2 4 | 5 0 | 0 7 | 7 4 | 6 6 | 2 6 | 7 7 | 5 6 |
| 23 | 7 6 | 9 2 | 4 8 | 8 9 | 3 9 | 2 2 | 8 6 | 9 0 |
| 24 | 9 3 | 4 7 | 2 1 | 4 7 | 1 8 | 8 8 | 2 3 | 2 1 |
| 25 | 2 7 | 2 8 | 4 0 | 0 8 | 2 3 | 5 1 | 5 2 | 9 7 |
| 26 | 3 0 | 9 3 | 5 8 | 1 7 | 1 5 | 1 8 | 6 5 | 3 8 |
| 27 | 2 4 | 6 4 | 9 2 | 3 6 | 3 3 | 8 0 | 6 8 | 6 8 |
| 28 | 9 0 | 1 7 | 3 8 | 4 0 | 0 0 | 8 6 | 7 0 | 4 5 |
| 29 | 6 2 | 7 9 | 9 6 | 5 3 | 7 8 | 0 6 | 0 5 | 3 1 |
| 30 | 3 8 | 0 8 | 5 5 | 4 1 | 7 3 | 7 1 | 4 9 | 9 5 |
| 31 | 8 5 | 3 9 | 9 7 | 1 1 | 9 6 | 8 6 | 4 2 | 3 0 |
| 32 | 9 7 | 3 6 | 3 1 | 4 9 | 8 2 | 8 8 | 9 2 | 9 1 |
| 33 | 9 2 | 7 7 | 8 5 | 7 0 | 9 2 | 8 1 | 8 7 | 1 0 |
| 34 | 8 6 | 2 3 | 0 5 | 8 2 | 3 7 | 6 2 | 5 9 | 7 4 |
| 35 | 0 8 | 0 0 | 6 4 | 9 3 | 2 1 | 2 5 | 1 4 | 1 6 |
| 36 | 0 7 | 7 3 | 6 0 | 1 2 | 3 0 | 2 0 | 1 6 | 8 9 |
| 37 | 9 1 | 4 9 | 8 3 | 3 3 | 3 1 | 0 1 | 2 4 | 9 8 |
| 38 | 6 5 | 4 9 | 1 1 | 1 9 | 0 9 | 3 0 | 1 9 | 8 4 |
| 39 | 6 8 | 5 9 | 5 0 | 7 5 | 7 5 | 8 0 | 0 9 | 1 9 |
| 40 | 8 5 | 5 5 | 3 3 | 9 9 | 5 0 | 8 4 | 3 7 | 9 4 |

## TABLE OF $\chi^2$

| $n$ | P = ·99 | ·98 | ·95 | ·90 | ·80 | ·70 |
|---|---|---|---|---|---|---|
| 1 | ·000157 | ·000628 | ·00393 | ·0158 | ·0642 | ·148 |
| 2 | ·0201 | ·0404 | ·103 | ·211 | ·446 | ·713 |
| 3 | ·115 | ·185 | ·352 | ·584 | 1·005 | 1·424 |
| 4 | ·297 | ·429 | ·711 | 1·064 | 1·649 | 2·195 |
| 5 | ·554 | ·752 | 1·145 | 1·610 | 2·343 | 3·000 |
| 6 | ·872 | 1·134 | 1·635 | 2·204 | 3·070 | 3·828 |
| 7 | 1·239 | 1·564 | 2·167 | 2·833 | 3·822 | 4·671 |
| 8 | 1·646 | 2·032 | 2·733 | 3·490 | 4·594 | 5·527 |
| 9 | 2·088 | 2·532 | 3·325 | 4·168 | 5·380 | 6·393 |
| 10 | 2·558 | 3·059 | 3·940 | 4·865 | 6·179 | 7·267 |
| 11 | 3·053 | 3·609 | 4·575 | 5·578 | 6·989 | 8·148 |
| 12 | 3·571 | 4·178 | 5·226 | 6·304 | 7·807 | 9·034 |
| 13 | 4·107 | 4·765 | 5·892 | 7·042 | 8·634 | 9·926 |
| 14 | 4·660 | 5·368 | 6·571 | 7·790 | 9·467 | 10·821 |
| 15 | 5·229 | 5·985 | 7·261 | 8·547 | 10·307 | 11·721 |
| 16 | 5·812 | 6·614 | 7·962 | 9·312 | 11·152 | 12·624 |
| 17 | 6·408 | 7·255 | 8·672 | 10·085 | 12·002 | 13·531 |
| 18 | 7·015 | 7·906 | 9·390 | 10·865 | 12·857 | 14·440 |
| 19 | 7·633 | 8·567 | 10·117 | 11·651 | 13·716 | 15·352 |
| 20 | 8·260 | 9·237 | 10·851 | 12·443 | 14·578 | 16·266 |
| 21 | 8·897 | 9·915 | 11·591 | 13·240 | 15·445 | 17·182 |
| 22 | 9·542 | 10·600 | 12·338 | 14·041 | 16·314 | 18·101 |
| 23 | 10·196 | 11·293 | 13·091 | 14·848 | 17·187 | 19·021 |
| 24 | 10·856 | 11·992 | 13·848 | 15·659 | 18·062 | 19·943 |
| 25 | 11·524 | 12·697 | 14·611 | 16·473 | 18·940 | 20·867 |
| 26 | 12·198 | 13·409 | 15·379 | 17·292 | 19·820 | 21·792 |
| 27 | 12·879 | 14·125 | 16·151 | 18·114 | 20·703 | 22·719 |
| 28 | 13·565 | 14·847 | 16·928 | 18·939 | 21·588 | 23·647 |
| 29 | 14·256 | 15·574 | 17·708 | 19·768 | 22·475 | 24·577 |
| 30 | 14·953 | 16·306 | 18·493 | 20·599 | 23·364 | 25·508 |

For larger values of $n$, the expression $\sqrt{2\chi^2} - \sqrt{2n-1}$

This table is reproduced, by kind permission of the author and publishers, 6th edition, 1936, Oliver & Boyd, Edinburgh and London.

The meaning of the footnote to it is this. If the value of $n$ is greater value is found to be less than 1·65, the differences observed may well have if it is 2·33, then P is ·01 ; if it has a still greater value, P is less than ·01.

## TABLE OF $\chi^2$ (*contd.*)

| ·50 | ·30 | ·20 | ·10 | ·05 | ·02 | ·01 | $n$ |
|---|---|---|---|---|---|---|---|
| ·455 | 1·074 | 1·642 | 2·706 | 3·841 | 5·412 | 6·635 | 1 |
| 1·386 | 2·408 | 3·219 | 4·605 | 5·991 | 7·824 | 9·210 | 2 |
| 2·366 | 3·665 | 4·642 | 6·251 | 7·815 | 9·837 | 11·341 | 3 |
| 3·357 | 4·878 | 5·989 | 7·779 | 9·488 | 11·668 | 13·277 | 4 |
| 4·351 | 6·064 | 7·289 | 9·236 | 11·070 | 13·388 | 15·086 | 5 |
| 5·348 | 7·231 | 8·558 | 10·645 | 12·592 | 15·033 | 16·812 | 6 |
| 6·346 | 8·383 | 9·803 | 12·017 | 14·067 | 16·622 | 18·475 | 7 |
| 7·344 | 9·524 | 11·030 | 13·362 | 15·507 | 18·168 | 20·090 | 8 |
| 8·343 | 10·656 | 12·242 | 14·684 | 16·919 | 19·679 | 21·666 | 9 |
| 9·342 | 11·781 | 13·442 | 15·987 | 18·307 | 21·161 | 23·209 | 10 |
| 10·341 | 12·899 | 14·631 | 17·275 | 19·675 | 22·618 | 24·725 | 11 |
| 11·340 | 14·011 | 15·812 | 18·549 | 21·026 | 24·054 | 26·217 | 12 |
| 12·340 | 15·119 | 16·985 | 19·812 | 22·362 | 25·472 | 27·688 | 13 |
| 13·339 | 16·222 | 18·151 | 21·064 | 23·685 | 26·873 | 29·141 | 14 |
| 14·339 | 17·322 | 19·311 | 22·307 | 24·996 | 28·259 | 30·578 | 15 |
| 15·338 | 18·418 | 20·465 | 23·542 | 26·296 | 29·633 | 32·000 | 16 |
| 16·338 | 19·511 | 21·615 | 24·769 | 27·587 | 30·995 | 33·409 | 17 |
| 17·338 | 20·601 | 22·760 | 25·989 | 28·869 | 32·346 | 34·805 | 18 |
| 18·338 | 21·689 | 23·900 | 27·204 | 30·144 | 33·687 | 36·191 | 19 |
| 19·337 | 22·775 | 25·038 | 28·412 | 31·410 | 35·020 | 37·566 | 20 |
| 20·337 | 23·858 | 26·171 | 29·615 | 32·671 | 36·343 | 38·932 | 21 |
| 21·337 | 24·939 | 27·301 | 30·813 | 33·924 | 37·659 | 40·289 | 22 |
| 22·337 | 26·018 | 28·429 | 32·007 | 35·172 | 38·968 | 41·638 | 23 |
| 23·337 | 27·096 | 29·553 | 33·196 | 36·415 | 40·270 | 42·980 | 24 |
| 24·337 | 28·172 | 30·675 | 34·382 | 37·652 | 41·566 | 44·314 | 25 |
| 25·336 | 29·246 | 31·795 | 35·563 | 38·885 | 42·856 | 45·642 | 26 |
| 26·336 | 30·319 | 32·912 | 36·741 | 40·113 | 44·140 | 46·963 | 27 |
| 27·336 | 31·391 | 34·027 | 37·916 | 41·337 | 45·419 | 48·278 | 28 |
| 28·336 | 32·461 | 35·139 | 39·087 | 42·557 | 46·693 | 49·588 | 29 |
| 29·336 | 33·530 | 36·250 | 40·256 | 43·773 | 47·962 | 50·892 | 30 |

may be used as a normal deviate with unit variance.

from *Statistical Methods for Research Workers*, by R. A. Fisher, Sc.D., F.R.S.,

than 30, the value of $\sqrt{2\chi^2} - \sqrt{2n-1}$ should be calculated. If this latter occurred by chance; if it is 1·65, then P is ·05; if it is 2·05, then P is ·02;

## TABLE OF "$t$"

| $n$ | P = ·50 | ·20 | ·10 | ·05 | ·02 | ·01 |
|---|---|---|---|---|---|---|
| 1 | 1·000 | 3·078 | 6·314 | 12·706 | 31·821 | 63·657 |
| 2 | ·816 | 1·886 | 2·920 | 4·303 | 6·965 | 9·925 |
| 3 | ·765 | 1·638 | 2·353 | 3·182 | 4·541 | 5·841 |
| 4 | ·741 | 1·533 | 2·132 | 2·776 | 3·747 | 4·604 |
| 5 | ·727 | 1·476 | 2·015 | 2·571 | 3·365 | 4·032 |
| 6 | ·718 | 1·440 | 1·943 | 2·447 | 3·143 | 3·707 |
| 7 | ·711 | 1·415 | 1·895 | 2·365 | 2·998 | 3·499 |
| 8 | ·706 | 1·397 | 1·860 | 2·306 | 2·896 | 3·355 |
| 9 | ·703 | 1·383 | 1·833 | 2·262 | 2·821 | 3·250 |
| 10 | ·700 | 1·372 | 1·812 | 2·228 | 2·764 | 3·169 |
| 11 | ·697 | 1·363 | 1·796 | 2·201 | 2·718 | 3·106 |
| 12 | ·695 | 1·356 | 1·782 | 2·179 | 2·681 | 3·055 |
| 13 | ·694 | 1·350 | 1·771 | 2·160 | 2·650 | 3·012 |
| 14 | ·692 | 1·345 | 1·761 | 2·145 | 2·624 | 2·977 |
| 15 | ·691 | 1·341 | 1·753 | 2·131 | 2·602 | 2·947 |
| 16 | ·690 | 1·337 | 1·746 | 2·120 | 2·583 | 2·921 |
| 17 | ·689 | 1·333 | 1·740 | 2·110 | 2·567 | 2·898 |
| 18 | ·688 | 1·330 | 1·734 | 2·101 | 2·552 | 2·878 |
| 19 | ·688 | 1·328 | 1·729 | 2·093 | 2·539 | 2·861 |
| 20 | ·687 | 1·325 | 1·725 | 2·086 | 2·528 | 2·845 |
| 21 | ·686 | 1·323 | 1·721 | 2·080 | 2·518 | 2·831 |
| 22 | ·686 | 1·321 | 1·717 | 2·074 | 2·508 | 2·819 |
| 23 | ·685 | 1·319 | 1·714 | 2·069 | 2·500 | 2·807 |
| 24 | ·685 | 1·318 | 1·711 | 2·064 | 2·492 | 2·797 |
| 25 | ·684 | 1·316 | 1·708 | 2·060 | 2·485 | 2·787 |

# INDEX